A Practical Approach to
Sedimentology

TITLES OF RELATED INTEREST

Adjustments of the fluvial system
D. D. Rhodes & G. P. Williams (eds)

Aeolian geomorphology
W. G. Nickling (ed.)

British rivers
J. Lewin (ed.)

The dark side of the Earth
R. Muir Wood

Dynamic stratigraphy of the British Isles
R. Anderton *et al.*

Elements of dynamic oceanography
D. Tolmazin

Environmental chemistry
P. O'Neill

Experiments in physical sedimentology
J. R. L. Allen

Fluvial geomorphology
M. Morisawa (ed.)

Groundwater as a geomorphic agent
R. G. LaFleur (ed.)

Hydraulics in civil engineering
A. Chadwick & J. Morfett

Introducing groundwater
M. Price

Petroleum geology
F. K. North

Petrology of the sedimentary rocks
J. T. Greensmith

Physical processes of sedimentation
J. R. L. Allen

Principles of physical sedimentology
J. R. L. Allen

Sedimentary structures
J. D. Collinson & D. B. Thompson

Sedimentology
M. R. Leeder

Tectonic geomorphology
J. T. Hack & M. Morisawa

A Practical Approach to Sedimentology

ROY LINDHOLM

Roy C. Lindholm
The George Washington University
Washington

London
ALLEN & UNWIN
Boston Sydney Wellington

Allen & Unwin, Inc.,
8 Winchester Place, Winchester, Mass. 01890, USA
the U.S. company of
Unwin Hyman Ltd

PO Box 18, Park Lane, Hemel Hempstead, Herts HP2 4TE, UK
40 Museum Street, London WC1A 1LU, UK
37/39 Queen Elizabeth Street, London SE1 2QB, UK

Allen & Unwin (Australia) Ltd,
8 Napier Street, North Sydney, NSW 2060, Australia

Allen & Unwin (New Zealand) Ltd in association with the Port Nicholson Press Ltd
60 Cambridge Terrace, Wellington, New Zealand

First published in 1987

Library of Congress Cataloging in Publication Data
Lindholm, Roy C., 1937–
A practical approach to sedimentology.
Bibliography: p.
Includes index.
1. Sedimentology. I. Title.
QE471.L534 1987 551.3 86–28899
ISBN 0–04–551131–4 (alk. paper)
ISBN 0–04–551132–2 (pbk. : alk. paper)

British Library Cataloguing in Publication Data
Lindholm, Roy C.
A practical approach to sedimentology
1. Sedimentology
I. Title
551.3′04 QE471
ISBN 0–04–551131–4
ISBN 0–04–551132–2 Pbk

Set in 10 on 12 pt Times Roman by Columns of Reading
and printed in Great Britain
by St Edmundsbury Press, Suffolk

To my wife Betty, without whose patience and understanding this book would not have been written

Preface

This book is designed for a one-semester course in sedimentology taken by advanced undergraduate or graduate students. It gives detailed descriptions of sedimentary features and the analytical methods used to evaluate them and is intended to support and reinforce principles presented in lectures. Discussion of principles and processes is found in complimentary texts, such as Leeder's (1982) *Sedimentology: process and product* and selected readings in professional journals.

This book is not an exhaustive treatise of laboratory techniques and theory. The subject matter includes topics generally covered in courses entitled "Sedimentology" or "Sedimentation". Sandstone and carbonate petrography is commonly given in a separate course. Furthermore, this topic is covered in several current texts. For these reasons I have omitted petrographic methods, with the exception of those applying to heavy minerals. I have included a rather extensive discussion of heavies because this topic is generally lacking in most modern texts. Every course in sedimentology is highly individualistic and material covered varies with the interests, background, and point of view of the instructor. For these reasons some topics presented in this book are not necessarily covered in all courses. Similarly some instructors may find that their favorite topic is missing. I can only hope that this problem is minimal.

Several chapters contain precise exercises to be completed by the student. Some must be done in the classroom, where specimens are available for study. Others may be done outside of the classroom. In some case (e.g. sedimentary structures) the materials will have to be provided by the instructor. In others (e.g. measurement of cross-bed azimuths) the data given in this book may be supplemented or replaced by data collected by the student.

I have tried to present methodology in a step-by-step format which allows independent student work. Some techniques which are standard fare in most sedimentology courses include determination of vector mean, vector magnitude, and grain-size parameters, as well as Markov chain analysis of vertical sequences. Several useful tests (chi-square and Mann–Whitney *U*) are presented to stress the value and need for statistical analysis in sedimentologic research. Extensive presentation of two-theta values and sample diffractograms are included to allow students to become familiar with X-ray diffraction techniques, even if the necessary equipment is not available. Detailed descriptions, together with identification keys, will aid in the identification of heavy minerals and trace fossils.

Roy C. Lindholm

Acknowledgments

I gratefully acknowledge the following persons for reading part or all of this text in its various stages and for their advice and comments: V.P. Carter, M.R. Leeder, J. Mazzulo, M.F. Miller, B.S. Pierce, M.D. Ruth, K.S. Schindler, and J.S. Schindler. I owe a special debt of gratitude to F.R. Siegel for reading part of the text and providing much needed encouragement throughout its preparation. Obviously any residual errors are my own responsibility. I thank F.J. Collier for helping to locate the trace fossils illustrated in Figures 4.43–4.45 and the Smithsonian Institution, Division of Paleobiology, for allowing me to photograph these fossils. I also thank Thomas DuRant for his assistance in obtaining the cover photograph which was provided by courtesy of the National Park Service Photo Collection. It was taken in Zion National Park by Richard Frear. I would be remiss if I did not acknowledge my teachers who nourished my interest in sedimentology, especially L.I. Briggs, R.L. Folk, E.F. McBride, and F.J. Pettijohn. I greatly appreciate the help and encouragement given by Roger Jones of Allen and Unwin during the preparation of this text and the splendid editorial work done by Geoffrey Palmer and Dorothy Sharp.

I am grateful to the following authors and copyright holders who have given permission for the reproduction of illustrative material (numbers in parentheses refer to text figures):

Society of Economic Paleontologists and Mineralogists (1.4, 1.19, 1.21, 1.35, 4.3a, 4.4, 4.42, 7.14, 8.2, 11.1, 11.8, 11.9); H. E. Reineck and Springer-Verlag (1.20); D. R. Lowe (1.35); American Association of Petroleum Geologists (1.37, 8.13–15, 11.13, 12.2); H. E. Cook (1.37, 12.2); Elsevier Science Publishers (1.40); Maryland Geological Survey (1.39, 8.10); C. K. Chamberlain (4.3a); J. D. Howard (4.42); R. L. Folk (7.1, 7.2, 8.7, 8.8, 8.13, 8.14); F. J. Pettijohn (7.8, 9.2, 9.3, 9.7); D. K. Davies (9.1); R. Anderton and Blackwell Scientific Publications (11.2); R. G. Walker (11.7–11.10); Figure 11.12 reproduced from *Stratigraphy and sedimentology*, 2nd edn, by W. G. Knumbein and L. L. Sloss, copyright © 1963 W. H. Freeman & Company; D. G. McCubbin (11.13).

Contents

Preface *page* ix
Acknowledgments xi
List of tables xvii

1 Description of sedimentary structures 1

1.1 Introduction 1
1.2 Structures on the upper bedding surface 2
1.3 Internal structures 14
1.4 Structures on the lower bedding surface: sole marks 28
1.5 Structures formed by soft-sediment deformation 30
1.6 Exercises: sedimentary structures 38

2 Analysis of sedimentary structures 43

2.1 Paleocurrent analysis 43
2.2 Correction of data for tectonic tilt 43
2.3 Graphic presentation of directional data 46
2.4 Vector mean and vector magnitude 47
2.5 Moving-average maps 50
2.6 Factors that cause variability in cross-bed dip azimuths 50
2.7 Exercises 54

3 Primary grain fabric 59

3.1 Introduction 59
3.2 Sand-grain orientation 59
3.3 Pebble orientation in conglomerate 60
3.4 Intraclast orientation in limestone 61
3.5 Orientation of fossils 62
3.6 Exercise 63

4 Trace fossils 65

4.1 Introduction 65
4.2 Classification 66
4.3 Keys for trace fossil identification 71
4.4 Descriptions of common trace fossils 80
4.5 Behavioral classification 98

4.6 Features that may be misidentified as trace fossils 99
4.7 Value of trace fossils in sedimentology 100
4.8 Exercises: trace fossils 102

5 Particle morphology 107

5.1 Definitions 107
5.2 Measurement 110
5.3 Factors that control particle morphology 111
5.4 Reasons for studying particle morphology 113
5.5 Sample statistical analysis using the chi-square test 113
5.6 Exercises: roundness and chi-square 119

6 Mineral identification using X-ray diffraction 124

6.1 Introduction 124
6.2 Mineral identification (exclusive of clays) 126
6.3 Clay mineral identification 128
6.4 Chemical composition in solid-solution series 130
6.5 Quantification of mineral content 130
6.6 Sample preparation 132
6.7 Exercises: X-ray diffraction 132

7 Grain size 154

7.1 Grain-size classification 154
7.2 Grain-size analysis of unconsolidated sediment 157
7.3 Grain-size analysis of sedimentary rock 161
7.4 Graphic presentation of data 163
7.5 Statistical parameters of grain size 166
7.6 Variation in grain size with distance of transport 175
7.7 Exercises: grain size 176

8 Sedimentary rock classification 184

8.1 Sandstone 184
8.2 Mudrock 194
8.3 Conglomerate 195
8.4 Limestone 195
8.5 Sample statistical analysis using the Mann–Whitney *U*-test 200
8.6 Exercises: rock classification 204

9 Heavy minerals 208

9.1 Introduction 208
9.2 Heavy mineral assemblage 208
9.3 Factors that control heavy mineral assemblages 208
9.4 Methods of separation and analysis 214
9.5 Mineral descriptions 218

10 Rock color 231

10.1 Descriptions of colors 231
10.2 Factors that influence color 231

11 Environmental analysis 235

11.1 Introduction 235
11.2 Field data 235
11.3 Facies analysis of vertical sections 240
11.4 Facies maps 250
11.5 Facies models 255
11.6 Exercise: facies relationship diagram 256
11.7 Exercise: isopach and facies map 257

References 260
Index 270

List of tables

1.1 Characteristics of undulatory bedforms 3
1.2 Comparison of terminology for large-scale bedforms produced by unidirectional currents 4
1.3 Terminology for stratification thickness 14
1.4 Comparison of terminology for climbing-ripple cross lamination 19
1.5 Criteria for distinguishing structures produced by soft-sediment deformation versus tectonic activity 31
2.1 Results of analysis for Exercise 2 55
2.2 Problem sets for analysis of paleocurrent data 56
5.1 Grain counts for roundness of two sand samples 114
5.2 Tally sheet for computing mean roundness for beach sand and dune sand 116
5.3 Analysis of roundness data using the chi-square test 117
5.4 Problem sets for analysis of roundness 120
5.5 Table to use in calculating mean roundness 121
5.6 Table to use in calculating chi-square 122
6.1 Comparison of XRD data for unknown mineral specimen and barite standard 127
6.2 Data for identification of clay minerals in an oriented mount using X-ray diffraction 129
6.3 2θ values for the four most intense reflections in the range 2–40° 2θ for minerals found in bulk samples of sediment and sedimentary rock 136
6.4 2θ values for the four most intense XRD reflections in the range 2–40° 2θ for minerals found in heavy mineral separations 140
6.5 2θ values for the four most intense XRD reflections in the range 2–40° 2θ for minerals found in sediment and sedimentary rock 145
6.6 2θ values for XRD reflections in the range 2–40° 2θ for minerals found in sediment and sedimentary rock 147
7.1 Udden–Wentworth size classes 155
7.2 Calculation of moment measures 169
7.3 Formulas and verbal scales for graphic size parameters 171
7.4 Grain-size parameters calculated by method of moments using different estimates of the grain size present on the pan 173
7.5 Problem sets for grain-size analysis 178
7.6 Results of grain-size analysis 179

7.7 Table to use in calculating moment measures (millimeter midpoint) 180
7.8 Table to use in calculating moment measures (ϕ midpoint) 182
8.1 Composition of 23 sandstone beds from Formation A and Formation B 201
8.2 Samples ranked in terms of feldspar abundance 202
8.3 Method for calculating Mann–Whitney *U*-test statistic 203
8.4 Partial list of critical values of *U* for the Mann–Whitney *U*-test 204
8.5 Problem set: sandstone composition for five samples 204
8.6 Problem set: limestone composition for four samples 206
8.7 Problem sets 207
9.1 Detrital heavy mineral suites characteristic of source rock types 209
11.1 Binomial probability for facies transitions in Battery Point Sandstone 248
11.2 Tally matrix for a hypothetical coal measure 256
11.3 Thickness of the Elk Point Group and its constituent lithologies 257

1 Description of sedimentary structures

1.1 Introduction

Primary sedimentary structures are formed at the time of deposition or shortly thereafter. The character of these structures depends mainly on current velocity, water depth, grain size, and sedimentation rate. As such they are critical to the understanding of the processes and conditions of deposition and lead to an interpretation of the depositional environment. In addition, some are useful in determining "stratigraphical-up" or "way-up" in folded sequences and paleocurrent directions.

All too often the terminology used is unnecessarily complex and confusing. One problem is that a particular structure may be quite variable in shape, and each variant is given a different name. Tool casts, for example, are subdivided as groove casts, chevron casts, prod casts, bounce casts, brush casts, and roll casts. This mainly reflects the complex nature of natural phenomena and to a certain extent it is unavoidable. A bigger problem is the use of numerous terms to describe a single feature, or worse, the use of the same term to describe different structures. In this book I have tried to present the most commonly used terms. This will meet your primary need to have a working vocabulary. You will also require an expanded vocabulary in order to use the literature, so I have included frequently used synonyms in the tables and have introduced them parenthetically in the text.

The organization of this chapter is based on the position of the structure relative to the bedding surface. The purpose is to familiarize you with the most common structures and give you an appreciation of their significance. Details concerning the processes involved in their formation can be found in books by Blatt *et al.* (1980) and Leeder (1982) as well as in those listed below. This text contains numerous illustrations, but you should look at as many other examples as possible. This is best done in the field and in the laboratory with hand specimens. Photographs will further enhance your ability to recognize sedimentary structures and to appreciate their variability. Especially recommended are books by Potter and Pettijohn (1963, 1977), Pettijohn and Potter (1964), Picard and High (1973), Reineck and Singh (1975), Allen (1982 a & b), Collinson and Thompson (1982), and Scholle and Spearing (1982).

1.2 Structures on the upper bedding surface

1.2.1 Undulatory bedforms produced by unidirectional water currents

Most bedforms produced in unidirectional water currents are asymmetric with a gentle surface sloping up-current (stoss surface) and a steeper surface (25–35°) sloping down-current (lee surface or slipface) (Fig 1.6b). Bedforms migrate in the direction of flow as sediment is accreted onto the lee surface. As water passes over the crest, the flow separates from the bed to form a zone of reverse flow (backflow) (Fig. 1.15). At the point where the mainflow reattaches to the bed, turbulent eddies are produced. In the case of bedforms with irregular (three-dimensional) crestlines, the erosive power of these eddies is concentrated on the bed to form spoon-shaped scours which migrate ahead of the crest. Scour pits of this sort are absent in straight-crested bedforms.

Current ripples are the smallest subaqueous forms commonly developed on silt to medium sand beds. They do not occur in sand coarser than 0.6 mm. Only in water depths of a few centimeters are ripple forms coupled with surface waves, and as is the case with megaripples, they are out of phase. Ripple height ranges from 0.5 to 5 cm, and ripple wavelength ranges between 10 and 60 cm (Table 1.1). The ripple index (L/H) ranges between 10 and 40. In plan view, ripple crests are straight (referred to as two-dimensional – see Fig. 1.1) or irregular (three-dimensional – see Fig. 1.2). Some work suggests that the variation from 2-D to 3-D ripples is systematically related to flow conditions (especially velocity and depth). However, it does not seem that these variations are regular, or large enough to be useful in the interpretation of paleoflow conditions (Harms *et al.* 1982: 2–17).

Megaripples (also known as dunes) are dynamically different from ripples. Although similar in shape, they are separated by a distinct difference in size (Table 1.1). Megaripple size increases with greater water depth, for depths of a few meters.

The term **sand wave** is used by some geologists to describe bedforms that are usually larger than megaripples (Table 1.1). Sand waves have less relief and generally straighter crests than megaripples (based on studies of streams and in laboratory flumes). Some workers do not agree with such a distinction, but consider both to be elements in a single bedform type, simply called large ripples (Harms *et al.* 1982). This rather basic, and as yet unresolved, problem is complicated by a lack of uniform usage (see Table 1.2).

Small bedforms are commonly superimposed on the stoss surfaces of larger ones. Examples include ripples on megaripples and sand waves,

Table 1.1 Characteristics of undulatory bedforms. From numerous sources (especially Reineck & Singh 1975 and Allen 1982a). Values commonly represent a compromise which I hope is near the truth.

Origin	Name	Height (H)	Length* (L)	Ripple index* (L/H)	Ripple symmetry index	Plan view shapes†	Other terms
subaqueous – currents	current ripples	0.5–5 cm	15–30 cm (10–60 cm)	10–40	2.5–15	3-D (2-D)	ripples, small ripples, small-scale ripples
subaqueous – currents	megaripples	10–200 cm	1–4 m (0.5–30 m)	10–40	high	3-D, 2-D	dunes, large ripples
subaqueous – currents	sand waves	1–20 m	20–200 m (5–100 m)	10–100	?	2-D (3-D)	large ripples, giant ripples, bars of various types
subaqueous – waves	antidunes	0.5–50 cm	0.1–5 m	low	low	2-D (3-D)	
subaqueous – waves	wave ripples	0.5–20 cm	2–100 cm	6–8 (2–16)	1–3	2-D, partly bifurcating	oscillation or symmetrical ripples when RSI < 1.5; wave-current or asymmetrical wave ripples when RSI > 1.5
wind	wind sand ripples	0.5–5 cm (0.2–10 cm)	5–80 cm (2–200 cm)	15–40 (10–70)	2–4 (1.5–8)	2-D, partly bifurcating	wind ripples, ballistic ripples
wind	wind granule ripples	2.5–60 cm	2.5–20 m	12–20	?	2-D, 3-D	wind ripples
wind	dunes	0.1–100 m	3–600 m	–	–	2-D, 3-D	numerous varieties (e.g. barchan, transverse, seif)

* Length and ripple index: complete range in parentheses if greater than commonly occurring range.
† Plan view shape: if one shape is markedly subordinate it is in parentheses.

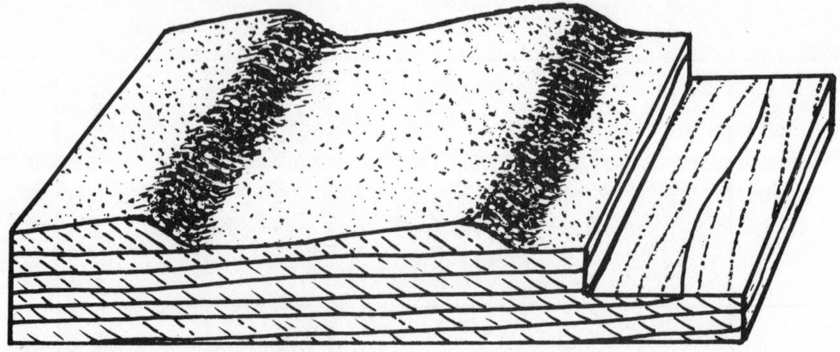

Figure 1.1 Two-dimensional (asymmetrical) current ripples and associated tabular cross bedding. Flow is from left to right.

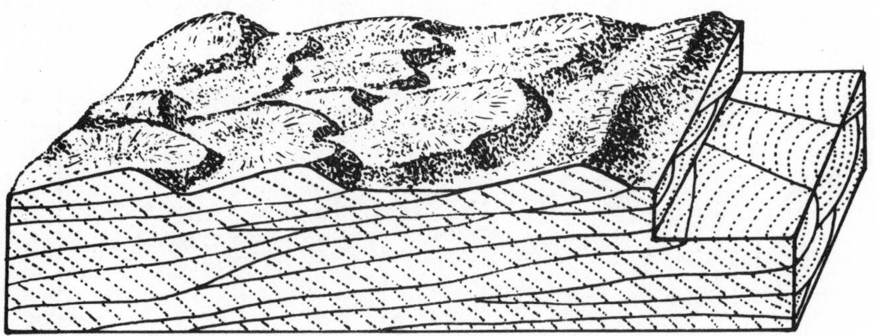

Figure 1.2 Three-dimensional (asymmetrical) current ripples and associated trough bedding. Linguoid ripples on left side and a single sinuous ripple on the right. Flow is from left to right.

Table 1.2 Comparison of terminology for large-scale bedforms produced by unidirectional currents. The various terms used to describe megaripples are given in column A and those used to describe sand waves in column B.

A	B	References
megaripple	sand wave	this book, Davis (1983)
megaripple	giant ripple	Reineck and Singh (1975)
dune	sand wave	Blat *et al.* (1980), Tucker (1981, 1982), Collinson and Thompson (1982)
large ripple (2-D and 3-D)	large ripple (2-D)	Harms *et al.* (1982)
dune	bar	Leeder (1982)
dune	dune	Allen (1982a)
type 2 megaripple	type 1 megaripple	Dalrymple *et al.* (1978)

and megaripples on sand waves. It is not certain whether the superimposed bedforms (especially megaripples on sand waves) are in equilibrium during particular flow conditions or whether they reflect variations in flow strength with time.

Sand waves and megaripples are almost never preserved as bedforms in ancient deposits, except in some Pleistocene sediments. For example, in Washington State, sand waves with heights of up to 3 m and wavelengths of up to 80 m were produced by catastrophic floods resulting from rapid draining of the glacial Lake Missoula.

Antidunes are fundamentally different from all the bedforms discussed above. They are rather symmetrical in vertical section, with broadly rounded crests and troughs (Fig. 1.27). The prefix "anti-" refers to the tendency of antidunes to migrate up-current. They develop in very fast shallow currents and are in phase with water-surface waves. Antidunes have a very low preservation potential because, as flow velocity decreases, the bedform is rapidly transformed to a plane bed by the still energetic flow.

1.2.2 Plane beds produced by unidirectional water currents

Under certain flow conditions, the sand-bed surface is nearly flat and horizontal. This bed configuration, called a **plane bed** (or flat bed according to some), is generally formed by fast currents with rapid sediment transport. Some sandstones are the product of deposition on a plane bed. They are rather fissile and, when split, show a distinct linear pattern on the bedding surface. This structure, known as **parting lineation**, occurs as a series of minute ridges and hollows (Fig. 1.3), which lie parallel to the current-flow direction. As such they indicate the line of movement, but not the direction of movement. You will often see parting lineation on flagstone used in patios and walks.

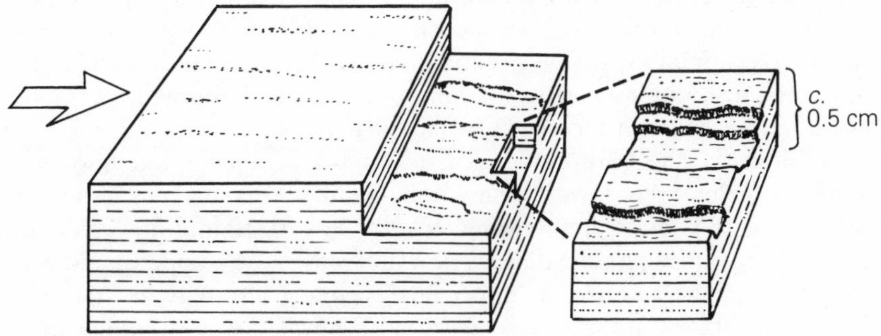

Figure 1.3 Plane bed and associated horizontal stratification. Bedding plane surface shows parting lineation. Arrow indicates flow direction.

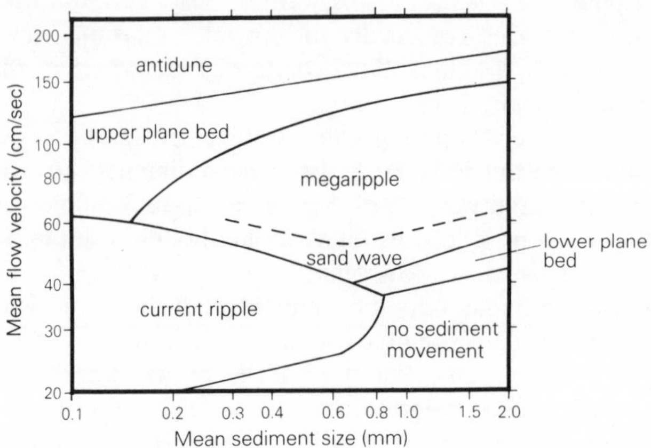

Figure 1.4 A size–velocity diagram for shallow depths (18–22 cm) showing stability fields of different bedforms (modified from Blatt *et al.* 1980: Fig. 5.4, Harms *et al.* 1982: Fig. 2.5).

1.2.3 Factors that control bedforms produced by unidirectional water currents

The three main factors that control the bedforms produced by unidirectional water currents are: (1) mean flow velocity, (2) grain size, and (3) water depth. A sequence of bedforms results from a regular increase in velocity (Fig. 1.4). For silt to very fine sand it is: ripple → upper plane bed → antidune; for medium sand: ripple → sand wave → megaripple → upper plane bed → antidune; and for coarse to very coarse sand: lower plane bed → sand wave → megaripple → upper plane bed → antidune. Note that plane beds may form under quite different conditions depending on grain size. One develops in relatively low velocities, but only on beds coarser than 0.6 mm, and is referred to as a **lower plane bed**. This bedform is not known to produce internal lamination. The other develops in higher-velocity flows, and is commonly preserved by internal laminae (see Section 1.3.2). There is a marked tendency for larger bedforms (megaripples and sand waves) to become progressively more three-dimensional with increasing velocity (Fig. 1.5).

Traditionally, the bedforms discussed above are separated into two groups. Ripples, the lower plane bed, sand waves and megaripples characterize the **lower flow régime** where flow resistance is high and bedforms are out of phase with surface-water waves. The upper plane bed and antidunes characterize the **upper flow régime** where flow resistance is low and antidunes are in phase with surface-water waves, which may migrate up-current.

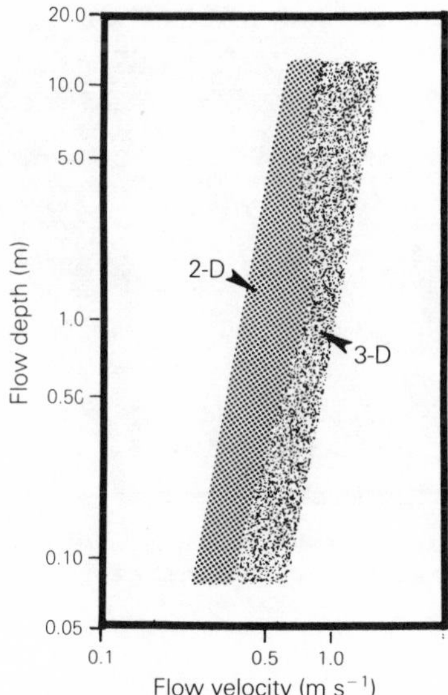

Figure 1.5 A depth–velocity diagram showing effect of flow velocity on plan-view geometry of dunes and sand waves (modified from Harms *et al.* 1982: Fig. 2.7).

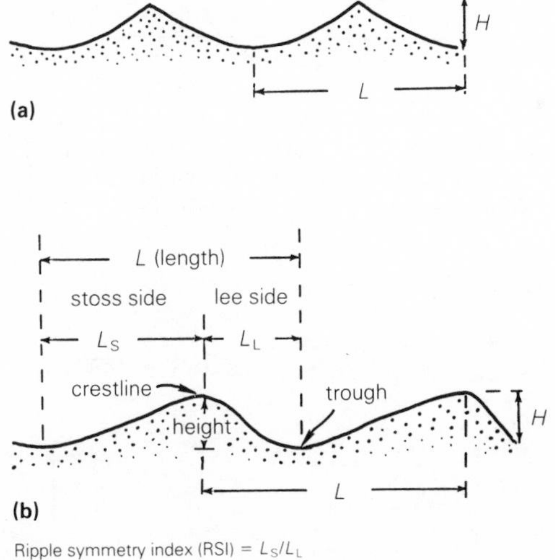

Figure 1.6 Diagrams for terms used in describing ripples seen in vertical profile: (a) symmetrical ripples; (b) asymmetrical ripples.

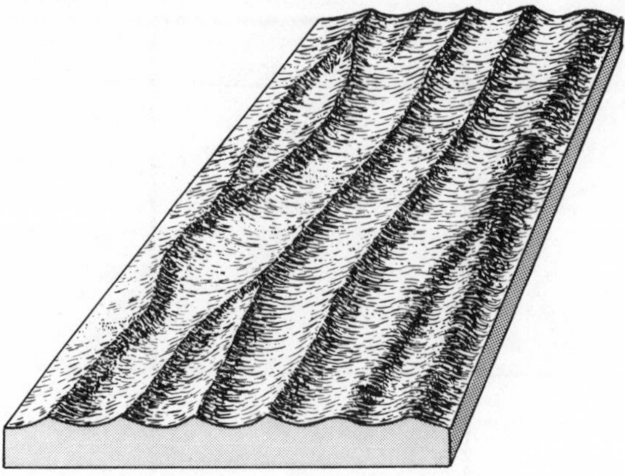

Figure 1.7 Two-dimensional symmetrical ripples with crestline bifurcation. Most show typical peaked crest; those to right have rounded crest.

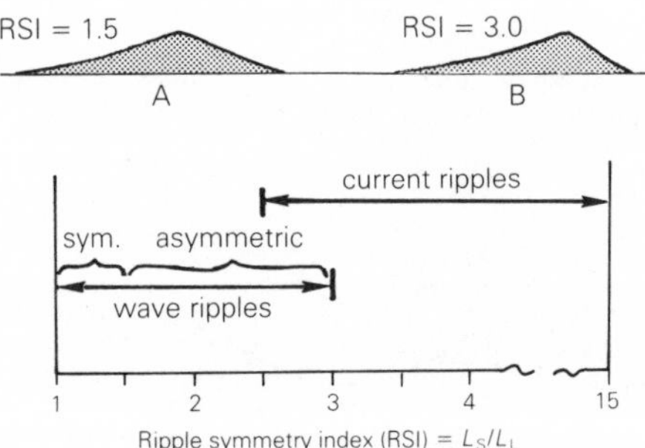

Figure 1.8 The ripple symmetry index range for current- and wave-formed ripples. A, Profile of typical wave ripple; B, profile of typical current ripple. Solid line represents most frequently occurring values. See Figure 1.6 for explanation of RSI. (Based on data from Tanner 1967.)

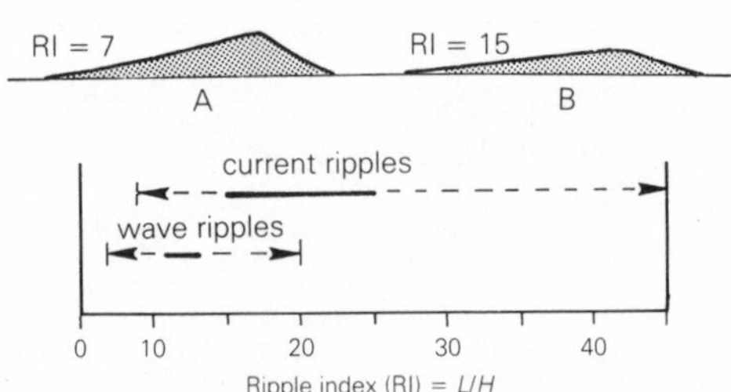

Figure 1.9 The ripple index range for current and wave ripples: A, B, profiles of asymmetrical wave ripples showing range of variation. See Figure 1.6 for explanation of RI. (Based on data from Tanner 1967.)

1.2.4 Undulatory bedforms produced by wave action

In nearshore marine and lacustrine environments, bedforms are strongly influenced by the oscillatory motion of wind-generated waves. The back-and-forth motion of the water near the bed produces symmetric ripples with peaked or somewhat rounded crests (Fig. 1.6a). Crestlines are relatively straight (2-D) and **bifurcation** is common (Fig. 1.7). Heights range upward to 20 cm and wavelengths to 1 m, depending on grain size, wave size and water depth. Shoaling waves or waves combined with currents moving in the same direction produce asymmetric ripples, called **wave-current ripples**. Although similar to ordinary current ripples, wave-current ripples have lower ripple symmetry index values and lower ripple index values (Figs 1.8 & 1.9). In addition, crestline straightness and bifurcation of wave-current ripples serve to distinguish them from current ripples.

Interaction between two wave-sets or between waves and currents may generate complex **interference ripple patterns** (for illustrations see Reineck & Singh 1975: 366–8). In cases where two sets of ripples form, they may be equally well developed or one may be dominant. The crestlines of the two sets may be parallel (Fig. 1.10a) or, as is usually the case, divergent (Fig. 1.10 b–e). In some situations they form rectangular or hexagonal outlines (Fig. 1.10b).

Gently undulating or **hummocky bedding surfaces** occur in some fine-grained sandstones (see Harms *et al.* 1982: Fig. 2.15, and Collinson & Thompson 1982: Fig. 6.61). Spacing between the broad and gentle domes (hummocks) ranges upward to 5 m, and heights range upward to several decimeters (Fig. 1.26). In some cases this bedform is attributed to large storm waves acting on shelf sands and in other cases to bedforms produced during upper-flow-régime conditions in unidirectional flow. Oscillatory flow generated by very large waves, with high orbital velocities, may produce a flat and featureless bed.

1.2.5 Undulatory bedforms produced by wind

Wind blowing over dry sand produces a variety of bedforms. This occurs mainly in deserts, coastal areas, and glacial outwash plains. The smaller bedforms, called **wind-sand ripples**, are composed of very fine to medium sand. Heights range upward to 5 cm and wavelengths to several decimeters (Table 1.1). They have ripple index values mostly in the range of 15 to 40, which is higher than for wave ripples. Ripple symmetry index values generally range between 1.5 and 4.0, lower than for most current ripples. Use of these two indices thus provides a reasonable basis for distinguishing wind-sand ripples from those formed in water (Fig. 1.11). In addition, ripples produced by wind action commonly lack well defined

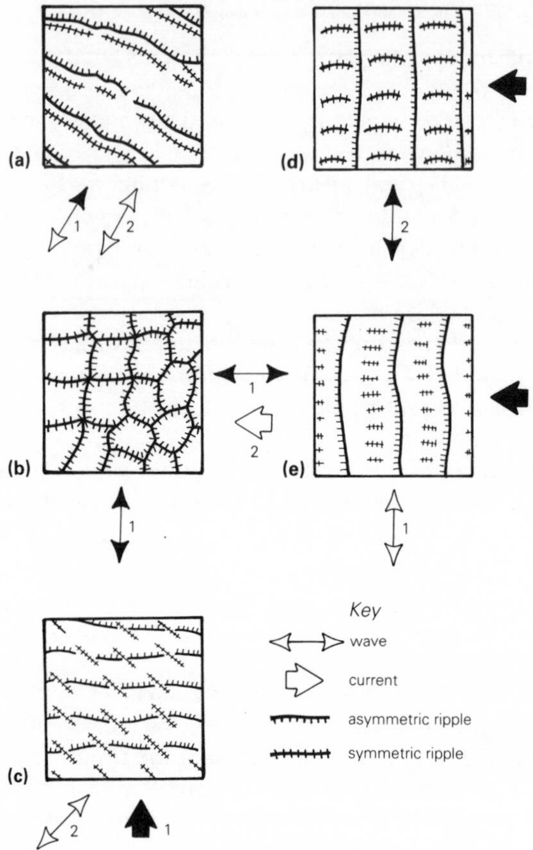

Figure 1.10 Some complex interference ripple patterns: (a) multiple and parallel ripple crests are "explained in terms of either the tide ebbing or the abatement of wind and wave" (Allen 1982a: 433, Fig. 11.11); (b)–(e) ripples formed by waves or currents moving in different directions. Solid arrow indicates dominant wave or current direction; darker crestline indicates larger-scale ripple; numbers denote relative time of activity, the same number reflecting simultaneous activity. (Based mainly on Reineck & Singh 1975: Figs 526 & 527.)

internal lamination and have relatively coarse sand grains concentrated near their crests – two aspects which further distinguish them from subaqueous ripples.

Larger aeolian bedforms (**dunes**), although common in the modern world, are not preserved in the rock record. Their former presence is indicated by extensive cosets of large-scale cross bedding (see Section 1.3.3a).

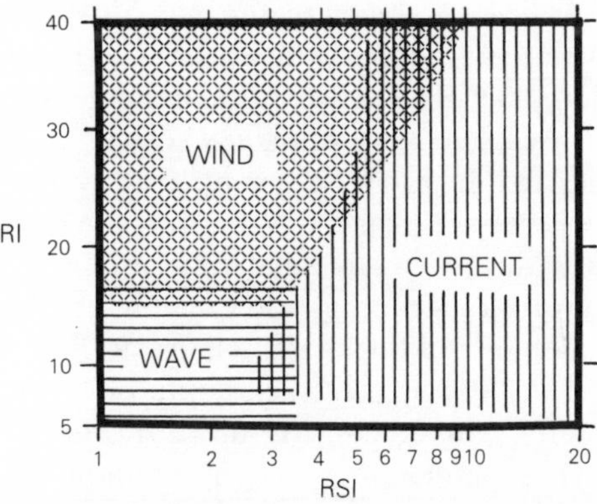

Figure 1.11 The variation of the ripple index (RI) and ripple symmetry index (RSI) for wind-, current-, and wave-formed ripples (modified from Tanner 1967: Fig. 1).

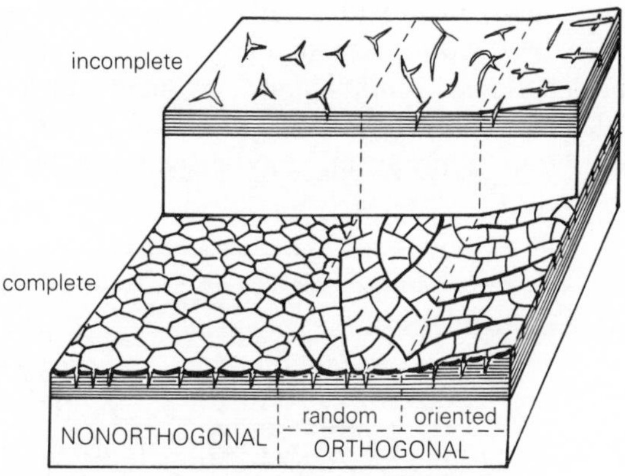

Figure 1.12 The classification of mudcracks as seen on bedding surface (based on Lachenbruch 1963 and Allen 1982b).

1.2.6 Mudcracks

Mudcracks (also called desiccation or shrinkage cracks) form in fine-grain sediment as shrinkage occurs during drying. In plan view they are described as **orthogonal** or **nonorthogonal**, depending on the angle of intersection (Fig. 1.12). Orthogonal cracks are usually normal to one another, and thus bound four-sided polygons. Complete orthogonal mudcracks are the commonest type (Allen 1982b: 546), occurring in a great variety of marine and nonmarine deposits. Complete oriented orthogonal systems develop in muddy beds that thicken in a particular direction or lie on a slope greater than 5°. Examples are known from exposed lacustrine mud deposits near the lake margin (Donovan & Archer 1975, Leeder 1982: Fig. 11.6 c & g), although other depositional environments are possible. Nonorthogonal cracks commonly outline hexagonal polygons and form in sediment that is homogeneous and relatively brittle where shrinkage is uniform. Although frequently illustrated in the literature, they are relatively rare.

Mudcrack polygon size ranges from a few centimeters to several meters and is mainly a function of bed thickness. Allen (1982b: 552) suggests that the polygon size is 3 to 8 times the crack depth or layer thickness.

Polygons are generally curved concave upward (Fig. 1.13,B), although flat or concave-down examples are known. Erosion of thick polygons produces mud clasts. Thin mud layers become strongly curved upon drying, to produce **mud curls** (Fig. 1.13,A). Although rarely preserved they are known and should not be confused with **dish structures** (see Section 1.5.3b).

Mudcracks are usually filled with relatively coarse sediment deposited on the desiccated bed. Some remain open and are filled with sparry calcite after burial. This occurs mainly in small cracks only a few millimeters wide. In vertical sections the mudcracks usually taper downward (Fig. 1.13,C), producing a V-shaped profile. Parallel-sided

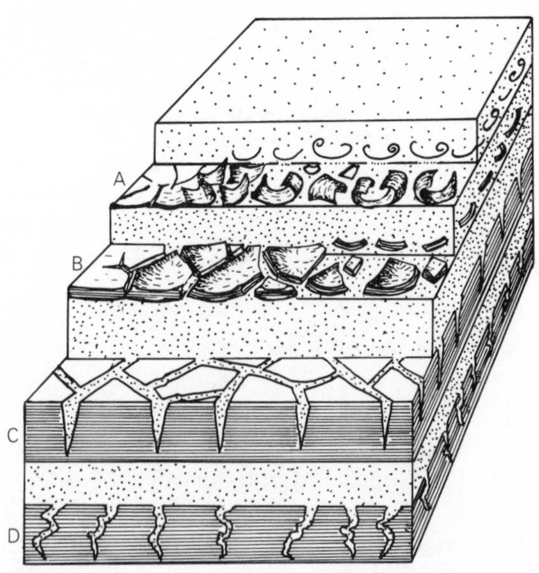

Figure 1.13 Mudcracks: A, thin mud layer with mud curls; B, desiccated mud bed showing gently curved concave-up polygonal fragments; C, sand-filled downward tapering mudcracks; D, sand-filled mudcracks deformed by compaction of muddy bed. Stipple pattern indicates sandy bed.

cracks, which also occur, may be mistaken for burrows. The surest way to avoid this error is observation of polygonal outlines on a bedding surface. Early compaction (prior to cementation) of the enclosing muddy bed may cause folding of a sandy infill (Fig. 1.13d) and should not be confused with tectonic deformation.

Some shrinkage cracks are thought to form in a subaqueous environment without benefit of exposure and drying. Commonly called **synaeresis cracks**, they are attributed to a decrease in volume when clay is rapidly flocculated or subjected to an increase in pore-water salinity. Synaeresis cracks are *typically* lenticular and discontinuous and are similar in appearance to incomplete orthogonal and nonorthogonal cracks (Fig. 1.12), which could be produced simply by rapid burial of a partially desiccated mud bed. Indeed Pettijohn (1975: 123) notes that criteria for distinguishing cracks formed by desiccation versus synaeresis are "obscure", a view echoed by Allen (1982: 553), who goes further in questioning the existence of synaeresis cracks in natural muddy deposits.

The problem regarding synaeresis notwithstanding, complete mudcracks are firm evidence for periodic subaerial exposure. Although the environmental importance of random orthogonal versus nonorthogonal cracks is not clear – indeed there may be none – oriented orthogonal systems may be useful in identifying depositional surfaces with slopes greater than 5° (e.g. muddy nearshore lacustrine or tidal-pond environments). Tapered mudcracks which bound concave-upward polygons are good "stratigraphic-up" indicators.

1.2.7 Raindrop imprints

Shallow pits, with slightly raised rims, are attributed to raindrops or hailstones falling on damp mud (Fig. 1.14a). **Stranded bubbles** produce a similar structure, but they are less regularly distributed on the sediment surface and do not overlap (compare Fig. 1.14 b & c). Moussa (1974)

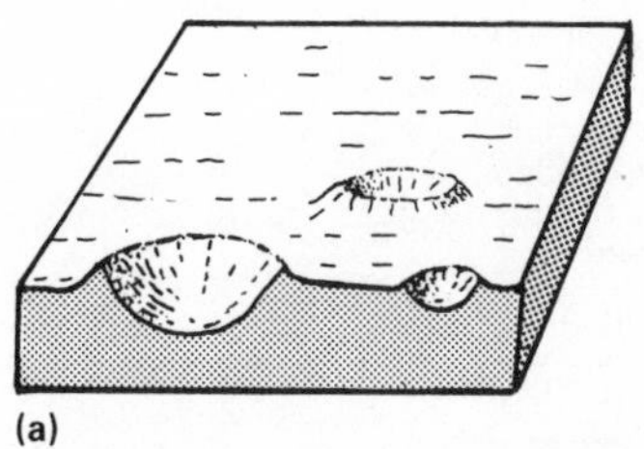

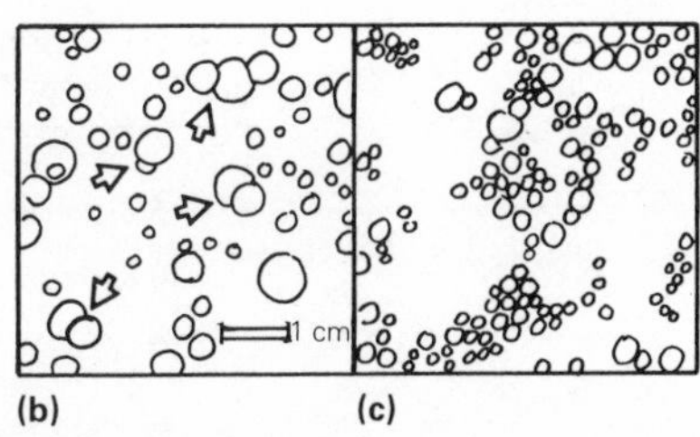

Figure 1.14 Raindrop imprints and impressions of stranded bubbles: (a) diagram of raindrop imprints showing raised rims; (b) plan view of raindrop imprints (note overlapping imprints shown by arrows); (c) plan view showing impressions of stranded bubbles (note irregular distribution). (Modified from illustrations in Shrock 1948.)

argues that many structures interpreted as raindrop imprints are really formed as gas bubbles rise through drying mud and escape to the atmosphere. In truth, the exact mechanism is not very important. The significance of these shallow pits is that they provide evidence of **subaerial exposure**.

A more serious problem involves mistaking these imprints for burrows that penetrate clay films on bedding surfaces in some rocks. Careful examination will show that burrows disturb the underlying sediment and the burrow traces on the bedding surface lack raised rims.

1.3 Internal structures

1.3.1 General characteristics

The one structure common to most sedimentary rock is primary stratification. It may be deposited on horizontal or inclined surfaces and is manifest by differences in grain size, mineralogy, or color. Boundaries between strata may be sharp or gradational, parallel or nonparallel. Strata may be planar or wavy, and in some cases they may be laterally discontinuous or lenticular.

Beds are defined as strata thicker than 1 cm and **laminae** as strata thinner than 1 cm. Further subdivision, as proposed by Ingram (1954), is shown in Table 1.3.

1.3.2 Planar stratification

The term "**planar stratification**" is used to describe strata with little or no primary dip. You will note that this is a restricted use of "planar", which is also used to describe one type of cross bedding (see Section 1.3.3a). The difficulties of terminology are briefly discussed in Harms *et al.* (1982: 3.23–3.24).

Table 1.3 Terminology for stratification thickness (after Ingram 1954).

Thickness boundary	Term
	very thickly bedded
1 m	
	thickly bedded
30 cm	
	medium bedded
10 cm	
	thinly bedded
3 cm	
	very thinly bedded
1 cm	
	thickly laminated
3 mm	
	thinly laminated

The most commonly reported planar stratification (or lamination) is produced by deposition on a plane bed which is a stable bed configuration in rapidly flowing water (upper flow régime) (Section 1.2.3). This type, called **horizontal stratification** (Harms & Fahenstock 1965) or **upper tractional planar lamination** (Harms *et al.* 1982: Table 3.2), shows parting lineation on bedding surfaces (Fig. 1.3). Although a plane bed also exists at lower velocities (lower flow régime) for sand coarser than 0.6 mm, it is probably not significant in the production of planar stratification. High-energy waves seaward of the surf zone can form flat and featureless beds and presumably planar stratification as well (**oscillatory planar lamination**, Harms *et al.* 1982).

Another type, called **flat stratification** (Lindholm 1982), is produced by migration of very small ripples (height less than 5 mm and wavelength less than 10 cm) in **shallow** water (less than 5 cm). Its recognition is based on association with very small ripples or microscale cross bedding (sets 1–2 mm thick). When present it indicates deposition in shallow flowing water and could be an important clue in evaluating certain sedimentary environments.

Deposition on a subhorizontal surface by settling of silt- and clay-size material from suspension also produces planar stratification (**settling planar stratification**, Harms *et al.* 1982).

Be aware that interpreting the origin of planar stratification is difficult and sometimes impossible. Not only is it difficult to differentiate between the types described above, but in some cases it is hard to distinguish true planar stratification from low-angle inclined stratification (see Sections 1.1.3 c & d).

1.3.3 Inclined stratification

As the name indicates, inclined stratification consists of strata with a primary dip, bounded by major bedding planes. Each of these units is called a **set**. Vertically contiguous sets of similar type are called **cosets** (see Fig. 1.17).

(a) Cross bedding

Cross bedding is produced by migration of bedforms, mainly ripples, megaripples and sand waves, in response to current action; it is one of the most familiar and useful structures found in sedimentary rock. The inclined strata, called **foresets**, have dips that range from 20 to 35°. Set boundaries are deposited subhorizontally, especially as seen on vertical sections parallel to flow.

Foresets are formed by deposition on the lee surface of a migrating bedform. Individual foresets are recognizable because of slight variations in grain size which may be produced by several mechanisms. One

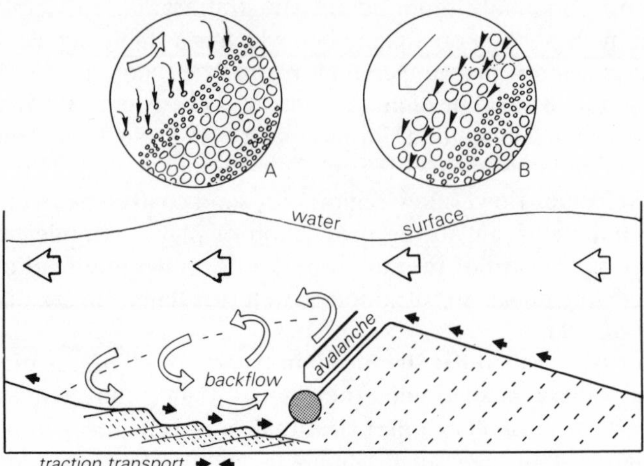

Figure 1.15 The zone of separation in the lee of a megaripple resulting in backflow. The traction load moves up the stoss face of the megaripple, periodically avalanching down the lee face. The coarsest portion of the suspended load is deposited on the lee face (see detail A). Periodic avalanche deposits from the megaripple crest (see detail B) alternate with layers of suspended sediment producing cross-bed foresets as the dune migrates from right to left. In some cases ripples form in the backflow and migrate, left to right, in the opposite direction to the main flow. This produces small-scale cross bedding which dips in the opposite direction from foresets deposited on the lee face of the megaripple (see Fig. 1.22).

involves continuous sedimentation of the suspended load, carried up the lee surface by backflow currents (Fig. 1.15,A), which is punctuated by sporadic avalanches of coarser sediment from the crest (Fig. 1.15,B). In this way coarse and fine strata are alternately superimposed in a layered sequence. Such laminae are commonly curved (Fig. 1.16a).

Another mechanism involving intermittent sand-flow down the lee surface of megaripples, sand waves, and aeolian dunes produces foreset laminae with little if any curvature in cross sections parallel to the dip direction (Fig. 1.16b) (Hunter 1985). Such foresets show downward coarsening along the cross stratum, inverse grading and a small range of cross-stratum thickness within a set.

Cross bedding is classified on the basis of (1) the shape and attitude of foresets, (2) the shape of set boundaries, and (3) the thickness of sets.

Foresets are described as **planar** or **tangential**, on the basis of their shape as viewed in vertical sections parallel to the dip direction (Fig. 1.16). Planar foresets are nearly flat and intersect the lower set boundary at a relatively high angle. Some authors use "angular" instead of "planar." Tangential foresets are curved concave-up and intersect the lower set boundary at a low angle.

Cross bedding is further described as **tabular** or **trough-shaped**, on the

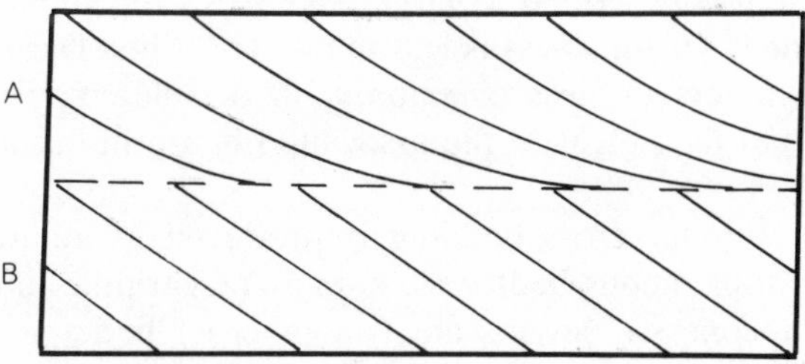

Figure 1.16 Vertical sections parallel to flow showing tangential (A) and planar (B) foresets.

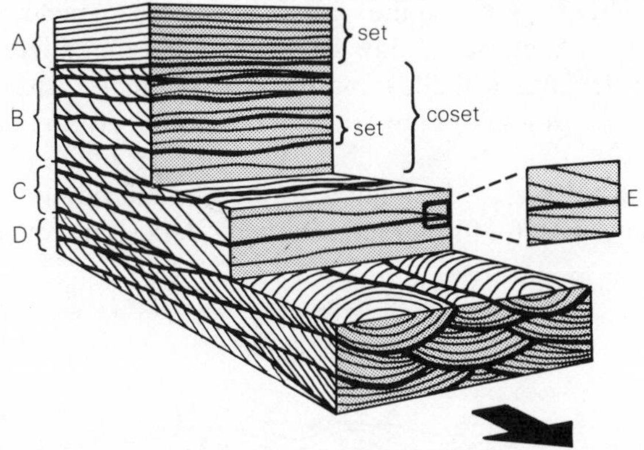

Figure 1.17 Cross-bed types based on set geometry: B, coset of tabular cross bedding with tangential foresets; C, coset of tabular cross bedding with angular foresets; D, coset of trough cross bedding; E, detail showing that foreset laminae in tabular cross bedding are not strongly conformable to lower set boundary (dips exaggerated). (Based on Harms *et al.* 1982.)

basis of the configuration of the set boundaries. In tabular cross bedding, **set boundaries** are characterized as being either planar or parallel, although in many cases they are somewhat undulatory and convergent (Fig. 1.17,B & C). In addition, foreset traces seen on horizontal surfaces are relatively straight.

Trough cross bedding sets have strongly curved concave-up lower set boundaries as seen in vertical sections transverse to flow (Fig. 1.17D). In plan view the foreset traces are markedly curved and concave in the down-current direction. This expression of trough cross bedding is sometimes referred to as **rib and furrow**. Trough sets result from the movement of three-dimensional (sinuously crested) bedforms into spoon-shaped scours which migrate ahead of the crest. In vertical sections parallel to flow it is often difficult to distinguish tabular and trough cross bedding.

Cross bedding is described as **large-scale** if set thickness exceeds 5 cm and **small-scale** if set thickness is less than 5 cm. Most large-scale sets are measured in meters or, less commonly, in decimeters. Set thickness is usually less than the height of the associated bedform because of erosion of the crest.

Large-scale tubular cross bedding is produced by relatively straight-crested (2-D) subaqueous bedforms, namely megaripples and sand waves (Fig. 1.1). In contrast, large-scale trough cross bedding is formed by irregular (3-D) subaqueous bedforms, namely megaripples (Fig. 1.2). Cross bedding produced by aeolian dunes typically occurs as cosets consisting of very large scale sets, each several (to 10 or more) meters thick. Although useful in the identification of aeolian deposits, size alone is not definitive. Some quite large scale cross bedding, especially occurring as isolated sets, may be formed by the migration of large bedforms in fluvial and shallow marine environments. Also some aeolian sandstones are dominated by relatively small sets or have no cross bedding at all.

Most small-scale cross bedding is formed by migrating current ripples. For extensive sets to form, net sediment deposition must take place.

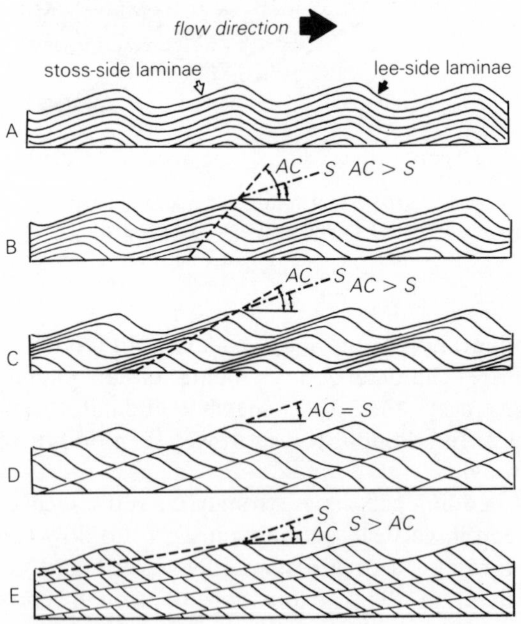

Figure 1.18 Climbing-ripple cross lamination. *AC*, angle of climb; *S*, stoss-side slope. A–D, Depositional-stoss climbing-ripple cross lamination; E, erosional-stoss climbing-ripple cross lamination. The sequence A–E shows a progressive decrease in the angle of climb. (Based on Harms *et al.* 1982.)

Table 1.4 Comparison of terminology for climbing-ripple cross lamination.

Description	Illustration in this text	Jopling and Walker (1968)	Reineck and Singh (1975)	Hunter (1977)	Harms *et al.* (1982)
no lateral migration of ripple crest; angle of climb at maximum	Fig. 1.18a	sinusoidal ripple lamination	ripple with laminae in phase	supercritical climbing translatent stratification	depositional-stoss climbing-ripple cross lamination
angle of climb greater than slope of stoss surface	Figs 1.18 b–c	type B ripple-drift cross lamination	type 1 ripple, laminae in drift		
angle of climb less than slope of stoss surface	Fig. 1.18e	type A ripple-drift cross lamination	type 2 ripple laminae in drift	subcritical climbing translatent stratification	erosional-stoss climbing-ripple cross lamination

When this happens, ripple crests will have a vertical component of motion as well as a horizontal component caused by ripple migration. The combined effect of these two components of movement is referred to as the **angle of climb**. If the angle of climb is greater than the stoss-side slope, stoss-side laminae are preserved (Fig. 1.18,A–D). Such cross bedding, where the stoss-side and lee-side deposits (foresets) form continuous laminae, is called **depositional-stoss climbing-ripple cross lamination** or more simply **climbing ripples** (see Table 1.4 for other terms). High angles of climb, caused by high rates of net deposition (mainly from suspension) may result from deceleration of flow, with a corresponding increase in sedimentation, as occurs during the waning stages of floods or turbidity flows. Changes in the angle of climb, within a given sequence (Fig. 1.19), reflect a delicate balance between variations in the rate of sedimentation and the rate of ripple migration caused by changes in flow conditions. An upward increase in the angle of climb, accompanied by a gradual decrease in grain size, is attributed to deceleration of flow, where increased sedimentation (vertical component) is more important than the decreasing migration rate (horizontal component).

If the angle of climb is less than the stoss-side slope, erosion occurs and only foresets are preserved (**erosional-stoss climbing-ripple cross lamination**, Fig. 1.18,E). Probably most small-scale cross bedding is produced by ripples climbing at small angles. This will not be obvious if the angle is

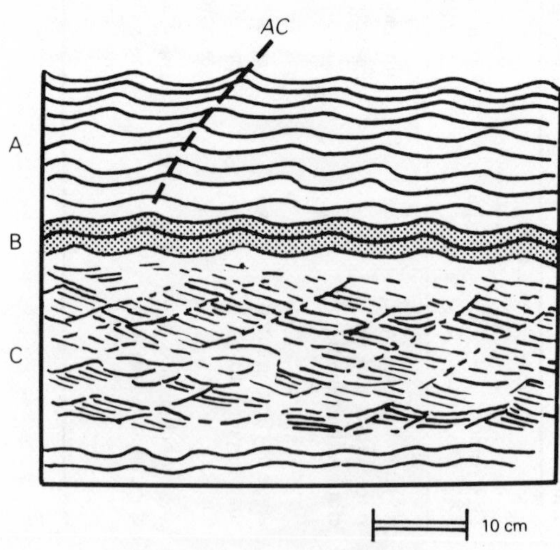

Figure 1.19 A sequence showing various types of climbing-ripple cross lamination in fine sand deposited on the flood plain of the Colorado River in Arizona. *AC*, angle of climb in set A. Which set (A, B, or C) shows the greatest angle of climb? (Based on photograph in McKee 1965: Fig. 3.c.)

very small or the upper and lower contacts of the coset are not exposed or are poorly defined.

In cases where ripples migrate (with zero angles of climb) across a muddy substrate, and the supply of sand or silt is limited, the isolated ripple train may be preserved as **form sets** (a form set is a unit in which the morphological character of a bedform is preserved). This structure, known as lenticular bedding (also called separated or starved ripples), is an end member in a sequence that includes wavy bedding and flaser bedding formed by interbedded mud and sand occurring in varying proportions (Fig. 1.20).

Small-scale cross bedding formed by **wave action** is variable in style (Fig. 1.21) and commonly occurs in form sets associated with lenticular,

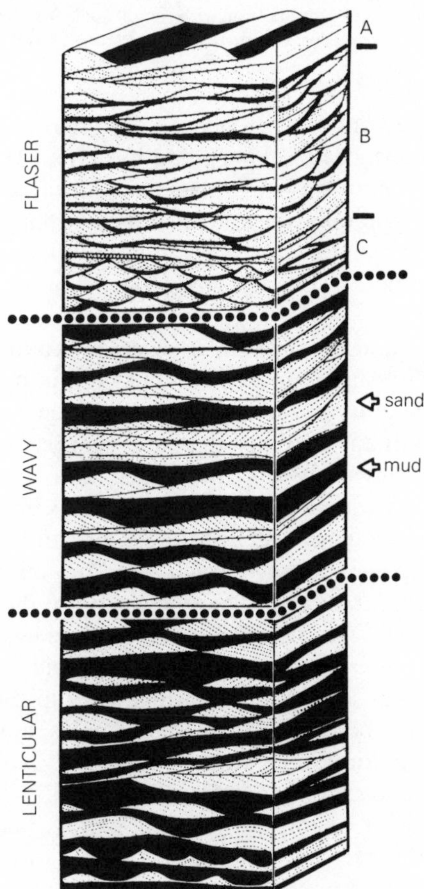

Figure 1.20 Bedding structures in interbedded sand and mud. What type of ripples formed cosets A, B, and C? (Modified from Reineck & Singh 1975: Figs 167, 168, 170, 171.)

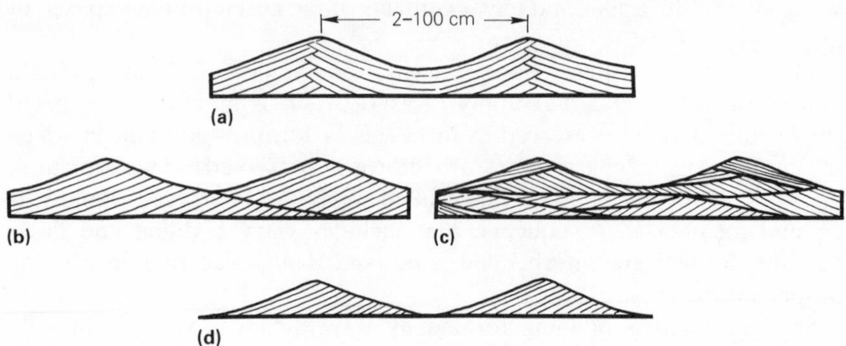

Figure 1.21 Cross bedding formed by oscillatory wave motion: (a) aggradation, no migration; (b) migration and aggradation with small angle of climb under constant wave conditions; (c) migration and aggradation with small angle of climb under variable wave conditions; (d) migration, no aggradation. (Modified from Harms *et al.* 1982: Fig. 3.13.)

wavy, and flaser bedding. Differences in the cross bedding are a function of the relative importance of (1) aggradation rate, (2) migration rate, and (3) variability (or uniformity) of wave size and direction of movement.

Aeolian ripples generally do not form well defined internal structures because migration is "less by repeated lee side avalanches than by saltation bombardment" (Leeder 1982: 97).

(b) Modifications and discontinuities in cross bedding

Cross bedding, with superimposed sets that dip in opposite directions, is called **herringbone cross bedding**. Such bidirectional cosets are deposited by ebb- and flood-tidal currents that are nearly equal in duration and strength. In tidal environments where one flow direction is dominant, herringbone cross bedding does not develop. Care must be taken to distinguish it from trough cross bedding, which in some vertical sections may appear to dip in opposite directions. For this reason at least two vertical sections (e.g. two joint faces) must be studied in order to verify the bidirectional aspect of herringbone cross bedding.

In some rather unusual cases, large-scale tabular sets are intimately associated with small-scale sets with opposite dip direction (Fig. 1.22). The small-scale cross bedding is formed by ripples moving in the backflow behind a larger bedform (megaripple or sand wave). Such ripples are known variously as **backflow**, **regressive**, or **counter-current ripples**. The terms are also used to name the resultant cross bedding. The marked difference in the thickness of opposed sets in this structure distinguishes it from herringbone cross bedding.

Some sets of large-scale cross bedding are interrupted by gently sloping surfaces, called **reactivation surfaces**, which separate otherwise conformable

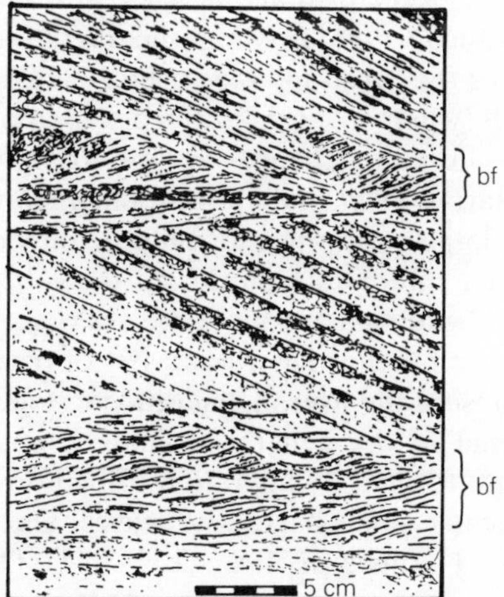

Figure 1.22 Large-scale cross bedding with small-scale backflow cross bedding (bf). See Fig. 1.15 for further explanation. (Based on photograph in Boersma *et al.* 1968.)

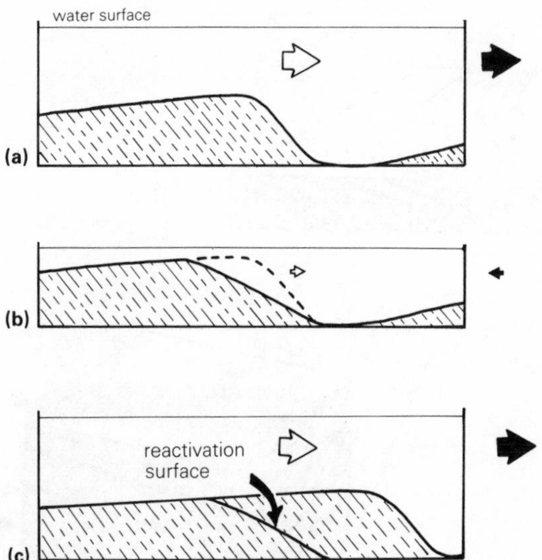

Figure 1.23 A reactivation surface formed by variable flow conditions in unidirectional flow (open arrows) or reversing tidal flow of unequal strength (solid arrows): (a) migration of large bedform; (b) erosion of crest and lee face, producing a gently inclined surface (**reactivation surface**); (c) renewed migration of bedform and re-establishment of slipface.

foresets (Fig. 1.23). Reactivation surfaces are produced by changes in flow conditions which *temporarily* halt the migration of a large bedform and cause erosion of the crest and lee surface. This may happen in very wide river channels when a large bedform is exposed to wave action during low flow or simply by changes in flow strength, which modify the bedform shape (Harms *et al.* 1982). In tidal régimes where one tidal phase is dominant, large bedforms may migrate only during the dominant phase and experience minor erosion during the subordinate phase.

Compound cross bedding contains large-scale sets of gently inclined bedding in combination with smaller-scale sets of **true** cross bedding. The large-scale sets represent the **overall depositional slope**, which may accrete parallel to or normal to the general sediment transport direction. The smaller-scale sets are formed by migration of bedforms across the master slope. Examples include point bars, sand waves, and some aeolian dunes (Allen 1982a: 371–3, Harms *et al.* 1982: 3.32–3.44). One variety known as **epsilon cross bedding** occurs in isolated tabular sandstone units 1–5 m thick. Gently inclined beds (dip = 5–15°), which extend through the full thickness of the unit, record successive positions of a laterally migrating point-bar surface (Fig. 1.24). Smaller-scale cross bedding indicates that flow was subparallel to the strike of the gently inclined beds. Interestingly, epsilon cross bedding is absent (or not recognized) in most point-bar sequences.

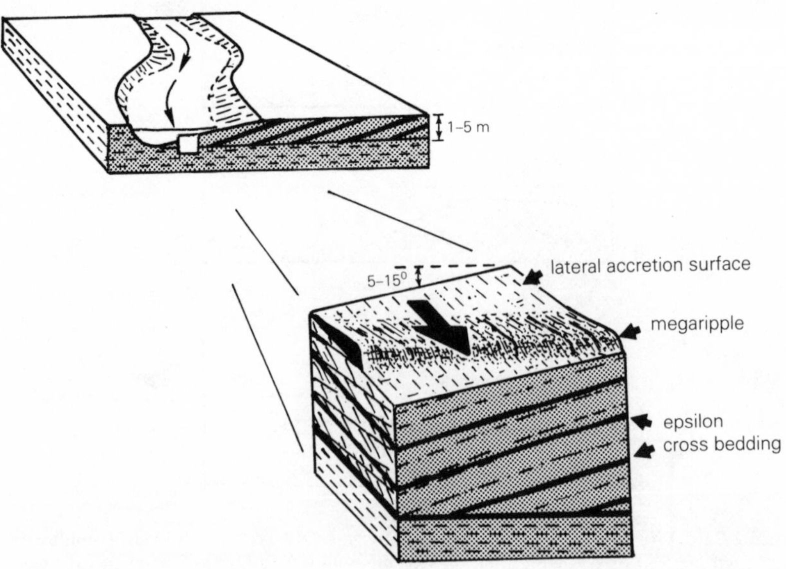

Figure 1.24 Epsilon "cross bedding" formed by laterally migrating point-bar surface.

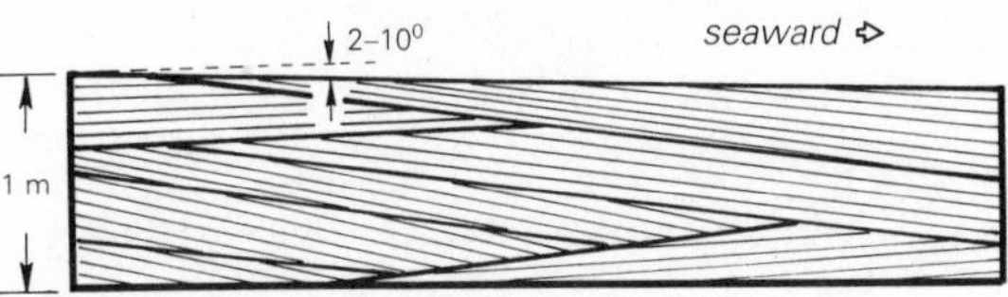

Figure 1.25 Swash cross stratification.

(c) Swash cross stratification

Swash cross stratification, formed in the beach swash zone, is characterized by seaward-dipping low-angle (2–10°) strata (Fig. 1.25). Sets tend to be wedge-shaped because of variations in the slope of the beachface, which changes with varying wave conditions. Laminae are subparallel to lower set boundaries and commonly show reverse textural grading.

(d) Hummocky cross stratification

Hummocky cross stratification consists of broadly undulating sets of rather gently dipping (generally less than 10°, although values may reach 15°) laminae composed of coarse silt to fine sand (Fig. 1.26). Dip directions are scattered and of no known use in evaluating paleoflow. Laminae parallel the lower set boundary but are truncated by the upper set boundary. They commonly show progressive thickening in the dip direction. Although hummocky cross stratification has not been observed in modern deposits or in the laboratory, the association with fossiliferous marine shale and wave ripples, especially at the top of hummocky cosets, suggests deposition on a marine shelf. This structure is thought to form by sedimentation of suspended material over low hummocks and shallow swales produced by large storm waves.

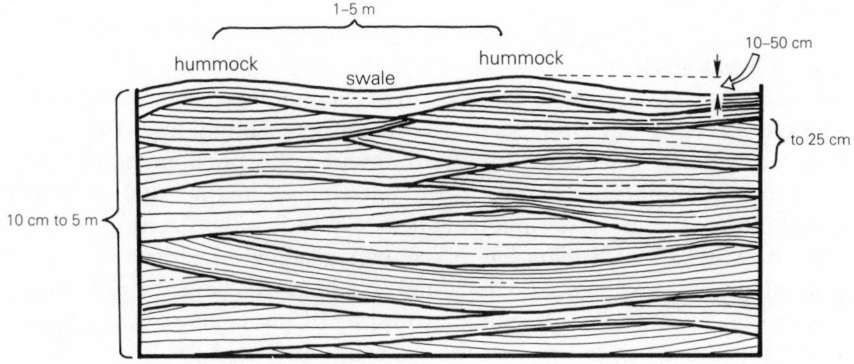

Figure 1.26 Hummocky cross stratification.

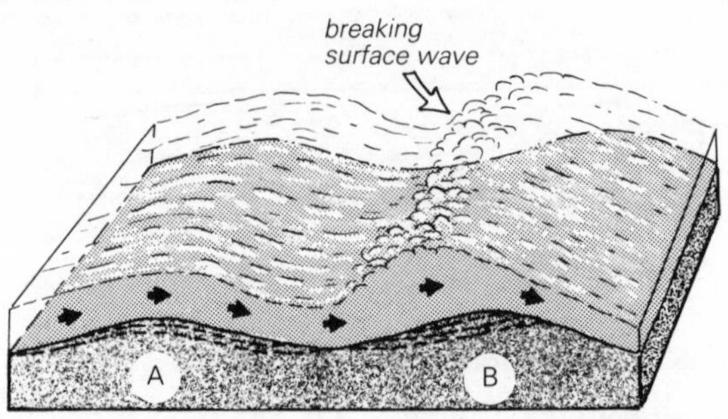

Figure 1.27 Antidune cross stratification: A, laminae draping over antidune crest; B, up-current dipping laminae. Solid arrows indicate flow direction. (Modified from Allen 1982: Fig. 10.21.)

(e) Antidune cross stratification

Antidune cross stratification occurs mainly as laminae which dip gently up-current (Fig. 1.27,B). Although the dip may reach 10°, it is usually much less. This structure is produced by sedimentation on the stoss side of the antidune as the surface wave "breaks" during up-current migration. The extreme *rarity* of this structure is not surprising because as flow velocity decreases the antidunes are destroyed and replaced by a plane bed. Also the formative mechanism lacks avalanching (an important process in the development of cross-bed foresets) and commonly may not produce any well defined stratification.

1.3.4 Graded bedding

The term "grading," applied to individual beds or laminae, is used to describe a progressive change in grain size from the base to the top of a sedimentation unit. There are two general types: normal grading and reverse grading.

(a) Normal grading

Normal grading, the most common type of grading, is manifest by an **upward decrease** in grain size. Many authors simply use the terms "graded bedding" or "graded bed" to describe this phenomenon.

Normal grading may reflect a gradual change in the total sediment distribution, in some cases involving a shift in the modal size (Fig. 1.28a). This type is called **distribution** or **content grading**. Another variety of normal grading, known as **coarse-tail grading**, is characterized by an upward decrease in the abundance (or size) of the coarsest size fraction with little change in the rest of the distribution (Fig. 1.28b).

Graded beds generally reflect deposition caused by "rapid" deceleration of the transporting current. This may involve dense sediment

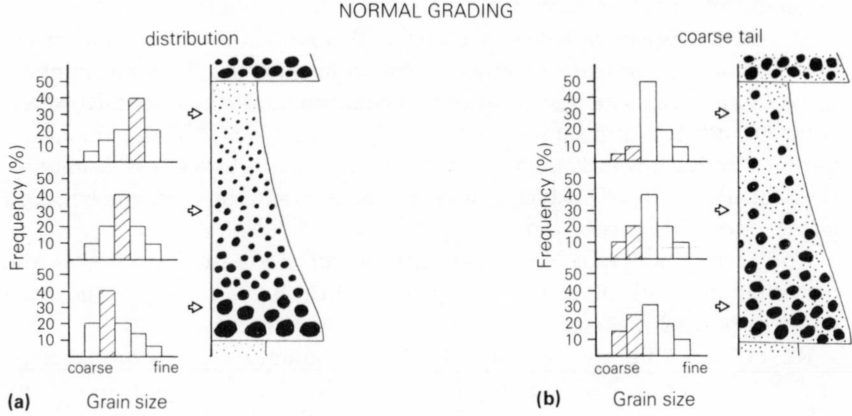

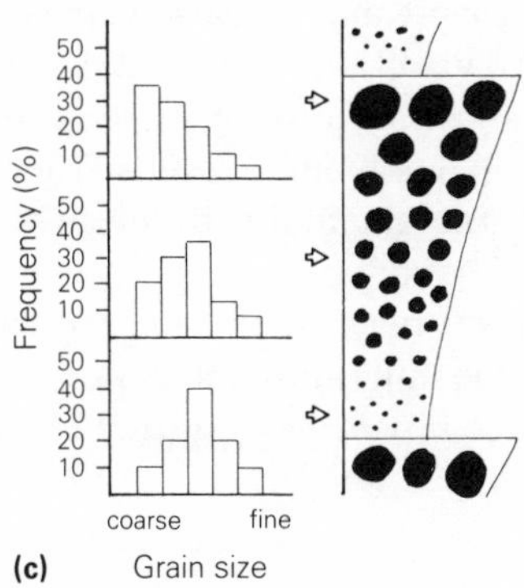

Figure 1.28 Graded bedding: (a) distribution grading; (b) coarse-tail grading; (c) reverse grading.

concentrations in which sorting is minimal. Such is the case for coarse-tail grading in some turbidites. In contrast, deposition during the waning stages of a flood may accompany more complete sorting and development of distribution grading.

Alternatively, the formation of graded beds may be caused by long-term changes in discharge and sediment load related to seasonal or climatic variability.

(b) Reverse grading (also called inverse grading)

Reverse grading describes an upward increase of grain size within a bed or lamination (Fig. 1.28c). It is generally associated wtih grain flows which are characterized by grain-to-grain collisions. Although the precise mechanism is unclear, dispersive stress and kinetic filtering are commonly mentioned. **Dispersive stress** is equal and opposite to the weight stress arising from the transfer of grain momentum onto the basal shear plane of the grain flow. The upward-directed component of the dispersive stress is far greater for larger particles than for smaller ones. "Hence the larger particles move upwards through the flow to equalize the stress gradient." (Leeder 1982: 76.) In **kinetic filtering** small grains filter down between larger ones during collision.

Conglomeratic grain flows, showing reverse grading, occur on the proximal portions of some subaqueous fans. Subaerial grain flow on dunes produces reverse grading in some sand laminae.

Reverse grading also occurs in backwash laminae formed on beaches, and in coarse volcanoclastic deposits. The latter may result from increased volcanic activity or from the tendency for larger pumice particles to become waterlogged more slowly than smaller ones.

(c) Fining-upward and coarsening-upward sequences

Many thick sequences show a gradual upward decrease in grain size (e.g. fluvial deposits); others show an upward increase (e.g. deltaic and some shoreline deposits). This phenomenon results from the lateral migration of environments and is fundamentally different from the graded beds described in (a) and (b) above.

The formative mechanism may be an integral part of the sedimentary model (**autocyclic**, e.g. the migration of a point bar in a meandering stream), or it may be caused by forces external to the sedimentary model (**allocyclic**, e.g. changes in sea level).

1.3.5 Massive bedding (also called homogeneous bedding)

Some beds that show no obvious sedimentary structures are in fact laminated or cross bedded as revealed when rock slabs are X-rayed (Hamblin 1962). Truly structureless units, especially thick sand beds, are formed by certain sedimentary gravity flows which lack a mechanism to produce primary structures. In others the structures are destroyed by upward movement of pore water or by bioturbation.

1.4 Structures on the lower bedding plane surface: sole marks

1.4.1 General characteristics

Preservation of structures on lower bedding surfaces occurs mainly on sandstone and siltstone beds that directly overlie mudrock. These structures, which stand out in positive relief, are referred to as **sole marks**

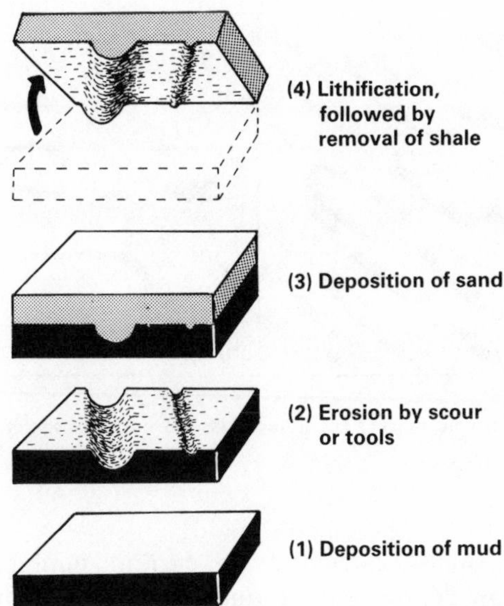

Figure 1.29 A sequence of events resulting in the formation of sole marks.

in reference to their position on the underside or **sole** of the bed (Fig. 1.29). In some cases the relief is exaggerated and the shape modified by loading (Section 1.5.2). Sole marks are produced by erosion of a cohesive mud substrate, followed by deposition of sand or silt. The erosional and depositional events are commonly phases of the same current. Episodic sedimentation, involved in the formation of sole marks, is especially common with turbidity flows but also occurs during "storm surges in shallow seas, sheet floods in semi-arid environments, and crevasse surges onto floodplains" (Collinson & Thompson 1982: 37).

1.4.2 Description

Some sole marks are caused by turbulent scour of a mud surface. **Flutes** (or flute casts), which are rather common, have an up-current end which is rounded or bulbous and a down-current end which flares out and merges with the bedding plane (Fig. 1.30a). Scour around an obstacle lying on the mud surface produces a horseshoe-shaped depression which is open in the down-current direction (Fig. 1.30b). These arcuate ridges, as seen on the sole of a bed, are called **current crescents**. Rarely, elongate scour pits form in a transverse direction to flow. If preserved as casts on the sole, they strongly resemble ripples and are sometimes given the rather misleading name **mud ripples** (Allen 1982b: 259–61).

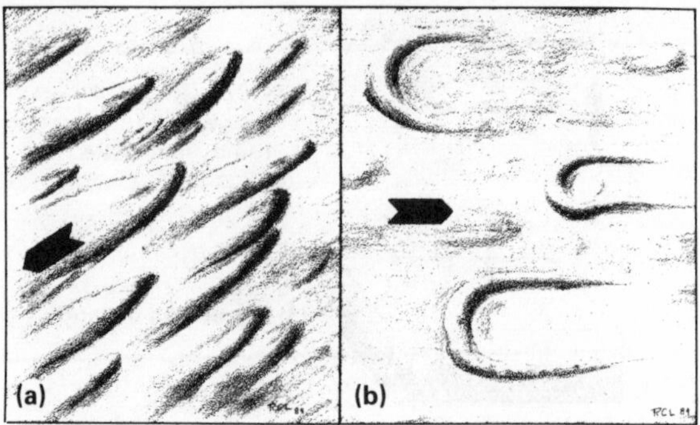

Figure 1.30 Common sole marks: (a) flute casts; (b) current crescents. Arrow indicates flow direction.

When objects (**tools**) carried by a current impinge on the mud substrate, a shallow depression is formed. The names applied to casts of these marks are generally descriptive of the inferred mode of origin. Collectively they are known as **tool casts**. **Groove casts** are straight, parallel, and generally continuous (on the scale of an outcrop). Width and relief are quite uniform and usually measured in millimeters – less commonly in centimeters. The other tool casts are discontinuous or repeated. **Prod casts** are asymmetrical with the down-current end being blunt and deep and the other gradational with the bedding surface.

Although tool casts of various types are commonly found together, they do not usually occur on the same surface with flutes. All sole marks can be used to establish stratigraphic-up. Although scour casts are useful in determining the paleoflow direction, tool casts, with the exception of prod casts, only indicate the line of movement.

1.5 Structures formed by soft-sediment deformation

1.5.1 Introduction

Rapid sediment accumulation on a slope may lead to deformation of the sedimentary mass. Soft-sediment deformation may occur at the time of deposition or shortly thereafter. It can involve lateral displacement downslope or vertical movement unrelated to slope.

Resultant structures are useful mainly as guides to relatively unusual and short-lived changes in the character of rapidly deposited sediment. As such they provide a significant insight regarding the sedimentary environment. Some structures point to deposition on a slope, and in some

Table 1.5 Criteria for distinguishing structures produced by soft-sediment deformation versus tectonic activity (summarized from Potter & Pettijohn 1963: 143).

Soft-sediment deformation	Tectonic activity
structure may be confined to a single bed "sandwiched" between undisturbed beds	all beds in a sequence are deformed
structures are spatially unrelated to larger structures of an area	structures (e.g. drag folds) are spatially related to larger structures (e.g. major folds or thrust faults)
structures may be truncated by penecontemporaneous erosion	structures are not truncated
structures are not intimately associated with vein filling, recrystallization, or rock cleavage	structures are associated with vein filling, recrystallization, or rock cleavage

cases they may be used to determine the attitude of the slope.

There is a great similarity between certain structures produced by penecontemporaneous deformation and those produced by tectonic deformation. Correct interpretation is critical to both sedimentologic and structural analysis. Criteria for distinguishing them are given in Table 1.5.

1.5.2 Structures produced by loading

Load structures are produced as a relatively dense bed sinks into a less dense bed. Superposition of more dense beds on top of less dense ones occurs when fine sand or coarse silt is deposited on mud. The density contrast is caused by a difference in initial porosity, with sand having lower porosity (approximately 45% but variable) than clay-rich mud (70–90%). A density inversion (heavy on top of light), although potentially unstable, may not result in loading, provided the sediment layers are strong enough. If the yield strength is decreased (or initially low), the sediment undergoes liquefaction and deformation occurs. The character of the resulting load structure depends on the density and thickness of the beds involved and on the degree of their liquefaction.

Loading may leave a sand bed intact or it may totally disrupt the bed. When not completely disrupted the loading is manifest by bulbous protuberances on the base of sand beds. These structures, called **load casts**, are most obvious when the underlying shale is removed by weathering (Fig. 1.31a). They are seen, in sections normal to bedding, as curved wedges of shale which project up between the sand lobes. This manifestation of load casts is called a **flame structure**, from the appearance of the curved and pointed tongues of shale (Fig. 1.31b). Spacing between lobes is usually 1–10 cm but may reach 10 m in unusual

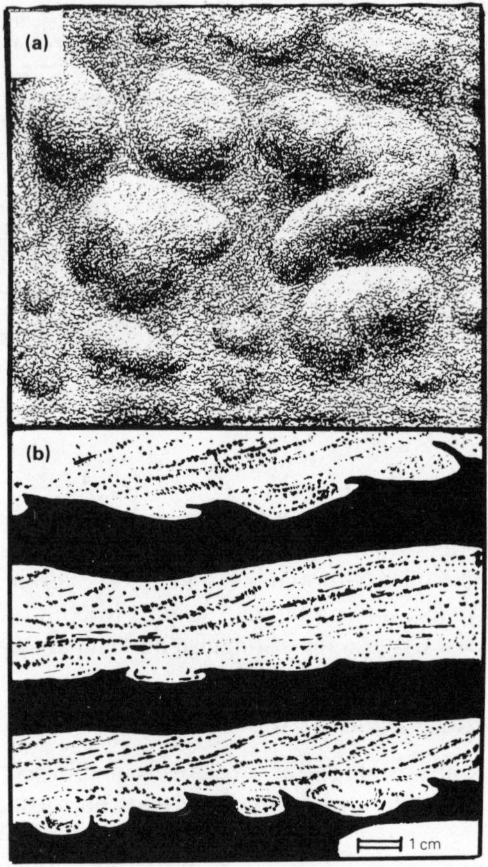

Figure 1.31 Load casts: (a) on sole of bed; (b) flame structure in section normal to bedding (modified from Potter & Pettijohn 1963: Fig. 6.2).

cases (Allen 1982b: 357). Irregularities on a muddy substrate may localize loading, as in the case of **load-casted flutes**, but this is not necessary for the development of load casts.

When loading completely disrupts a sand bed, elliptical or kidney-shaped sand bodies are formed by collapse into the underlying mud. In some cases this produces laterally continuous strings of isolated sand pods enveloped by mud. Called **pseudonodules**, they closely resemble a horizon of diagenetic concretions but are texturally different from the enclosing rock and may have internal laminations roughly parallel to the exterior of the sand body (Fig. 1.32,B). The **ball-and-pillow structure** occurs as extensive sheets composed of closely spaced, and sometimes stacked, sand "pillows" in a mud matrix (Fig. 1.32,C & Fig. 1.33). This structure

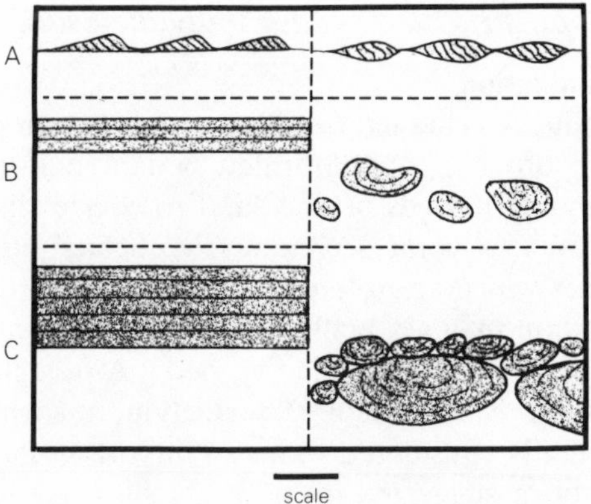

Figure 1.32 A schematic illustration of load structures (right side of figure): A, deformation of starved ripples by unequal loading; B, pseudonodules; C, ball-and-pillow structure.

Figure 1.33 A ball-and-pillow structure.

may result from foundering of several sand beds or repeated detachment of liquidized sand from the base of a thick sand bed. Individual sand "pillows" range in size from a few centimeters to several meters, and internal lamination is similar to that in pseudonodules. Some workers suggest that downslope movement is important in the formation of the ball-and-pillow structure, but this is questionable (Allen 1982b: 363).

Deformation may take place because of unequal loading and not because of liquefaction of the mud. As an example, **starved ripples** (see Section 1.3.3a) may sink into the underlying mud because of excess loading beneath the crest. This distorts the ripple shape as well as the internal lamination (Fig. 1.32,A).

1.5.3 Deformation structures within individual sand beds

(a) Convolute lamination

Convolute lamination is characterized by complex, intricate folding of laminae within an otherwise undeformed bed of uniform thickness. It occurs most commonly in beds of fine sand to coarse silt which range in thickness from 2 cm to several decimeters. Anticlinal crests are sharp in contrast to synclines which are relatively broad and open (Fig. 1.34). The degree of deformation may gradually decrease downward to undeformed stratification in the lower part of the bed. Although the origin of convolute lamination is uncertain, **liquefaction**, associated with rapid deposition, is generally considered to be an important mechanism. Other factors that have been suggested include: (1) shear caused by fluid flow acting on the sediment surface, (2) expulsion of pore water, (3) loading contemporaneous with deposition, and (4) lateral laminar flow of liquefied beds.

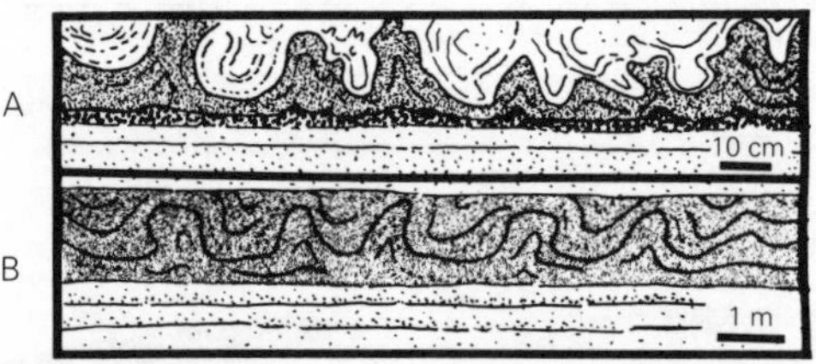

Figure 1.34 Convolute lamination: A, Brahmaputra River sediments (modified from Reineck & Singh 1975: Fig. 131). B, Precambrian fluvial sandstone (modified from Selley 1976: Fig. 83).

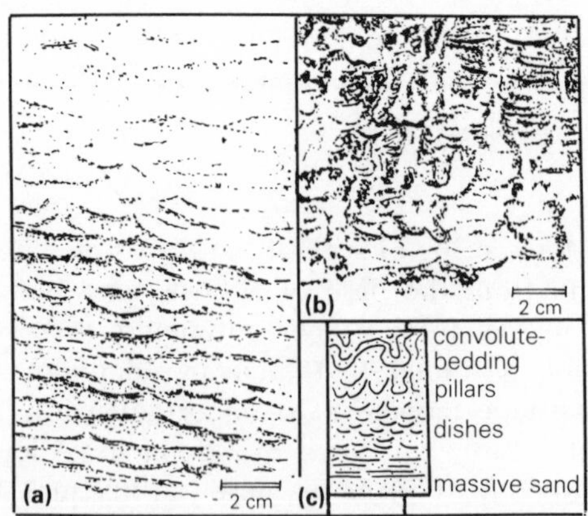

Figure 1.35 Dish-and-pillar structures in sandstone. Pillars are more strongly developed in (b) than in (a). Both these samples are from the Jackfork Group, Pennsylvanian, Oklahoma. A typical sequence for thick (> 0.5 m) sandstone beds is shown in (c). (Modified from illustrations in Lowe and LoPiccolo 1974.)

(b) Dish-and-pillar structure

This structure is produced in rapidly deposited clay-rich sand and silt by the upward escape of water (dewatering) during consolidation. **Dish structures** are dark pseudo-laminae formed by escaping water forced to follow horizontal flow paths beneath semi-permeable laminae. As the water moves through the sand, clay and organic material is removed and redeposited producing dish structures which range in thickness from 0.2 to 2 mm. These dark clay-rich pseudo-laminae are concave upward (Fig. 1.35a) and are commonly penetrated by structureless vertical **pillars** (Fig. 1.35b), which served as conduits for vertical water movement. They are often associated with convolute bedding in thick sandstone beds (greater than 0.5 m), where pillars and convolute bedding are more abundant upwards (Fig. 1.35c).

Their main value is as evidence of **rapid deposition** of relatively thick sand beds. Although characteristic of liquefied flows, they are probably not restricted to such deposits.

Dish structures superficially resemble several other structures, but are readily identified upon close examination. They lack foreset laminae present in small-scale cross bedding and well defined and tightly curled clay laminae in mud curls (Section 1.2.6). Vertical burrows are distinguished from pillar structures by having sharp margins and circular outlines on bedding surfaces.

(c) Deformed cross bedding

Within a coset of cross-bedded sandstone individual sets may show marked soft sediment deformation. **Overturned cross bedding** (Fig. 1.36,A), although absent in most cross-bedded sandstone, is locally abundant. It may result from liquefaction of sand in active megaripples or sand waves combined with shear stress exerted on the bed by flowing water. Foreset deformation is greatest near the surface because the shear effects gradually decrease downward. A second type of deformed cross bedding occurs as small folds without foreset oversteepening (Fig. 1.36,B). This structure may reflect buckling of a liquidized bedform, possibly after being subjected to an earthquake shock (Allen 1982b: 392).

1.5.4 Structures produced by downslope gravity transport

Gravity transport may involve beds just a few centimeters thick or sedimentary units tens to hundreds of meters thick. A great variety of structures are produced. A simple case involves gravity faults developed in sediments adjacent to river and tidal channels. The deformation commonly produces folds (Fig. 1.37) (called **slump folds**) and faults, as

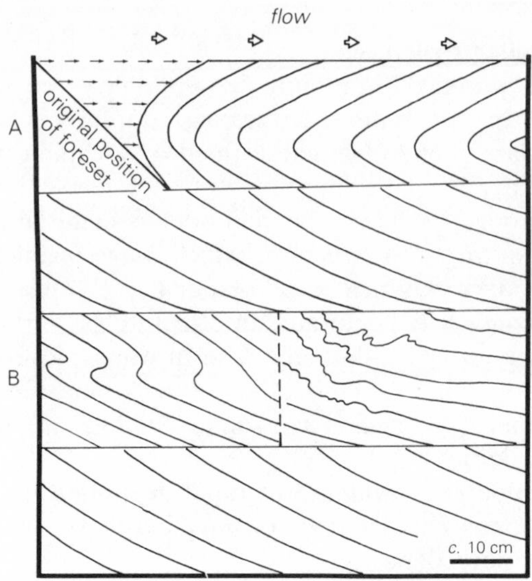

Figure 1.36 Deformed cross bedding: A, overturned foresets; B, small folds (two styles shown). (Modified from Allen & Banks 1972 and Allen 1982b.)

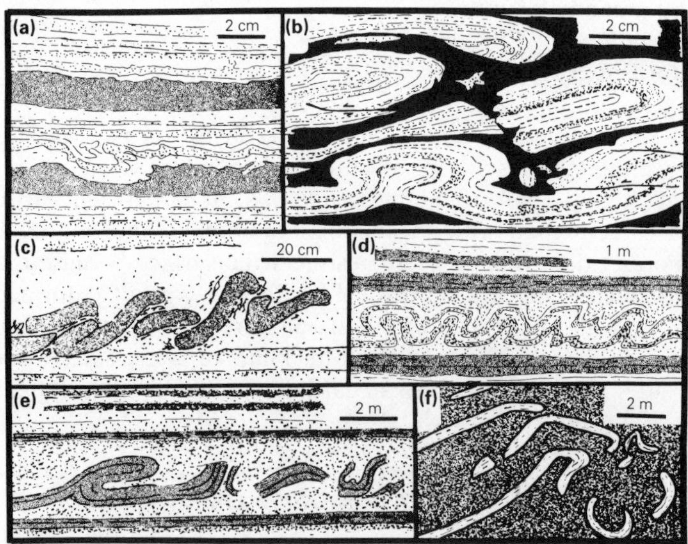

Figure 1.37 Folds produced by downslope gravity transport: (a) Eocene slope deposit, Oregon; (b) Triassic lacustrine deposit, Virginia; (c) Mississippian turbidites, Arkansas; (d) Pleistocene lacustrine deposit, Dead Sea, Israel; (e) Miocene slope deposit, New Zealand; (f) Miocene slope deposit, Italy. (Modified after Cook *et al.* 1982 (a, e, & f); Hentz 1981 (b); Morris 1971 (c); Allen 1982b (d).)

the sediment mass moves laterally on low-angle slide planes, which may be parallel to bedding.

Reconstruction of paleoslope using slump folds has intrigued geologists for several decades. Although it is generally assumed that the fold axes are normal to the downslope direction, some studies show that the folds may be rotated parallel to this direction (for a brief review see Rupke 1978: 376). In such a case the direction of slumping can be determined using the "separation angle" method (Hansen 1971). In some situations the folds may be so chaotic that analysis is impossible.

1.5.5 Structures produced by sediment injection

Sandstone dikes are tabular, discordant sandstone bodies, which range in thickness from a few centimeters to more than 10 m. They are caused by the injection of liquified sand *from below* (Fig. 1.38,B). Small sandstone dikes, which may show polygonal form in plan, should not be confused with mudcracks. Internally the sandstone may show faint lamination (parallel to the contact with the host rock) produced by shearing as the sand flowed upward (Fig. 1.38,C). In some cases sand may be injected as bedding-parallel sheets, called **sandstone sills** (Fig. 1.38,D). An uncommon variety of sandstone dike occurs as small, irregular and sinuous bodies (Fig. 1.39) formed when water-saturated sand and mud beds are subjected to extension (Selley 1976: 231). Apparently the host material was much less competent than that associated with the more common straight-sided sandstone dikes.

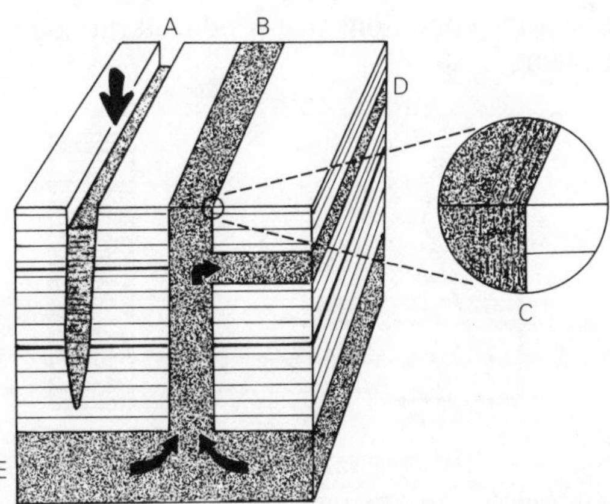

Figure 1.38 Structures produced by injection: A, Neptunian dike (arrow indicates sedimentation from marine water above); B, sandstone dike; C, faint lamination near margin of dike (formed during injection); D, sandstone sill; E, source bed for fluidized sand. Arrows indicate flow direction.

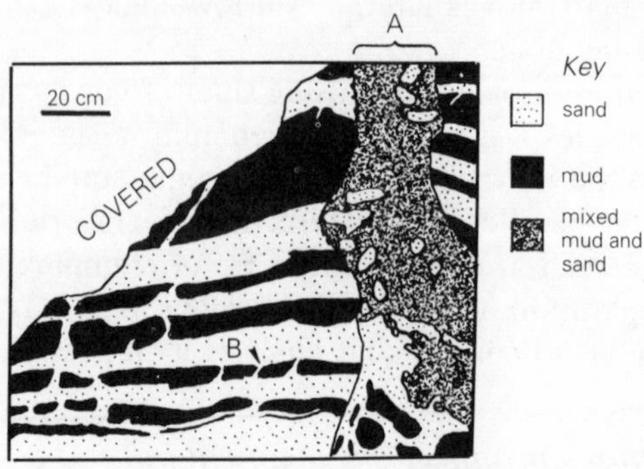

Figure 1.39 A sandstone dike (A) in a metamorphosed turbidite sequence (Lower Paleozoic, Maryland). Note small dikes (e.g. B) which penetrate muddy beds. (Based on photograph in Hopson 1964: Plate 16, Fig. 1, 298.)

Neptunian dikes and sills are produced by infilling of submarine fissures from above (Fig. 1.38,A). They are associated with pelagic deposits and are filled with relatively coarse sediment generally absent from the normal stratigraphic sequence (Jenkyns 1978: 359). The fractures may have been opened by slumping or penecontemporaneous tectonic activity.

1.6 Exercises: sedimentary structures

1 Answer the questions posed in the captions for Figures 1.19 and 1.20.

2 Briefly discuss the conditions that produced the sedimentary sequences shown in Figure 1.40.

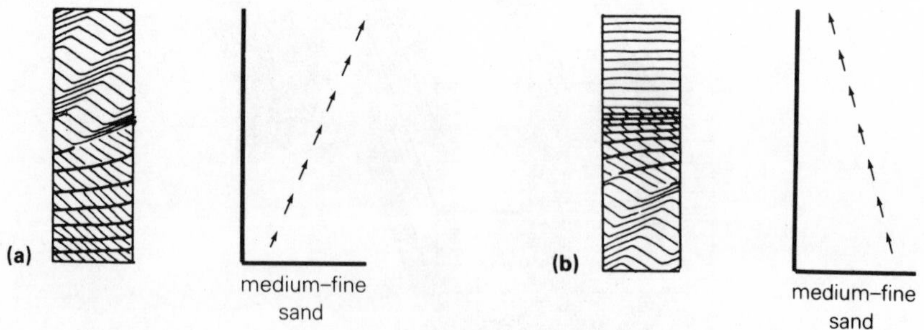

Figure 1.40 Sand sequences showing variation in sedimentary structures and grain size.

3 Describe as fully as you can the cross bedding in Figure 1.41 a–c. Indicate the general flow direction (e.g. flow from right to left).

4 Name the structures shown in Figure 1.41 d–i. Note that some samples may contain several different structures.

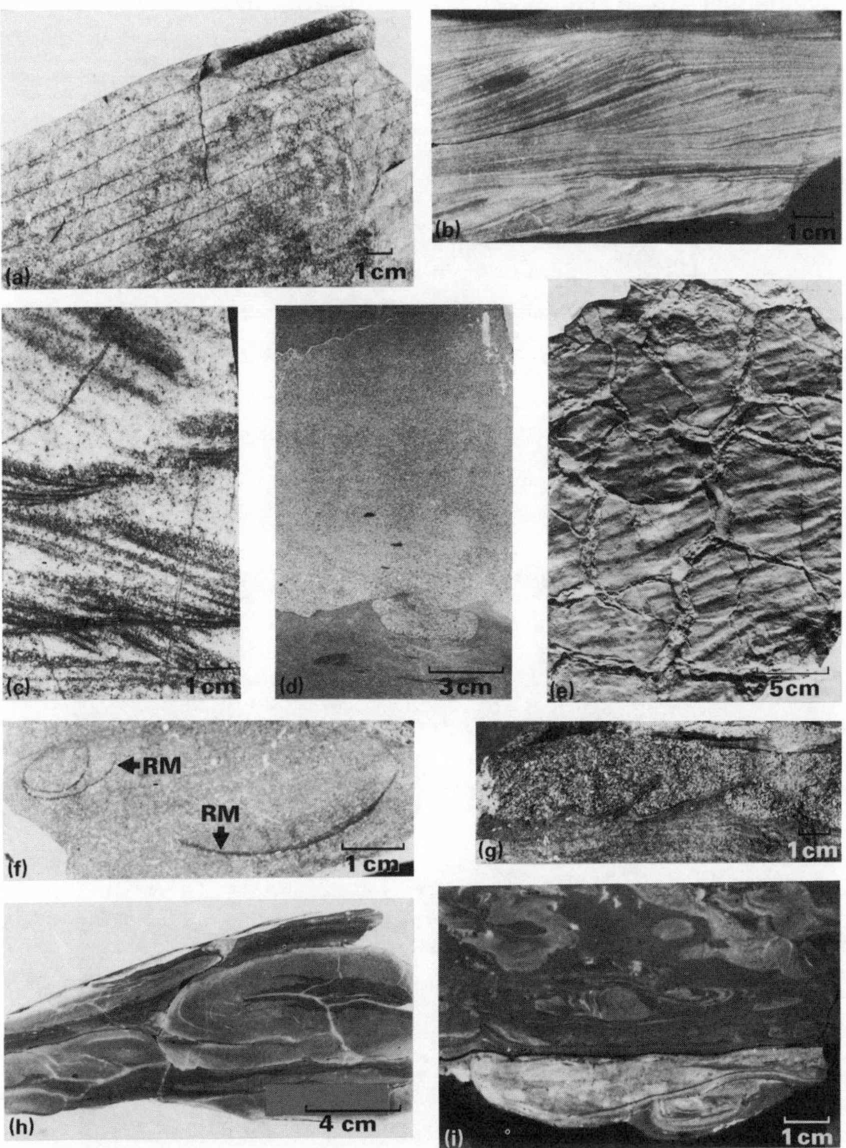

Figure 1.41 Sedimentary structures. All but (e) show faces normal to bedding; (e) shows upper bedding surface. RM in (f) refers to "clasts" of red mudrock.

5 Describe the ripples shown in Figure 1.42. Include in your description the character of the crestline, the ripple index, the ripple symmetry

index, and the internal structures. What does this indicate about the conditions operative during the formation of these ripples? What is "unusual" about the ripples in Figure 1.42 c.

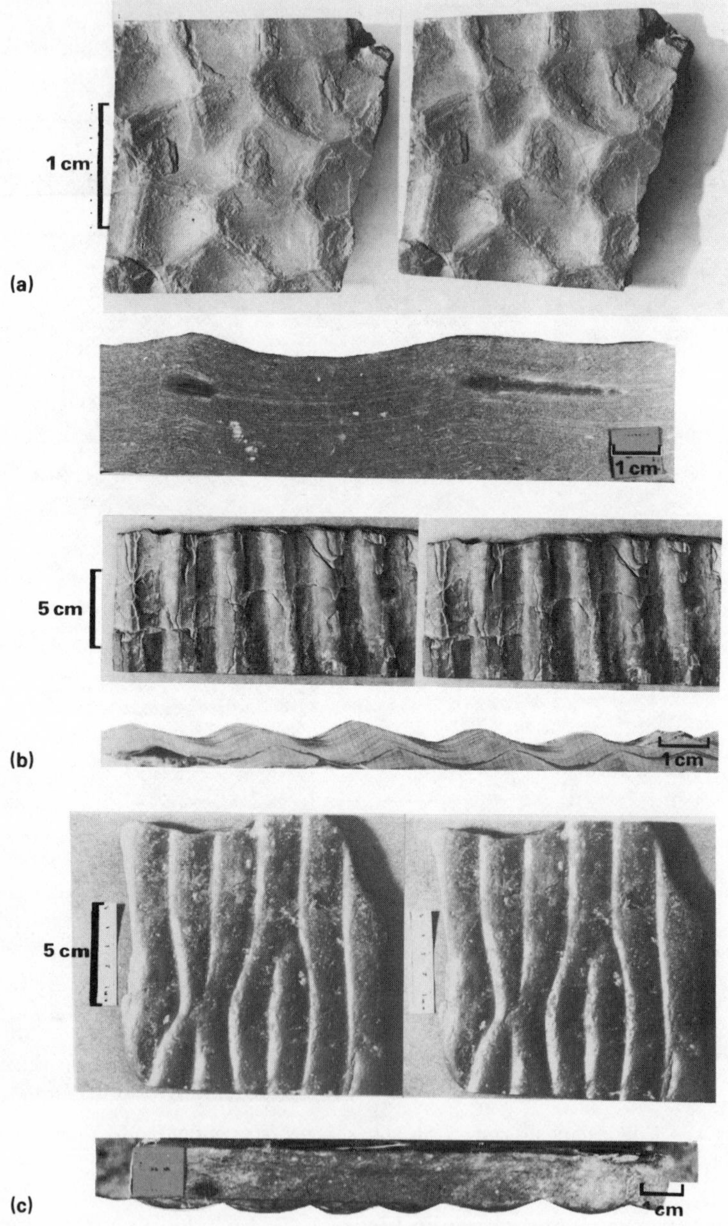

Figure 1.42 Ripples: A stereogram of a bedding surface above the corresponding cross section.

6 Name the structures shown in Figure 1.43. Determine the paleocurrent direction for each. Assume that *north* is toward the top of the page.

Figure 1.43 Stereograms of sole marks.

7 Name the structures shown in Figure 1.44 (over).

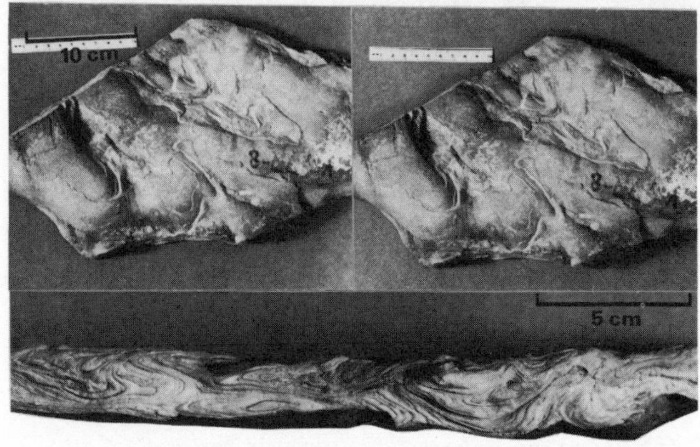

Figure 1.44 Stereograms of deformation structures: (b) shows the lower bedding surface.

2 Analysis of sedimentary structures

2.1 Paleocurrent analysis

Directional properties of sedimentary structures are important in paleoenvironmental interpretation. Generally they indicate the current flow direction at the time of deposition and provide an important key for evaluating paleogeography. In fluvial, deltaic, and most turbidite deposits, paleocurrent patterns indicate paleoslope. Paleocurrent studies may also provide important information regarding the geometry (e.g. elongation) of particular lithic units. Some of the most important structures which provide direction of movement data are cross bedding, current crescents, flute casts, and asymmetrical ripples. Those that indicate only the line of movement include parting lineation, groove casts, and symmetrical ripples.

2.2 Correction of data for tectonic tilt

Data are commonly collected from folded or tilted sequences and must be corrected in order to restore the bedding to its original horizontal position. This is done by rotating a line or a plane about a horizontal axis using stereographic projection (Fig. 2.1).

If the structural dip is less than 25°, the measured azimuth of linear structures needs no correction (Potter & Pettijohn 1963: 262). If the dip exceeds 25°, the effects of tilting must be removed. This can be done with a stereonet, as illustrated in Fig. 2.2.

The situation for planar structures (e.g. cross bedding) is different, because even very low tectonic dip values (anything greater than 5°) may introduce an appreciable error. As is the case for linear structures, rotation can be done using stereographic projection, as shown in Figure 2.3. The procedure is more complicated in the case of steeply plunging folds, and double rotation may be required (Ramsay 1961: 85). If the plunge is less than 10°, or if the dip is less than 45°, no correction for the plunge is necessary (Potter & Pettijohn 1963: 262).

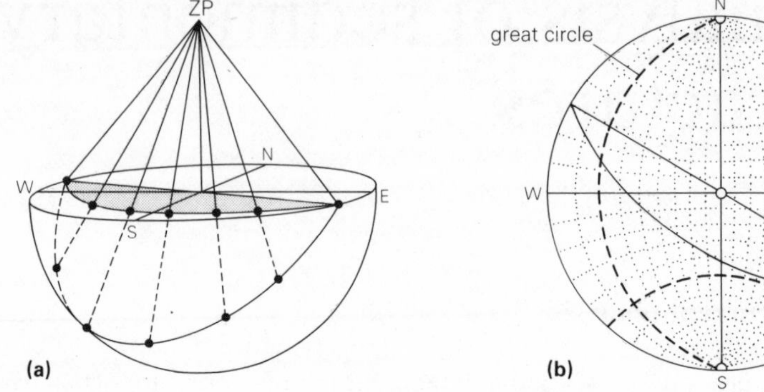

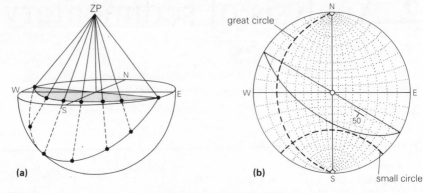

Figure 2.1 The stereographic projection of a plane. (a) Projection of a plane with a dip of 50°, and a dip direction of 210° (strike N60°W, dip 50°SW). ZP, zenith point. (b) Stereographic projection of the plane shown in (a). Also shown are projections of great circles (intersection of sphere with any plane passing through the center of the sphere) and small circles (intersection of sphere with any plane not passing through the center of the sphere) on the equatorial plane of the sphere. These are the basic elements of a **stereonet**.

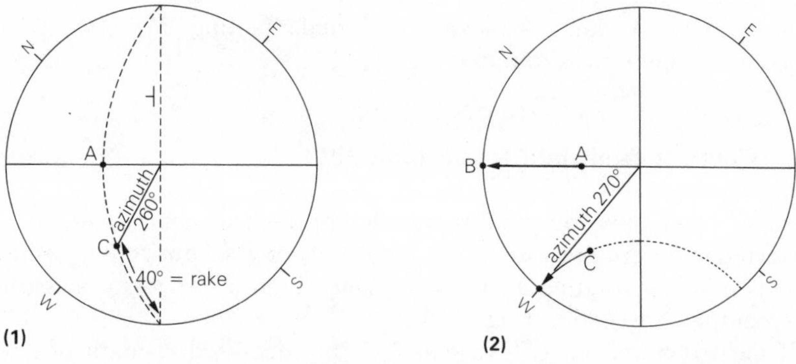

Figure 2.2 The correction of a linear structure for tectonic tilt using stereographic projection.

(1) Plot the plane of the bedding and linear structure (as a line) on the stereogram. In this example the bedding has a dip of 50° and a dip direction of 320° (strike N50°E, dip 50°W). The rake of the linear structure is 40°; the azimuth of a vertical plane, which passes through the linear structure, is 260°.

(2) Restore the bedding to horizontal (point A to point B). Move the intersection point of the linear structure with the great circle projection of the bedding point (point C) along the nearest small circle (dotted line) to the edge of the stereogram. Read the azimuth of the linear structure. In this example it is 270° (due west).

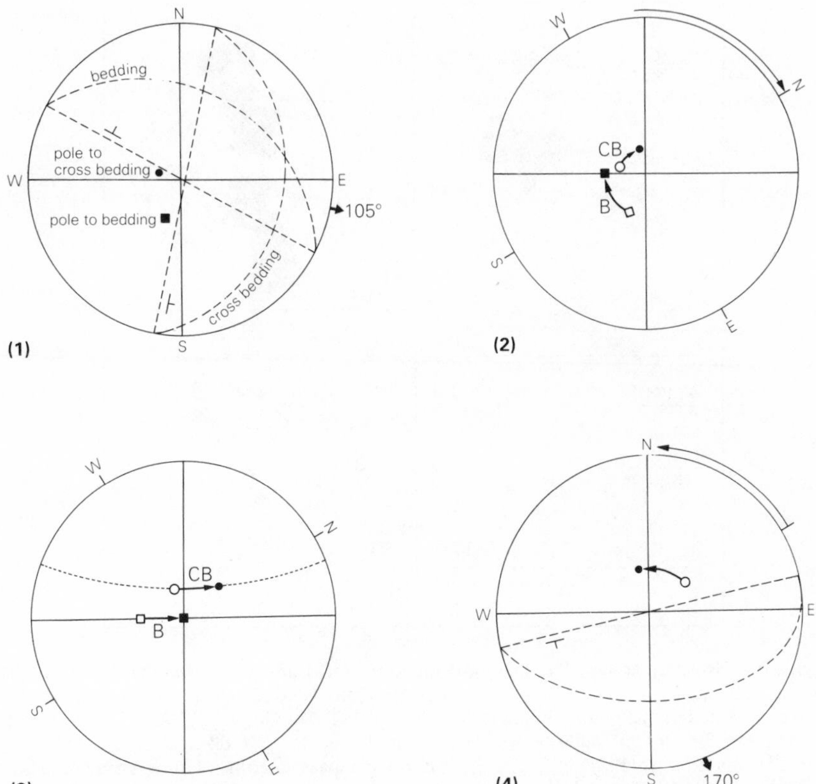

Figure 2.3 The correction of cross bedding for tectonic tilt using a stereographic projection.

(1) Plot the poles of the cross bedding and bedding on the stereogram. Sketching the projection of planes (dashed lines) is optional, but useful for those with little experience of using stereographic projections. In this example the bedding has a dip of 30° and a dip direction of 30° (strike N60°W, dip 30°NE). The tilted cross bedding has a dip of 20° and a dip direction of 105° (strike N15°E, dip 20°SE).

(2) Rotate the stereogram so that the pole of the bedding, B, comes to the equatorial line. In doing this you will also rotate CB, the pole of the cross bedding. Mark both points on the stereogram (i.e. on the tracing paper).

(3) Bring bedding to the horizontal by shifting B, the pole of the bedding, to the center of the stereogram. Move CB, the pole of the cross bedding, the same number of degrees (30) in the same direction, along the nearest small circle (dotted line).

(4) Rotate the stereogram back, so that its N–S line coincides with the N–S line on the stereonet. As before, sketching the projection of the plane of the cross bedding is optional. To read the dip direction (azimuth), draw a line from the pole, through the center, to the edge of the stereonet. In this example, the corrected cross-bedding dip direction (azimuth) is 170° (S10°E).

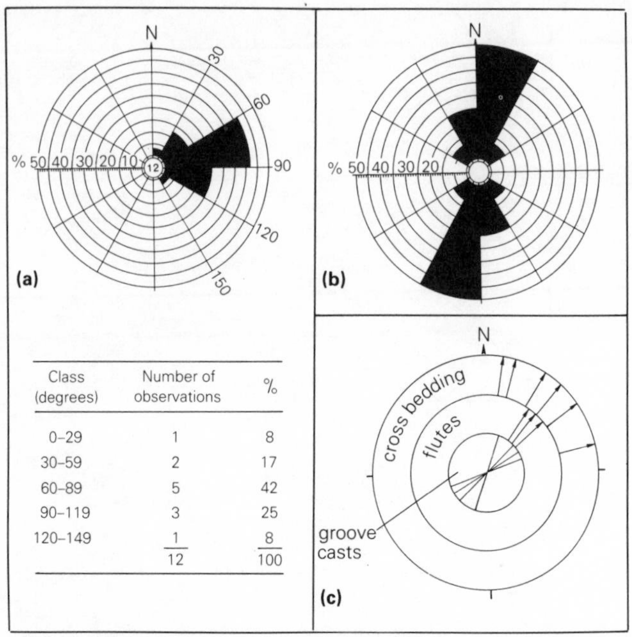

Class (degrees)	Number of observations	%
0–29	1	8
30–59	2	17
60–89	5	42
90–119	3	25
120–149	1	8
	12	100

Figure 2.4 Rose diagrams. The diagrams may utilize (a) direction of movement data, (b) line of movement data, or (c) data from several different structures. Data plotted: (a) twelve cross-bed dip azimuths (in degrees) – 10, 80, 112, 71, 130, 42, 58, 72, 67, 74, 99, 102; (b) compass bearing of eight groove casts (in degrees) – 20(200), 331(151), 340(160), 305(125), 15(195), 18(198), 39(219), 6(186); (c) compass bearing of four groove casts – 60(240), 71(251), 20(200), 39(219), three flute casts – 42, 37, 50, and six cross-bed dip azimuths – 17, 55, 33, 78, 10, 43.

2.3 Graphic presentation of directional data

A popular device for presenting directional data is the **current rose**, which is a histogram converted to a circular distribution. Various class intervals are used, but a 30° interval will meet most needs. It is better to plot the percentage of observations in each class than to plot the total number of observations (Fig. 2.4a). The class interval with the most observations is the **modal class**. When measurements of structures which show direction of movement are plotted (e.g. cross beds and flute casts), the rose diagram indicates the direction toward which the current moved. Most distributions produce a single dominant mode (**unimodal**), although some have two or more subequal modes (**bimodal, polymodal**). In the case of structures which show line of movement, each measurement is represented by two opposite azimuth values (e.g. 30 and 210°). The resulting current rose consists of two reflected halves (Fig. 2.4b). Measurements made from several different structures may be plotted on a single **composite** rose diagram (also called a composite ray diagram, radial line diagram, or spoke diagram) (Fig. 2.4c).

2.4 Vector mean and vector magnitude

2.4.1 Direction of movement data

Although the current rose gives a general idea of the paleocurrent direction, a more rigorous approach is needed. The vector mean is the most commonly used measure of the average flow direction. Strongly bimodal distributions may produce a vector mean that has little geologic significance.

The vector mean can be determined graphically (Reiche 1938) by assigning a vector of unit length to each measured value (Fig. 2.5b). The first observation is plotted as a vector starting at an arbitrary point of origin. The second is then plotted at the end of the first, and so on until all have been plotted. The line which connects the point of origin with the end of the last vector is the **graphical vector mean**.

Another method, involving summation of the sine and cosine for each direction of movement azimuth (e.g. cross bedding), is shown in Figure 2.5a. The vector mean is the arctan of the resulting tangent. It is important to keep in mind that in a 360° distribution any value of the tangent will have two possible azimuths that differ by 180°. For example, the tangent for a 10° angle and a 190° angle is 0.176. They are distinguished by the *sign* of the sine and cosine. In the first quadrant (azimuth = 10°) both will be positive and in the third quadrant (azimuth = 190°) they will be negative. These relationships are summarized in Figure 2.5a. Programs for use with programmable calculators are also available (Lindholm 1979a, Freeman & Pierce 1979).

In analyzing directional data, the dispersion of the data is given by the vector magnitude (Fig. 2.5). To facilitate comparison between samples, the vector magnitude should be expressed as a percentage (this is also known as the consistency ratio). High values, which indicate a clustering of observations around the vector mean (i.e. low dispersion), are produced by individual measurements generally trending in the same direction (Fig. 2.6a). Low values indicate a greater scatter (Fig. 2.6b).

To determine whether or not the measured azimuths are uniformly distributed, various **tests of significance** can be used (Potter & Pettijohn 1963). Two of the most commonly used are the **Rayleigh test** (Curray 1956) and the **chi-square test** (Chayes 1949). A graphical expression of the Rayleigh test is shown in Figure 2.7. Use of Anjne's A as an alternate test statistic is advocated by Dale and Ballantyne (1980).

	Azimuth	sin x	cos x
1	27°	+0.4540	+0.8910
2	172°	+0.1392	−0.9903
3	68°	+0.9272	+0.3746
4	112°	+0.9272	−0.3746
5	50°	+0.7660	+0.6428
6	123°	+0.8387	−0.5446
7	100°	+0.9480	−0.1736
8	137°	+0.6820	−0.7314
9	160°	+0.3420	−0.9397
10	111°	+0.9336	−0.3584
11	118°	+0.8829	−0.4695
12	146°	+0.5592	−0.8290
13	80°	+0.9848	+0.1736
14	96°	+0.9945	−0.1045
15	77°	+0.9748	+0.2250
	Σn	+11.3541	−3.2085

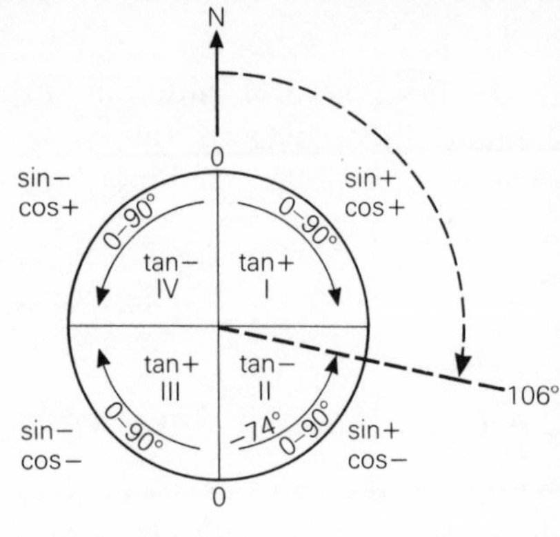

$$\tan x = \frac{\Sigma n \sin x}{\Sigma n \cos x} = \frac{11.3541}{-3.2085} = -3.539$$

arctan −3.539 = −74° or 106° = vector mean

$$R = \sqrt{[(\Sigma n \sin x)^2 + (\Sigma n \cos x)^2]}$$

$$R = \sqrt{(128.91 + 10.29)} = 11.8$$

$$L = R/n \times 100 = \frac{11.8}{15} \times 100 = 79 = \text{vector magnitude}$$

(a)

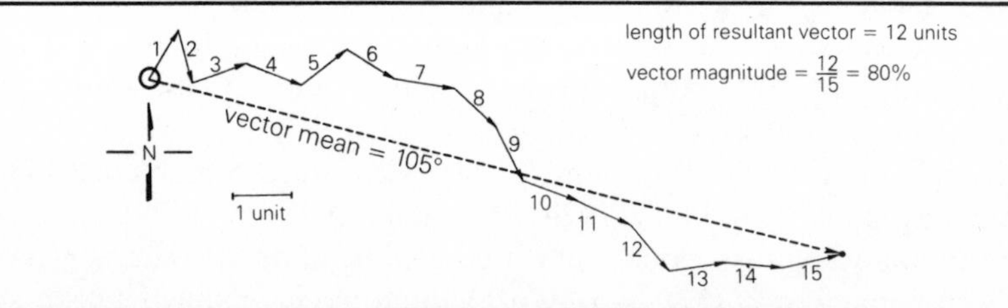

(b)

Figure 2.5 Methods for calculating the vector mean and vector magnitude.

(a) *Trigonometric method.* The tangent of the mean vector is calculated by dividing the sum of the sines by the sum of the cosines. The vector mean is the arctan of this value. It is critical that the *signs* of the trigonometric functions be accurately recorded. In this example the negative tangent (positive sine and negative cosine) lies in the 2nd quadrant, and the resultant azimuth (−74°) is plotted counterclockwise from zero at the bottom of the circle (see illustration to the right of the tabulated sines and cosines). According to standard geologic usage, this equals 106° (measured clockwise from zero (due north) or S74°E in the parlance of many geologists in the United States. The vector magnitude in percent (L) is determined by dividing R (11.8) by the number of measurements (15) multiplied by 100.

(b) *Graphical method.* Each measured azimuth is plotted as a unit vector. One unit of length can be 1 cm, 1 in. or whatever is convenient. In this illustration the unit vectors are labeled 1 to 15 (azimuths given in (a) above). The resultant vector, the line which connects the origin with the end of the last unit vector, is the vector mean. The vector magnitude is obtained by dividing the length of the resultant vector (12 units) by the total length of the unit vectors (15 units) multiplied by 100.

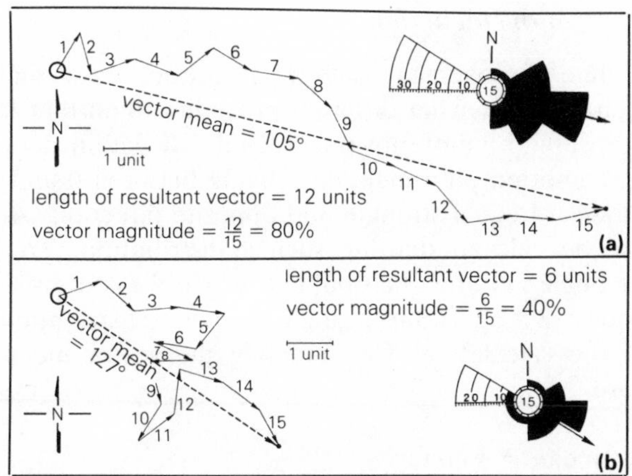

Figure 2.6 A graphic comparison of samples with (a) high vector magnitude and (b) low vector magnitude. Individual measurements for (a): 1, 27; 2, 172; 3, 68; 4, 112; 5, 50; 6, 123; 7, 100; 8, 137; 9, 160; 10, 111; 11, 118; 12, 146; 13, 80; 14, 96; 15, 77. Individual measurements for (b): 1, 70; 2, 136; 3, 83; 4, 98; 5, 214; 6, 280; 7, 117; 8, 268; 9, 169; 10, 209; 11, 50; 12, 2; 13, 108; 14, 130; 15, 157.

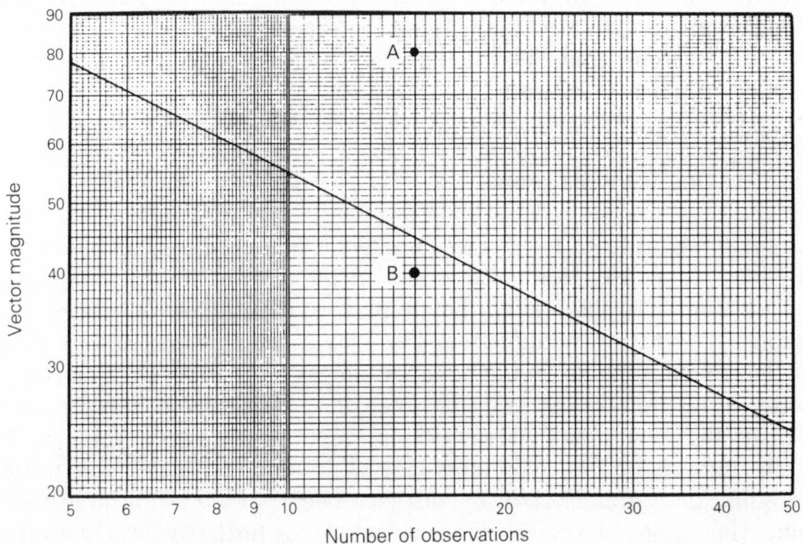

Figure 2.7 A graph to evaluate the significance (at 0.05) of the vector mean using the Rayleigh test. If the calculated vector magnitude is greater than the critical value for a given number of observations (i.e. it plots above the sloping line), the sample is considered to be from a population with a preferred orientation. This is the case for A (sample shown in Fig. 2.6a). If the calculated vector magnitude is less than the critical value for a given number of observations (i.e. it plots below the sloping line), the sample is considered to be from a population with no preferred orientation. This is the case for B (sample shown in Fig. 2.6b). (Modified from Curray 1956: Fig. 4.)

2.4.2 Line-of-movement data

Analysis of line-of-movement data (e.g. groove casts and symmetric ripples) requires a somewhat different procedure than that for direction-of-movement data. Line-of-movement data fall within a range of 0 to 180°, which, if plotted on a diagram ranging between 0 and 360°, would show two modes of equal strength and opposite direction. A valid vector mean cannot be calculated using such a distribution. To remedy this situation the angle (x) must be doubled, which transforms a distribution with two modes 180° apart into a single unimodal distribution (Krumbein 1939: 688). The calculations for obtaining the vector mean and vector magnitude are

$$\text{vector mean} = \tfrac{1}{2} \arctan \frac{\sum n \sin 2x}{\sum n \cos 2x}$$

$$\text{vector magnitude} = \frac{\sqrt{[(\sum n \sin 2x)^2 - (\sum n \cos 2x)^2]} \times 100}{\sum n}$$

Another way of analyzing line-of-movement data is to handle all measurements as if they fell into just two quadrants, e.g. the NE and NW, and make the calculations using the technique described in Section 2.4.1. Remember, though, that the vector mean is a bidirectional vector whose values are 180° apart.

2.5 Moving-average maps

Regional paleocurrent trends, which may be obscured by presentation of unrefined data, are more clearly shown by moving-average maps that smooth out local variations. To prepare a moving-average map, first establish a grid for the study area. This may be an arbitrary grid or a pre-existing system such as 7.5 minute quadrangles. Using all of the individual vector means in adjacent grid units, calculate a grand vector mean using one of the techniques described in Section 2.4. Plot this at the intersection of the four grid units (Fig. 2.8a: detailed map). Repeat the procedure until grand vector means have been plotted at all intersection points (Fig. 2.8b). To clarify the regional trends further you may want to include a more schematic interpretive map (Fig. 2.8c).

2.6 Factors that cause variability in cross-bed dip azimuths

Variability of cross-bed dip azimuths depends in part on the scale of comparison. In alluvial deposits the scatter of azimuths around the mean,

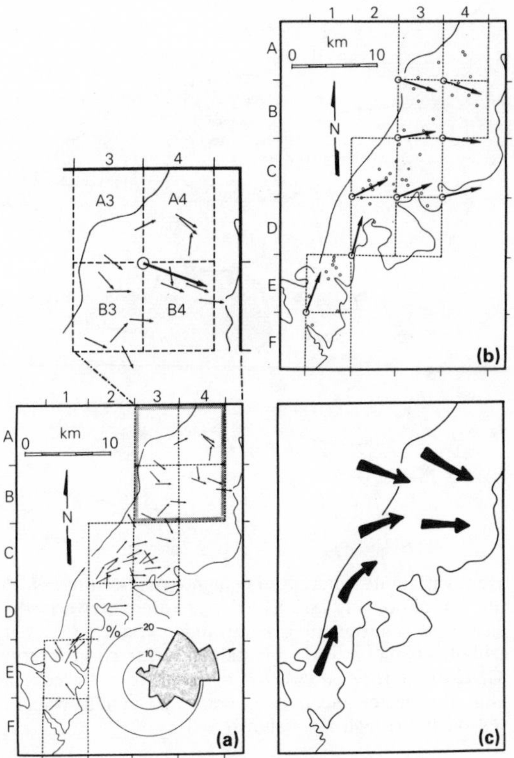

Figure 2.8 A moving-average map of cross-bed dip azimuths. (a) A map showing vector means calculated for each outcrop. The detailed map above shows the northern portion of the study area. The grand vector mean (large arrow) is calculated using the 15 outcrop vector means (small arrows) in sectors A3, A4, B3, and B4. (b) Completed **moving average map**. Each arrow is a grand vector mean calculated as described in (a). (c) Interpretive map. (Based on measurements in the Lower Cretaceous Potomac Group in northern Virginia by Weir 1976 and Adabi 1978.)

determined for a single outcrop, has many causes. They include characteristics inherent in the associated bedforms, in-channel processes, and flow out of the channel. In trough cross bedding, dip azimuth variability is an intrinsic feature of the foreset geometry (Fig. 2.9). In-channel processes which contribute to the nonuniform distribution of cross-bed dip azimuths include backflow in the lee of ripples, flow around bars and other obstructions, and lateral or oblique-to-flow migration of bars (Fig. 2.10 b–d). During floods, water spilling out of the channel may produce cross bedding in levee and crevasse splay deposits, with dip azimuths markedly divergent from the general flow system (Fig. 2.10e).

On a larger scale, the sinuous character of meandering stream channels

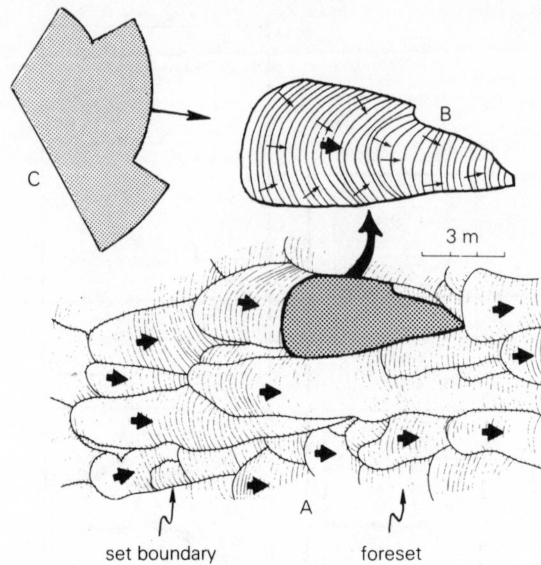

Figure 2.9 Paleocurrent variability inherent in trough cross bedding. A, Plan view of cross-bed sets in the Chinle Formation (Triassic), Arizona (after Stewart *et al.* 1972). Arrows indicate paleoflow directions determined from trough axes. B, One set showing twelve random foreset dip azimuths (small arrows) and paleoflow direction determined from trough axis (large arrow). C, Current rose and vector mean (arrow) based on the 12 azimuths shown in B. *Note* that the vector mean in C shows essentially the same paleocurrent direction as that based on the trough axis (shown in B).

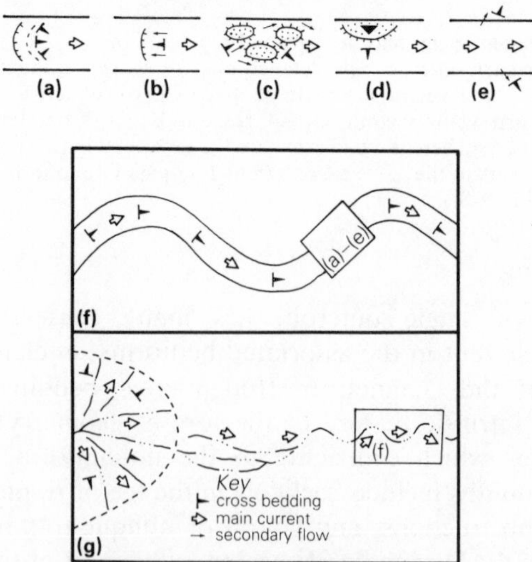

Figure 2.10 Schematic maps of alluvial systems showing their influence on paleocurrent variability. (a)–(e) Small segments of stream channel. (a) Trough cross bedding; (b) backflow in lee of large bedform; (c) flow around in-channel bars; (d) lateral migration of bar; (e) flow out of channel during flood; (f) meandering stream; (g) alluvial fan.

contributes to the variability of cross-bed dip azimuths (Fig. 2.10f). Depending on the outcrop size and the width of the paleomeander belt, this may or may not affect cross-bed variability within an outcrop.

On a regional scale, the paleocurrent pattern of alluvial deposits may show variability caused by local or regional changes in the paleoslope (Fig. 2.8c). Specific examples include radiating flow patterns on alluvial fans or deltas (Fig. 2.10g) and centripetal flow patterns associated with syndepositional basins (Fig. 2.11a) (Selley 1976).

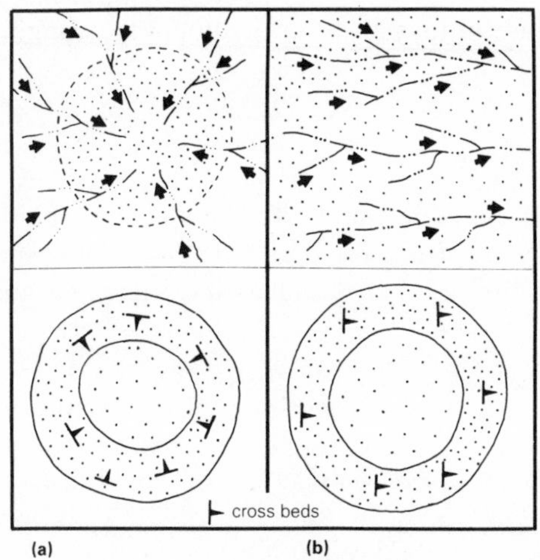

Figure 2.11 Schematic maps of basins showing associated paleocurrent patterns in fluvial deposits: (a) syndepositional basin with centripetal pattern toward the center of the basin that was a topographic low during deposition; (b) post-depositional tectonic basin in which paleocurrents show no relationship to the structural morphology of the basin. (Modified from Selley 1976: Fig. 95.)

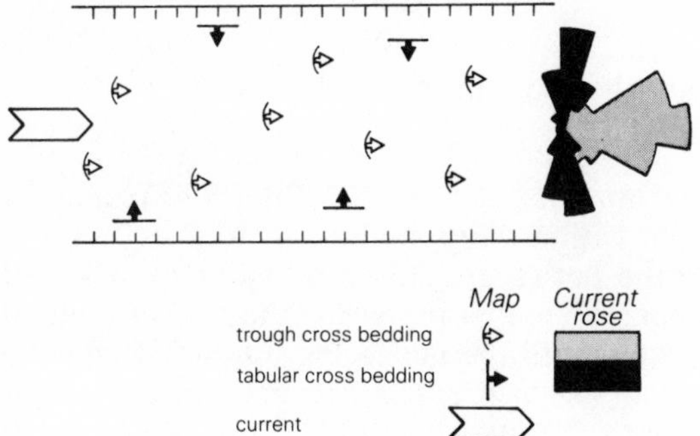

Figure 2.12 A hypothetical model for a polymodal paleocurrent pattern. The interpretation, discussed in the text, is based on a study by Cant and Walker (1976).

Significant insights regarding the paleoenvironment may be obtained by examining the paleocurrent data facies by facies – perhaps even isolating different sedimentary structures and comparing their directional patterns (Harms *et al.* 1982). This *important point* is illustrated by the hypothetical case shown in Figure 2.12. The tabular cross bedding shows a paleoflow direction that is markedly different from that indicated by the trough cross bedding. One interpretation is that the tabular sets represent lateral growth of bars into the stream channel and the trough sets represent down-channel migration of megaripples. Such an interpretation is certainly more informative than simply noting that the paleocurrent is polymodal. It also demonstrates why a vector mean calculated for a polymodal distribution may have no geologic meaning.

2.7 Exercises

1 The strike and dip of five cross-bed sets is given below, together with the strike and dip of the regional bedding. Using the stereonet (Fig. 2.13), restore the cross bedding to its original attitude (see Section 2.2).

	Tilted	*Restored*
Set A	N6°W,62°NE	____________
Set B	N35°W,80°NE	____________
Set C	N52°W,59°NE	____________
Set D	N12°E,30°SE	____________
Set E	N55°W,32°NE	____________

Regional strike and dip = N29°W,50°NE

Suggestions for using the stereonet. All poles to planes etc. are drawn on tracing paper with a *sharp* medium–hard pencil. The tracing paper is attached to the net (Fig. 2.13) with a thumb tack that pierces the center of the net. When first preparing the net, carefully push the tack through the *center*, with the net facing upward. Remove the tack and replace it so that the tack enters the back of the net and the point sticks up above the printed face of the net. Reinforce the center of both the tracing paper and the net with Scotch tape (attached to the back).

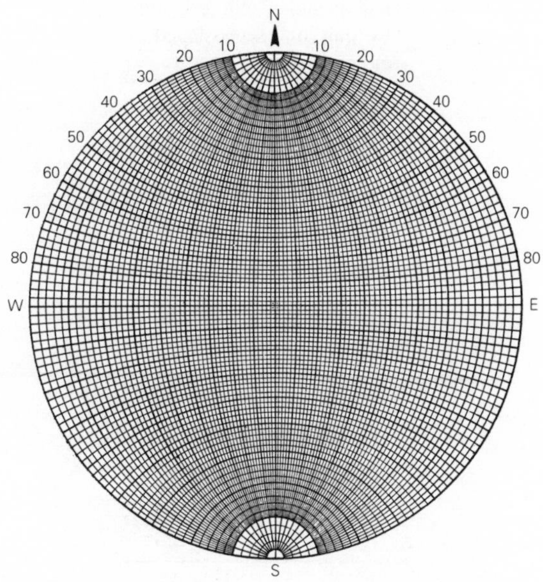

Figure 2.13 A stereonet.

2 Three sets of cross-bed dip azimuths are given below. Determine the vector mean and the vector magnitude for one set of data (as indicated by your instructor) by (a) the graphic method and (b) the trigonometric method using Figure 2.14 (also see Section 2.4). Put your answers in Table 2.1. These values can also be calculated by using a small computer or a programmable calculator (Freeman & Pierce 1979, Lindholm 1979a).

Use the graphic version of the Rayleigh test (Fig. 2.7) to determine whether the vector mean is significant at the 0.05 level.

Plot the data, as percentage of observations, on a current rose using 30° class intervals (see Section 2.3). Include an arrow for the vector mean as well as the number of observations (see Fig. 2.6).

Table 2.1 Results of analyses for Exercise 2.

Sample set _____	Vector mean	Vector magnitude
trigonometric method graphic method		

Is the vector magnitude significant at the 0.05 level?_____

Table 2.2 Problem sets for analysis of paleocurrent data. Data given as dip azimuths. Use only one set assigned by your instructor.

Set A	Set B	Set C
5	93	127
12	112	218
82	39	63
111	130	82
42	106	130
73	128	96
40	71	147
353	110	160
51	141	112
58	80	153
20	157	25
48	52	192
137	98	133
17	20	200
96	91	213

Azimuth (degrees)	sin x	cos x
1		
2		
3		
4		
5		
6		
7		
8		
9		
10		
11		
12		
13		
14		
15		
Σn		

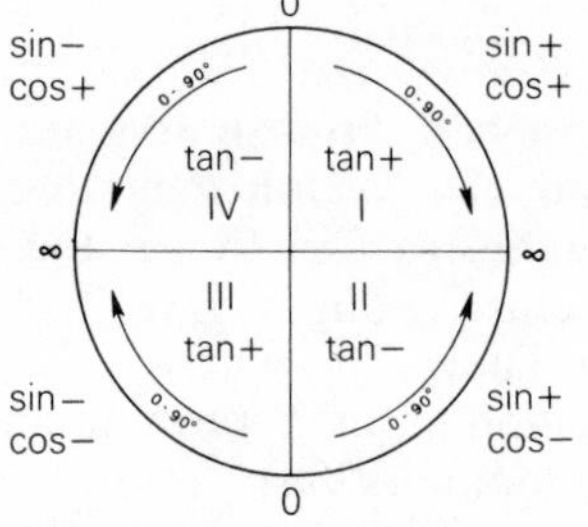

$$\tan \bar{x} = \frac{\Sigma n \sin x}{\Sigma n \cos x} = \text{———} = \text{———}$$

arctan ——— = ——— = vector mean

$$R = \sqrt{[(\Sigma n \sin x)^2 + (\Sigma n \cos x)^2]} = \sqrt{[(\quad)^2 + (\quad)^2]}$$

$$R = \sqrt{[\text{———} + \text{———}]} = \text{———}$$

$L = R/n \times 100 =$ ———/——— $\times 100 =$ ——— = vector magnitude

Figure 2.14 A work sheet for use in calculating vector mean and vector magnitude using data in Exercise 2.

3 A "do-it-yourself" outcrop is shown in Figure 2.16. Using the enlarged version provided at the back of the book, cut it out (along the dashed lines) and tape it together after folding along the dotted lines. Use a Brunton compass or a protractor to measure the foreset dip azimuth of as many cross-bed sets as possible. Calculate the vector mean and vector magnitude and construct a current rose using the measurements that you have made (use Fig. 2.15).

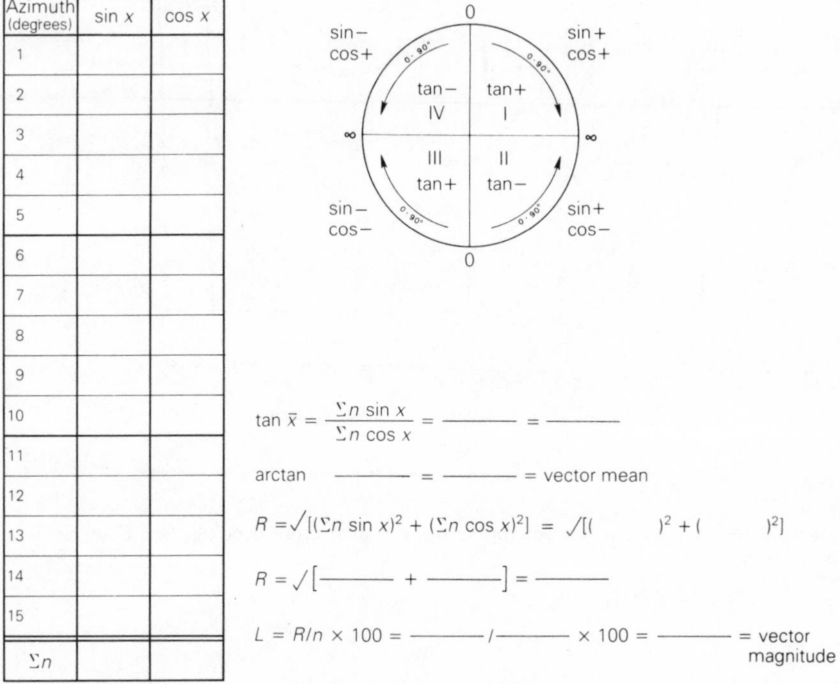

Figure 2.15 A work sheet for use in calculating vector mean and vector magnitude using measurements from Exercise 3.

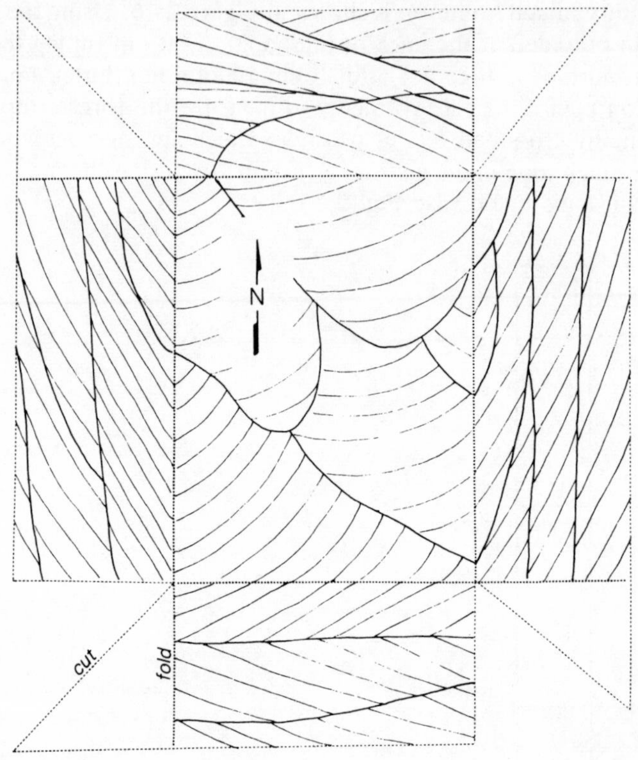

Figure 2.16 A model of an outcrop showing trough cross bedding. See Exercise 3 for instructions.

3 Primary grain fabric

3.1 Introduction

Dimensional grain fabrics produced during deposition are of interest mainly as a guide to paleocurrent direction and the transport mechanism. Such primary fabrics are manifest by elongate grains which show a preferred orientation. Some fabrics indicate the direction of movement (flow) and others only the line of movement. The methods of data presentation and analysis are the same as for directional sedimentary structures (Chapter 2).

3.2 Sand-grain orientation

Even though sand grains are generally nonspherical, they are not highly elongate. This, together with the small size, precludes field study of sand-grain orientation fabrics. Although indirect methods of orientation measurement allow rapid analysis (Sipple 1971, Shelton & Mack 1970) the procedure has not gained widespread popularity.

In most cases where preferred orientation has been demonstrated, the grains are oriented with their long axes parallel to flow. This generally occurs in sandstones with planar stratification (see Section 1.3.2).

In some sandstones, *grain alignment may parallel the direction of maximum permeability*. In fluvial deposits this direction coincides with the long axis of the sand body (i.e. a channel) and in nearshore marine deposits it is normal to the sand body (i.e. a bar sand) (Fig. 3.1).

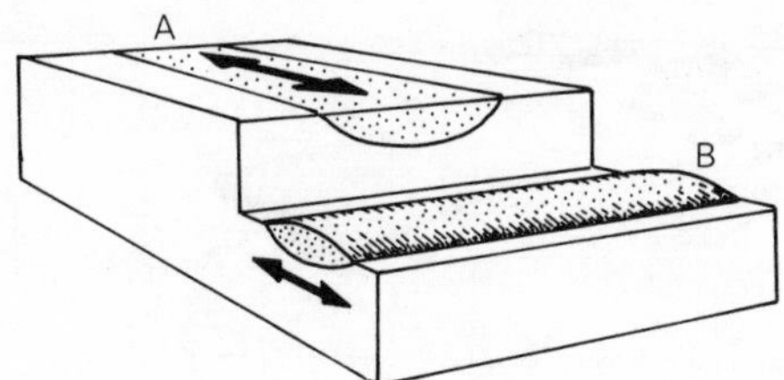

Figure 3.1 The relationship between sand-grain orientation and maximum permeability (arrows) to (A) fluvial-channel sand bodies and (B) marine sand bars (based on Pryor 1973).

3.3 Pebble orientation in conglomerate

Two aspects of pebble orientation are important. One involves the orientation of long axes. Measurements generally are made on bedding-parallel surfaces, but they can be made on vertical sections where pebbles stand out in relief. The other aspect relates to the orientation of flat pebbles not deposited in a horizontal position. Measuring the general dip direction is all that is needed, provided the orientation of the long axes is accurately recorded. This can be determined in vertical sections parallel to the dip direction or on bedding surfaces, provided there is adequate relief on the pebbles. A more elaborate analytical method is described by Davies and Walker (1974).

Flattened pebbles commonly dip at a low angle (10–30°) in the up-current direction of unidirectional flow. This fabric is called **imbrication**. It reflects the most stable configuration of grains lying on a horizontal surface under the influence of flowing water. Grains in any other position tend to be re-entrained. Imbrication is an excellent paleocurrent indicator in some coarse fluvial deposits (e.g. Lindsey 1972).

The orientation of elongate pebbles relative to the current direction is complex. In some cases elongate pebbles are aligned in a direction transverse (perpendicular) to the flow, and in others they are aligned parallel to the direction of the flow (Fig. 3.2). Coarse sediments with either orientation pattern may be imbricated. **Elongation transverse to flow** results from clasts rolling on the sediment surface and characterizes most fluvial deposits with a well developed fabric. Orientation of long

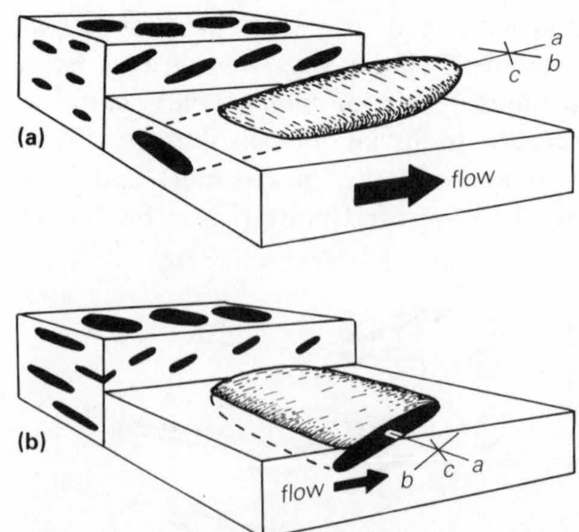

Figure 3.2 Pebble imbrication: (a) Long axes parallel to flow; (b) long axes transverse to flow. Reference axes are: *a*, long; *b*, intermediate; and *c*, short.

axes **parallel to flow** is generally interpreted as evidence for rapid transport capable of maintaining large clasts in the dispersion above the bed. It occurs in conglomerates associated with turbidite sequences and may be expected in alluvial-flash flood deposits (Harms *et al.* 1982: 6–4). Although pebble elongation parallel to flow may be a useful indicator of the transport mechanism, care must be taken to establish *beyond reasonable doubt* that such a relationship indeed exists.

Many conglomeratic deposits show no preferred orientation. This occurs when clasts are not able to react to the current (e.g. during very rapid deposition).

3.4 Intraclast orientation in limestone

Intraclasts in limestone, produced by penecontemporaneous erosion and redeposition, commonly show a well defined orientation fabric. Where bedding surfaces are exposed, the long-axis orientation and imbrication azimuth may be measured directly in the field. More commonly, oriented samples must be taken to the laboratory for analysis (Lindholm 1980: 1206). Comparison of intraclast orientation and cross-bedding dip azimuths indicate that long axes are transverse to flow (Fig. 3.3).

Intraclastic sediment is deposited in shallow marine shelf environments (e.g. platform margin ooid shoals and intertidal mud flats) and in deeper intrashelf basins. Studies of Cambrian carbonates in Virginia indicate that

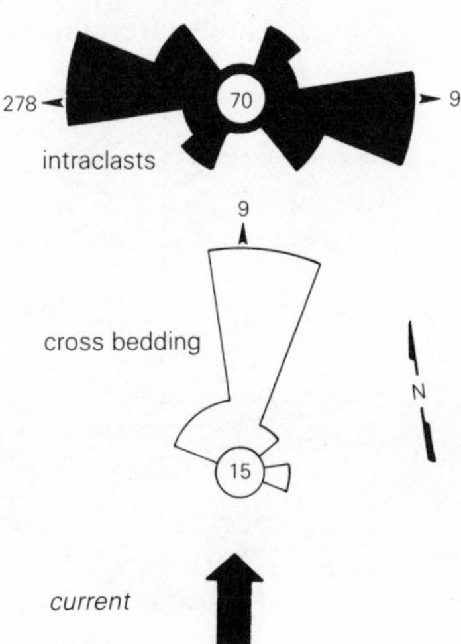

Figure 3.3 A current rose showing intraclast orientation transverse to flow direction, as determined from associated cross bedding. Ordovician Lincolnshire Limestone near Strasburg, Virginia. (Based on unpublished data collected by Scott Phillips 1981.)

intraclastic units displaying well developed imbrication were generated and deposited by storms (Whisonant *et al.* 1985). The paleocurrent system transporting these sediments was highly dispersed in the seaward areas but was more consistently landward-oriented in the shoreward direction. Whisonant and his colleagues are expanding their work to include the deeper-water deposits.

3.5 Orientation of fossils

Although the orientation of fossils may provide useful information regarding paleocurrents and the physical processes active during deposition, the fabric patterns are commonly obscure and difficult to interpret. This is due in part to the irregular shape of many fossils, as well as the fact that orientation may reflect the life position of the animal.

It is generally accepted that bivalve shells, subject to **traction transport**, lie with their **concave side down**, which is the hydrodynamically stable rest position (Fig. 3.4,C). Those carried in **suspension** commonly are deposited **concave-up**. This occurs in turbidity current deposits (Fig. 3.4,B) and in material deposited in local sediment traps (e.g. large open burrows) (Fig. 3.4,D). Bioturbation modifies bivalve shell fabric (Fig. 3.4,A) by greatly increasing the proportion of inclined and vertical shells (Salazar-Jimenez *et al.* 1982). An abundance of vertical and steeply inclined shells may simply record growth position, especially if articulated bivalves are present.

Unidirectional currents and wave action usually cause alignment of conical shells. Elongate conical shells are aligned parallel to flow in

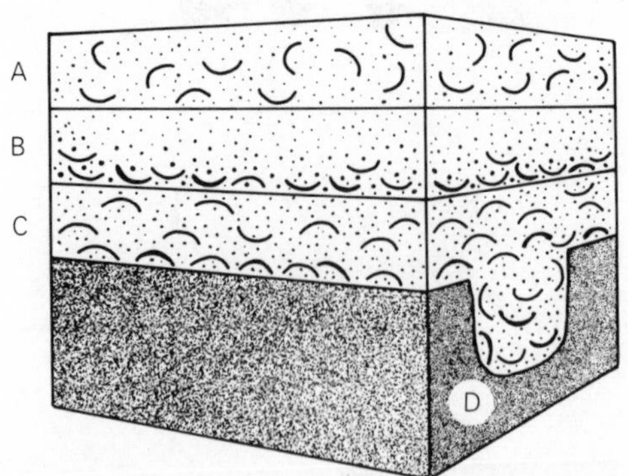

Figure 3.4 Orientation patterns for bivalve shells as seen in vertical section: A, bioturbated bed with great diversity of orientation; B, suspension deposit (turbidite) with dominance of concave-up shells; C, traction deposit with dominance of concave-down shells; D, sediment trap (large open burrow) with dominance of vertical and concave-up shells.

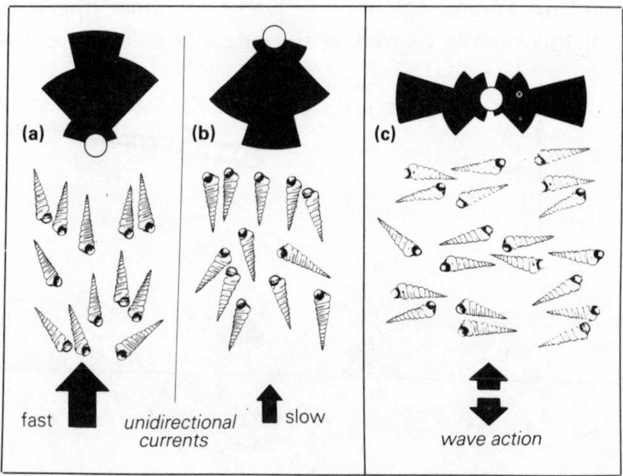

Figure 3.5 Orientation patterns for elongate conical shells as seen on bedding surface. Current roses drawn to indicate the directon in which the apex points. (Based mainly on Nagel 1967: Fig. 1, and Allen 1982a: Fig. 5.22.)

unidirectional currents, with the majority of shells pointing in one direction. Generally the **apex points up current** (Fig. 3.5b) (Nagel 1967). Low-spired gastropods swing around the heavy end, so the apex points down current, as apparently happens with high-spired forms in fast flow (Fig. 3.5a) (Allen 1982a: Fig. 5.22). Interpretation is further complicated by the observation that some deposits of oriented gastropods reflect life position, rather than particle orientation by moving water (Kidwell 1982). **Wave action** aligns conical shells **parallel to wave crests** (normal to the direction of wave propagation), with approximately half of the shells pointing in one direction and half pointing in the opposite direction (Fig. 3.5c).

Lack of orientation may reflect absence of currents or factors that inhibit free movement of shells by bottom currents (e.g. a grassy or muddy substrate, or burial of live animals). In addition, shells which are equidimensional or lack well defined symmetry do not produce useful orientation fabrics. Lastly, displaced centers of gravity due to uneven filling before burial may affect orientation.

3.6 Exercise

In Figure 3.6, measure the azimuth of as many of the conical fossils (*Tentaculites*) as you can. Plot your results as a current rose. Indicate the type of current (unidirectional or wave action) operative during deposition of this sample as well as the inferred paleocurrent direction.

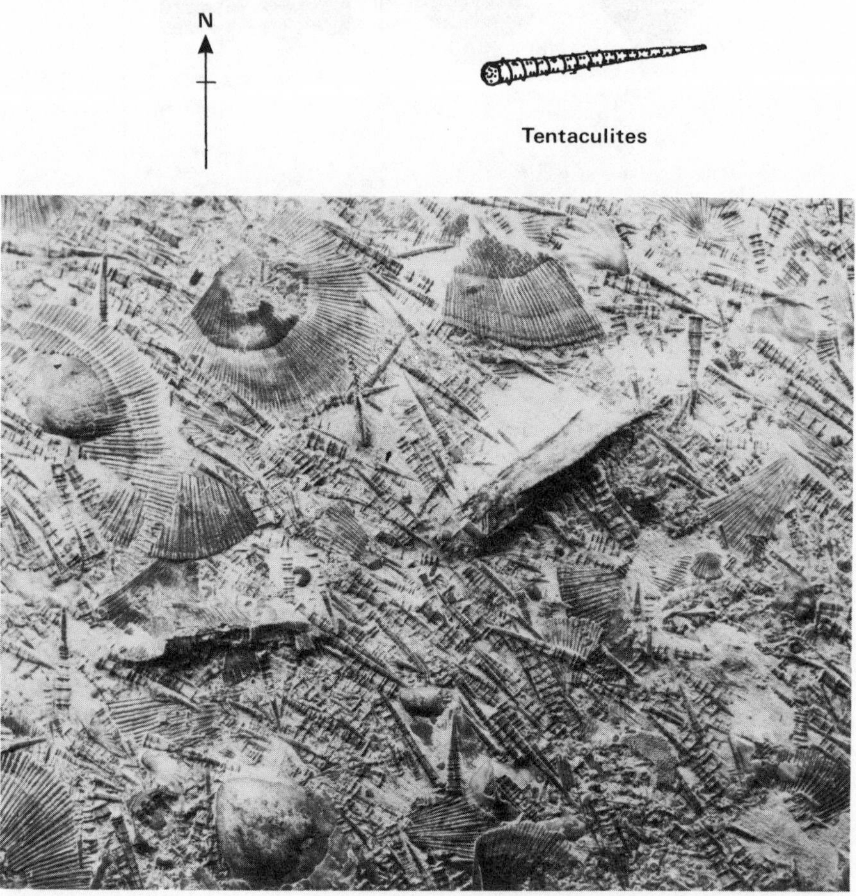

Figure 3.6 An upper bedding surface showing numerous conical fossils (*Tentaculites* – a fossil of uncertain affinity) and brachiopods. Silurian Keyser Formation, West Virginia.

4 Trace fossils

4.1 Introduction

Discrete structures produced by biogenic activity on the sediment surface or within the sediment are literally traces of ancient organisms and hence are called **trace fossils**. They differ from body fossils in that they are formed by an animal's **behavioral activity** in response to the substrate and other paleoecological paramaters rather than being part of an animal's body (also see Section 4.5). Synonyms include "ichnofossil" and "lebensspuren." Four characteristics of trace fossils that affect their value in geologic investigation are (1) long time range, (2) narrow facies range, (3) no secondary displacement, and (4) relatively great abundance in rocks with few body fossils.

Because trace fossils in sandstone and shale are more abundant and easier to study than in other lithologies, most work has focused on these rocks. Nonetheless, traces, especially borings, are important in some carbonate units (Kennedy 1975, Warme & McHuron 1978, ten papers in the March 1984 issue of *J. Paleont.* **58**(2)).

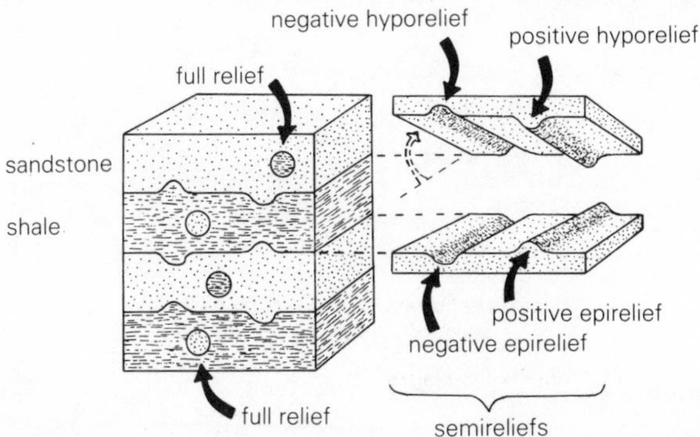

Figure 4.1 Preservational terminology used to describe trace fossils (based on toponomic classification by Seilacher 1964; terms in parentheses from Martinsson 1970).

Full relief traces preserved within a bed (endichnial burrows; exichnial burrows).
Semirelief traces at a sand–shale or comparable contact.
Epirelief (epichnia): semireliefs on the top surface of a sandstone bed; they may be concave positives (epichnial ridge) or convex negatives (epichnial groove).
Hyporelief (hypichnia): semireliefs on the bottom surface (sole) of a sandstone bed; they may be convex positives or concave negatives (hypichnial ridge or hypichnial groove cast).

4.2 Classification

When describing trace fossils, various preservational or morphologic features should be utilized. Primary among these is the position of the trace relative to the interface between muddy and sandy beds (Fig. 4.1). Those at the contact are **semireliefs** and those enclosed within a bed are called **full reliefs**. Semireliefs on the upper surface of a sandy bed are called **epireliefs**, and those on the lower surface are called **hyporeliefs**. Other morphological features are summarized in Figures 4.2 and 4.3.

I **Full reliefs** (traces within stratum) (see Fig. 4.1)

- A shape
  - 1 unbranched
    - a straight
    - b curved
      - (1) U-shaped
      - (2) J-shaped
      - (3) spirally coiled
  - 2 branched
    - a regular
    - b irregular
  - 3 diameter
    - a uniform
    - b nonuniform
      - (1) localized swelling
      - (2) tapering
- B wall character
  - 1 unlined
  - 2 lined
  - 3 crenulated
- C filling
  - 1 homogeneous
  - 2 patterned
    - a meniscate (see Fig. 4.3a)
    - b pelleted
- D spreite (see Fig. 4.3b)
  - 1 protrusive
  - 2 retrusive
- E size
- F orientation (with respect to bedding)
  - 1 horizontal
  - 2 vertical
  - 3 inclined (oblique)
  - 4 random
- G deformation of enclosing laminae

II **Semi-reliefs** (traces at sand–shale contact)

- A epirelief or hyporelief (Fig. 4.1)
  - 1 positive (convex)
  - 2 negative (concave)
- B shape
  - 1 radially symmetrical
    - a with or without axial vertical structure
    - b circular or ovoid
    - c multirayed
      - (1) shape of rays
      - (2) number of rays
  - 2 imprints (tracks) in rows (trackway) (see Fig. 4.6)
    - a uniformity of imprints
      - (1) all alike
      - (2) of different kinds
    - b character of rows
      - (1) continuous
      - (2) discontinuous
        - (a) clusters
        - (b) short rows oblique to trackway
    - c shape of imprints
      - (1) simple
        - (a) elongated
        - (b) circular or ovoid
      - (2) digitate (number of digits)
  - 3 ridges and furrows (trails) (see Fig. 4.5)
    - a pattern
      - (1) gently curving
      - (2) meandering
        - (a) no regular pattern
        - (b) zigzag or sine wave
        - (c) two orders of meanders
        - (d) highly attenuated "meander loops" (in contact)
      - (3) spiral
      - (4) honeycomb network (especially regular hexagons)
    - b branched or unbranched
    - c shape
      - (1) simple
      - (2) lobate
        - (a) bilobate
        - (b) trilobate
    - d ornamentation
      - (1) transverse
      - (2) oblique
- C internal structure
- D size
- E orientation (relative to north)

Figure 4.2 Morphologic characteristics used in describing trace fossils (expanded and modified after Horowitz's classification – in Frey 1971).

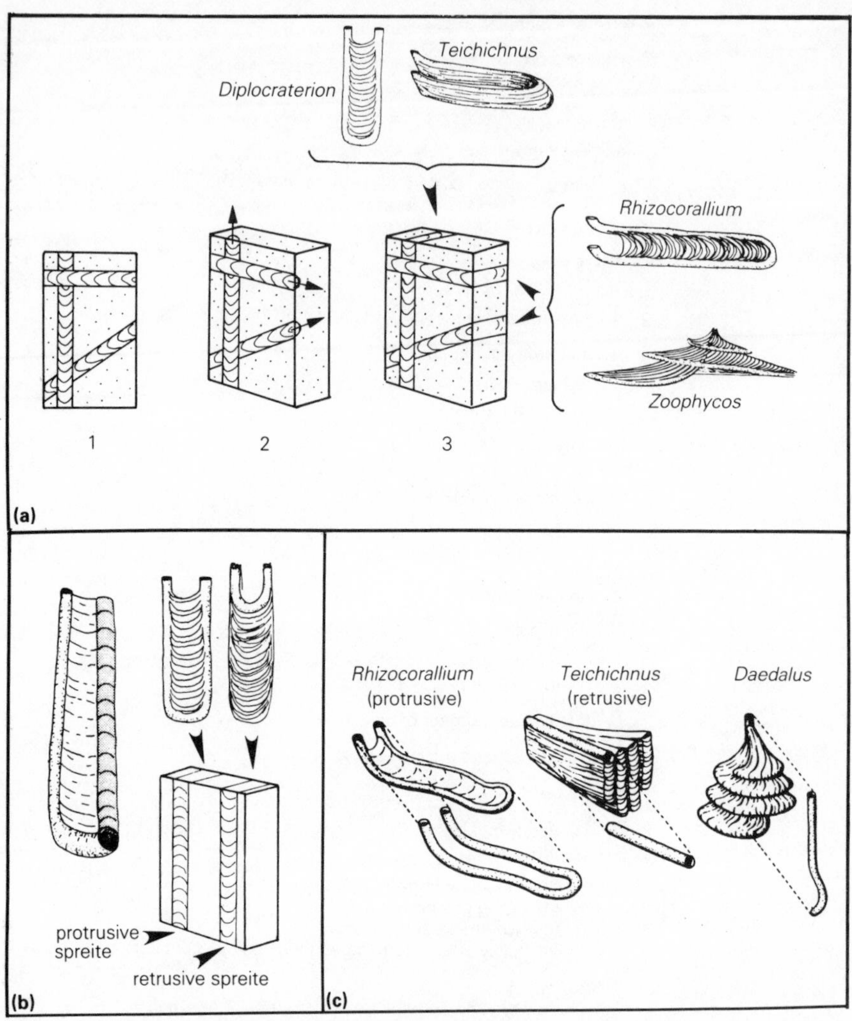

Figure 4.3 Spreite and meniscate structures in burrows.

(a) The arcuate laminate in the burrows shown in surface 1 may be meniscate, backfilled burrows or spreite-filled tabular structures. Block 2 shows the actual structure of a meniscate backfilled burrow. The curved laminae (meniscae) are concave in the direction that the burrowing animal moved (small arrows). Block 3 shows the actual structure of a spreite-filled tabular structure (spreite = sets of closely spaced, parallel or concentric traces). Vertical structure formed by translocation of burrows in a vertical plane as in *Diplocraterion* and *Teichichnus*. Horizontal structure formed by lateral translocation of burrow in horizontal plane as in *Rhizocorallium* and *Zoophycos*. (Modified from Chamberlain 1978.)

(b) Protrusive spreite are produced by the downward translocation of the vertical U-shaped burrow (*Rhizocorallium*). Concave-down laminae were formed as sediment was plastered onto the ceiling of the burrow. Retrusive spreite are produced by the upward translocation of the burrow. Concave-up laminae were formed as sediment was plastered on the floor of the burrow.

(c) Comparison of spreite in trace fossils as observed in rock (total structure above) and active burrow in modern sediment (extended below) (modified from Seilacher 1953).

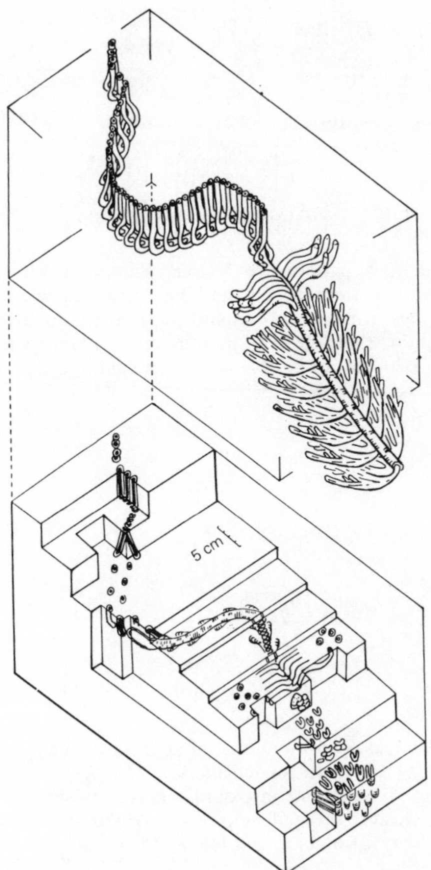

Figure 4.4 A compex trace fossil. Note the variety of possible expressions present in different horizontal and vertical planes through the trace fossil. From Paleocene submarine canyon deposits at Point Lobos, California (Hill 1981).

Difficulty in describing trace fossil morphology, especially full reliefs, stems from the fact that the geometry is difficult to determine in lithified material and that many traces are quite complex (Fig. 4.4) and strongly influenced by substrate consistency (e.g. wet versus dry or firm versus soupy). Although special techniques may be required (Farrow 1975), the best approach is to study the variously oriented cross sections provided by bedding and joint surfaces. Experience, knowledge of the way that modern animals move through sediment and a vivid imagination are also helpful.

Traces formed on the sediment surface by locomotion are called **trails** (Fig. 4.5) (a continuous groove or furrow) or **tracks** (Fig. 4.6) (impression left by a foot or podium). A **trackway** is a succession of tracks. Although

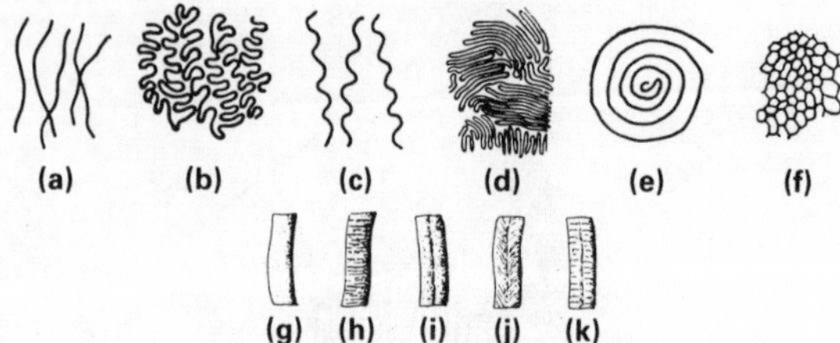

Figure 4.5 Typical trail patterns (e–f) and shapes (g–k). (a) Gently curving; (b) meandering – no regular pattern; (c) meandering – zigzag or sine wave; (d) meandering with highly attenuated loops in contact; (e) spiral pattern; (f) honeycomb network; (g) simple with no ornamentation; (h) simple with transverse ornamentation; (i) bilobate with no ornamentation; (j) bilobate with oblique ornamentation; (k) bilobate with transverse ornamentation.

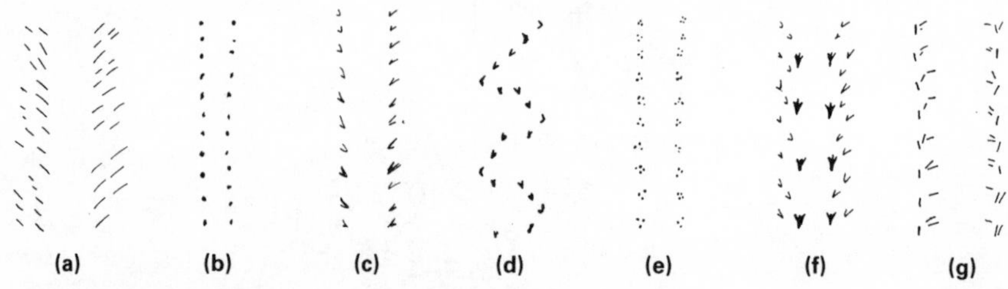

Figure 4.6 Typical tracks: (a–e) imprints all alike in trackway; (f–g) imprints of different kinds in trackway. (a) Elongate scratch marks – *Diplichnites*; (b) circular pits; (c) bifid marks – *Permichnium*; (d) imprints in groups arranged in short rows oblique to trackway – *Octopodichnus*; (e) clusters of small imprints – *Diplopodomorpha*; (f) bifid and digitate marks – *Kouphichnium*; (g) oblique and longitudinal marks – *Copeza*.

most marine tracks and trails are formed as depressions on a muddy substrate, they are commonly preserved as positive hyporeliefs. Some trails are formed by animals plowing through the sediment just below the water–sediment interface. **Burrows** are excavations generally filled with sediment which may be the product of active backfilling or passive filling after the burrow is abandoned. Dominantly horizontal burrows are called **tunnels** and dominantly vertical burrows are called **shafts**. **Borings** are excavations made in consolidated material such as lithified sediment, shell, or bone.

After trace fossils have been fully described they should be named. Informal designations (e.g. type 1, type 2, etc.) can be used effectively to describe the distribution of traces within facies in a localized study area. For comparison with other studies, **ichnogeneric names** should be used, or else the occurrence will be lost in the literature (M.F. Miller 1983: personal communication). Assignment of the correct names is done by comparison with descriptions in the Treatise volume on trace fossils (Häntzschel 1975). This is facilitated by the keys in Figures 4.7–4.16.

Keep in mind that an **ichnogenus** includes traces that are morphologically similar but generally produced by one of several different organisms which exhibit similar behavior (i.e. they have the same *modus vivendi*). Conversely, different activities of one organism may produce different *ichnogenera*.

Some ichnogenera are transitional one to the other, and one ichnogenus may grade into another within a few feet (e.g. *Ophiomorpha* transitional to *Thalassinoides* and *Asterosoma* transitional to *Rosselia*). Also some specimens have characteristics that would place them halfway between two distinct but similar ichnogenera.

4.3 Keys for trace fossil identification

These keys are intended to be used with the 1975 Treatise volume on trace fossils by Häntzschel (1975) as well as with the descriptions of 26 common trace fossils in Section 4.4.

First determine which of the categories, listed below, best fits the trace that you are trying to identify. Then proceed to the figure indicated. Using the characteristics that you have described for the unknown trace, follow the key to the ichnogeneric names on the right-hand side of the key. You may find that you still have several possible ichnogenera as candidates for your unknown trace. At this point you will need to consult the Treatise volume for more detailed information and illustrations for comparison (do this as a check even if the key leads to a single ichnogenus). If none seems correct, you should re-evaluate your original decision as to which broad category best describes your specimen. You may have been using the wrong key. It will be tedious at first but you will find this process more efficient than randomly thumbing through the Treatise volume trying to find an illustraton that resembles your unknown trace.

Please note that size measurements presented in these keys are based mainly on those in the Treatise volume. They should be used as a guide and not taken too literally. Some samples may be smaller or larger than indicated in these keys.

		Go to Figure
Trail-like traces	gently curving	4.7
	meandering	4.8
	miscellaneous	4.9
Track-like traces on bedding plane		4.10

Equant-to-oblong traces preserved as semireliefs (exclusive of tracks)	4.11
Traces radially symmetric in horizontal plane	4.12
Burrows horizontal or oblique to bedding (tunnels)	4.13
Vertical burrows (shafts)	4.14
Burrow network composed of vertical or horizontal traces	4.15
Traces with spreite	4.16

These keys are an expansion and modification of Simpson's (1975) morphologic classification. One asterisk (*) indicates that the ichnogenus is described in Figures 4.7 to 4.16; two asterisks (**) indicate that the ichnogenus is illustrated in Figure 4.6.

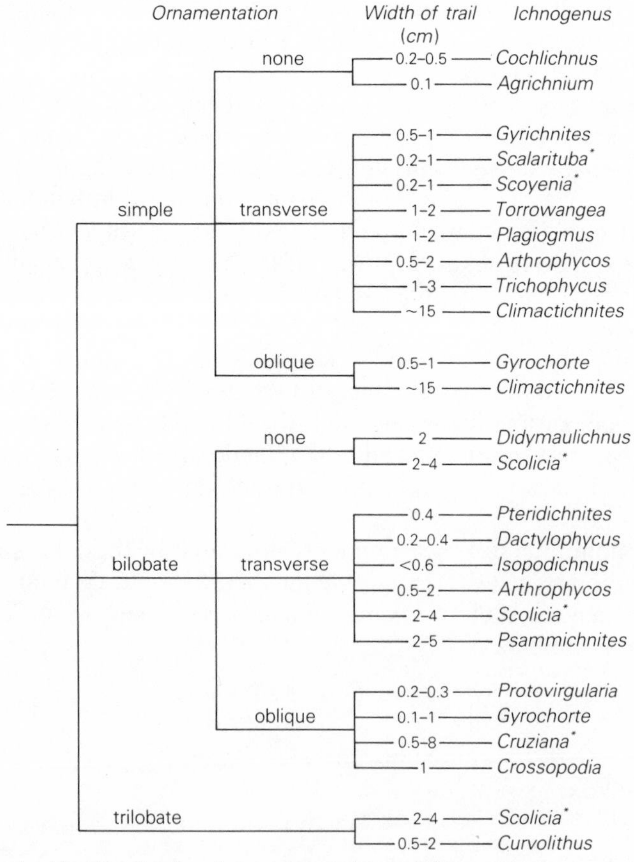

Figure 4.7 An identification key for gently curving trail-like traces.

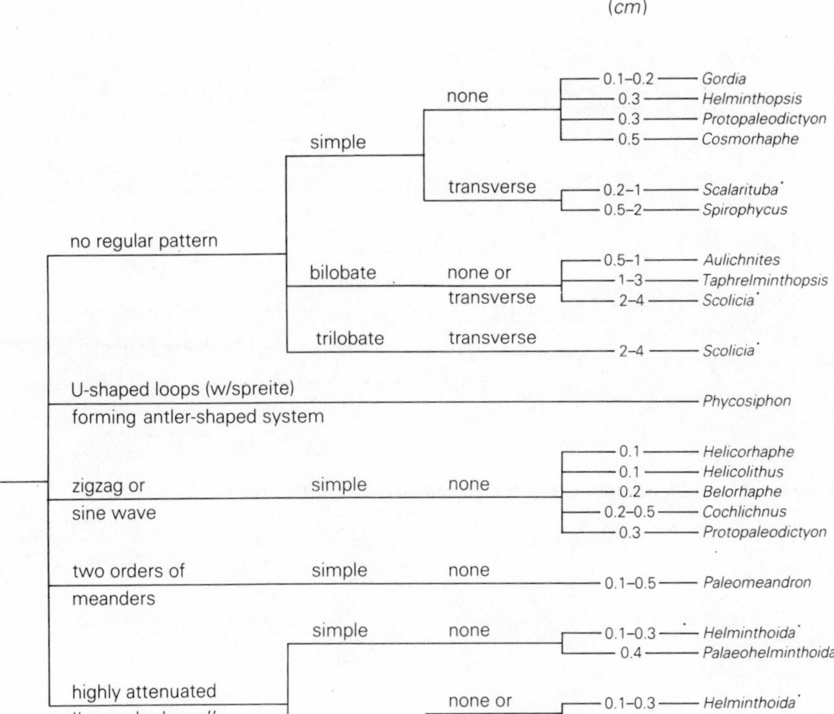

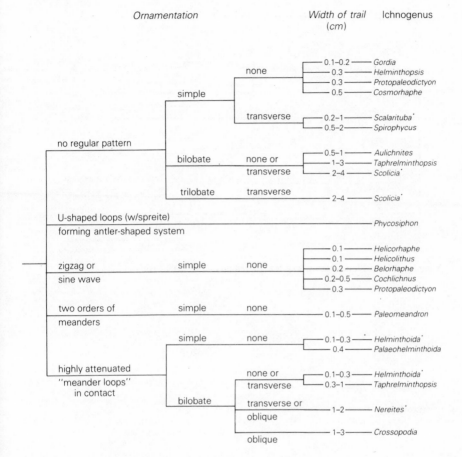

Figure 4.8 An identification key for meandering trail-like traces.

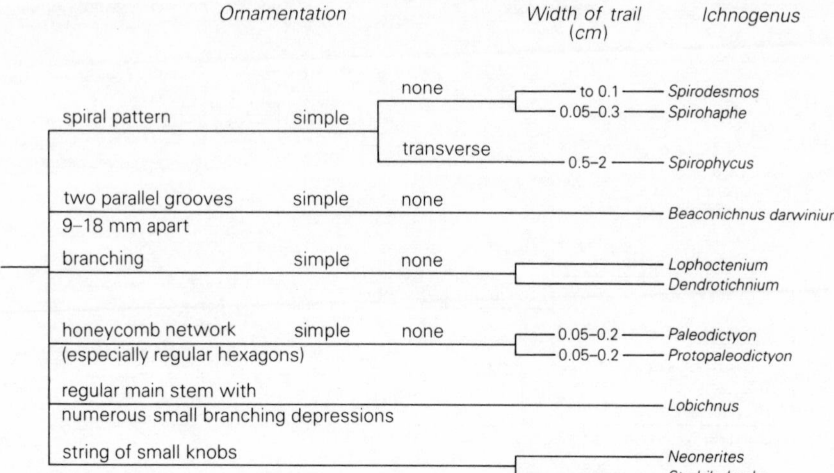

Figure 4.9 An identification key for miscellaneous trail-like traces.

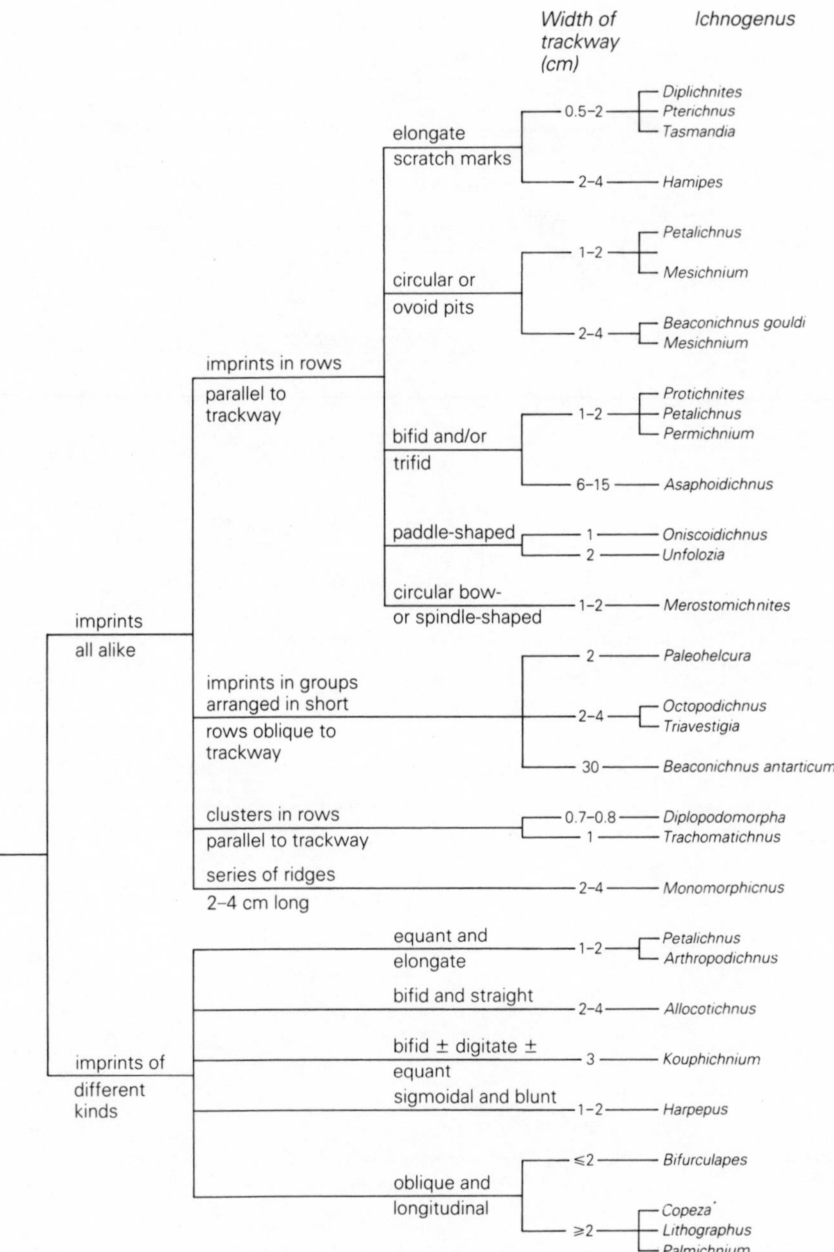

Figure 4.10 An identification key for track-like traces on bedding plane.

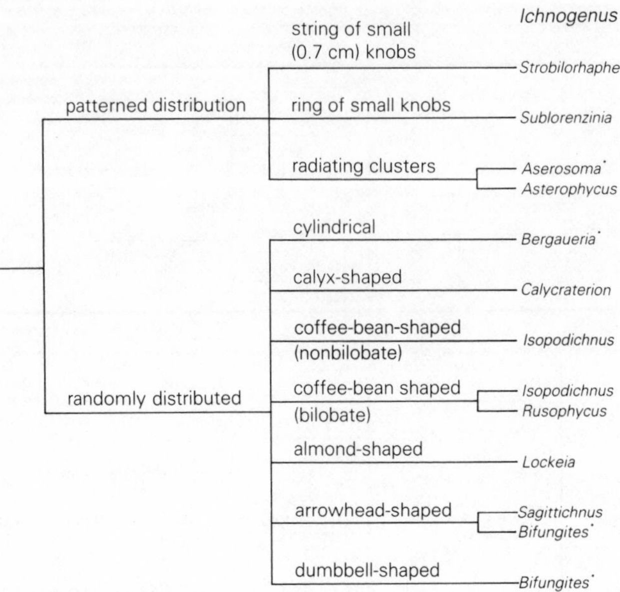

Figure 4.11 An identification key for equant to oblong traces preserved as semireliefs (exclusive of tracks).

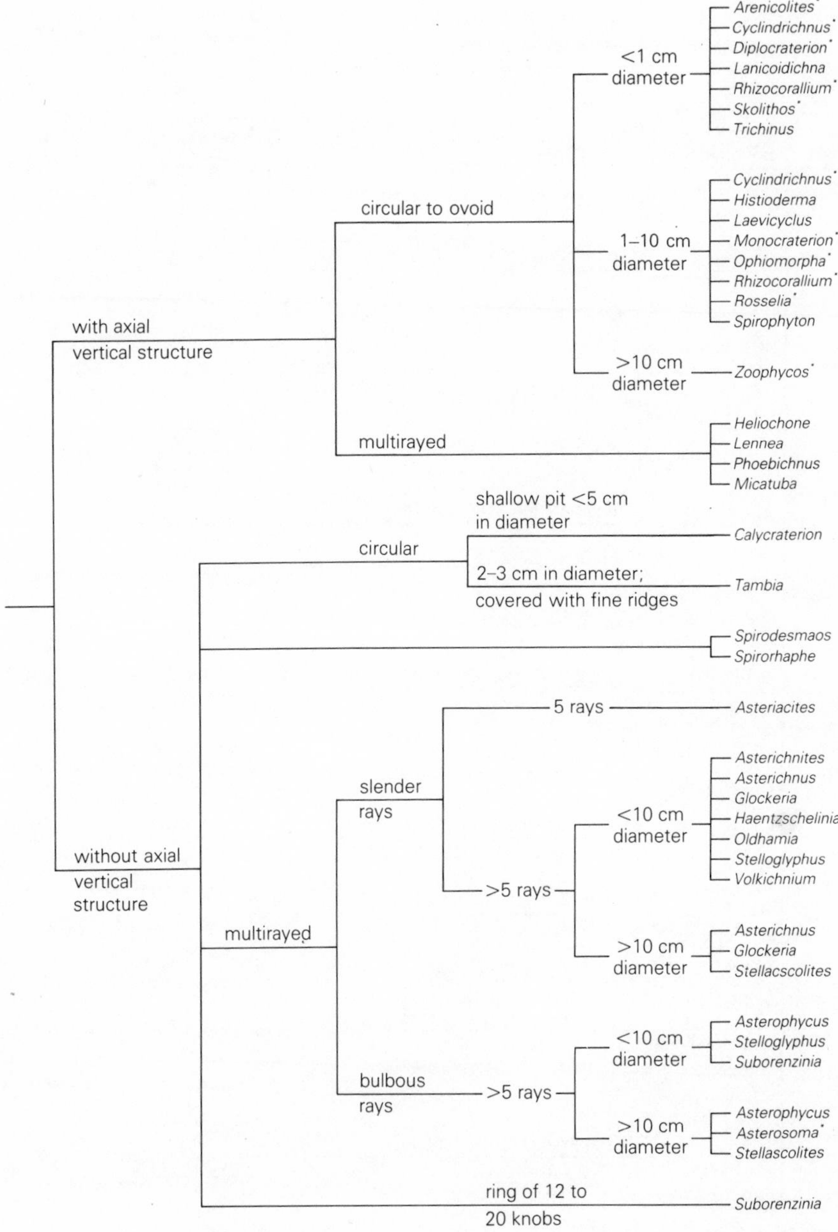

Figure 4.12 An identification key for traces radially symmetrical in the horizontal plane.

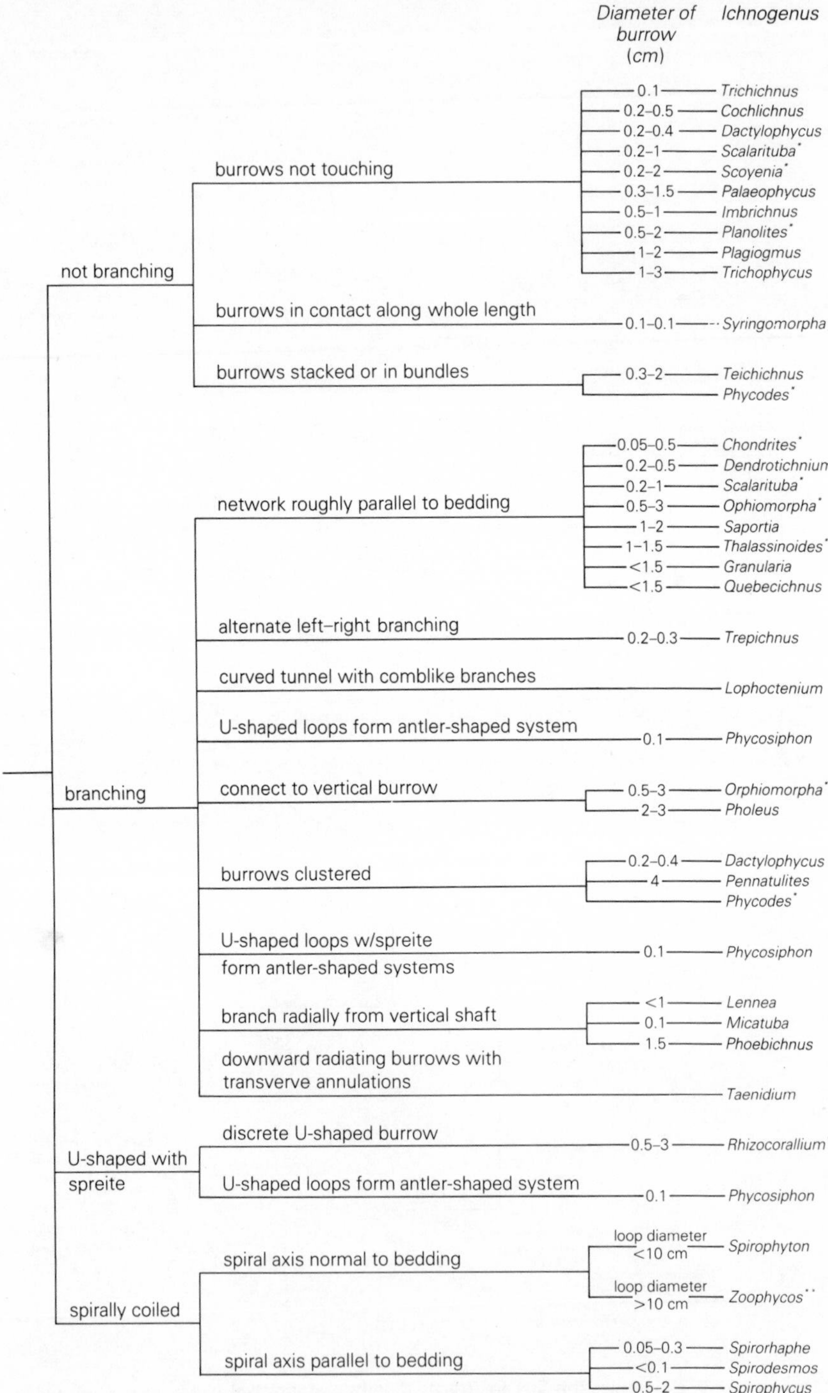

Figure 4.13 An identification key for burrows horizontal or oblique to bedding (tunnels).

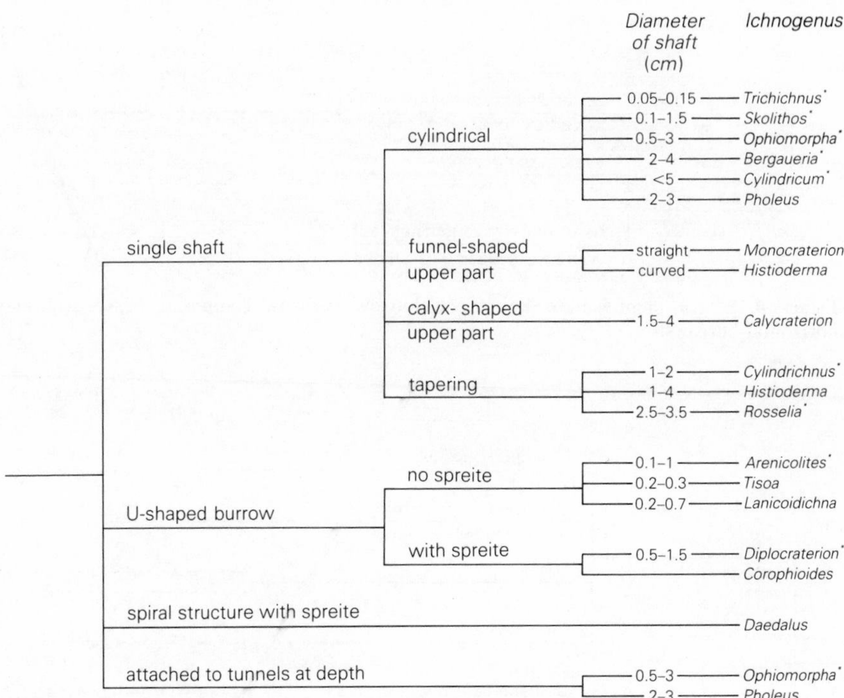

Figure 4.14 An identification key for vertical burrows (shafts).

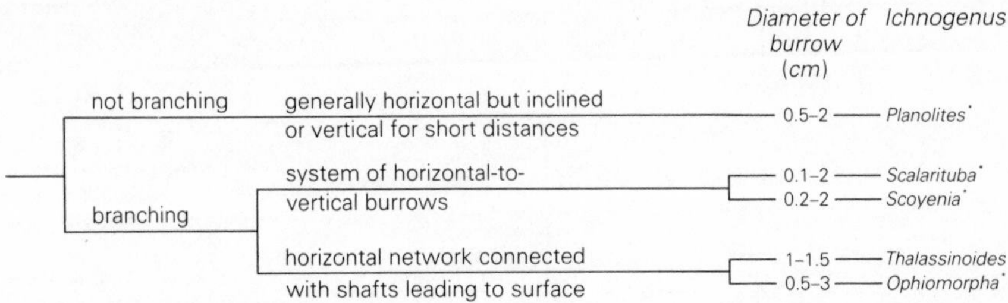

Figure 4.15 An identification key for a burrow network composed of vertical and horizontal burrows.

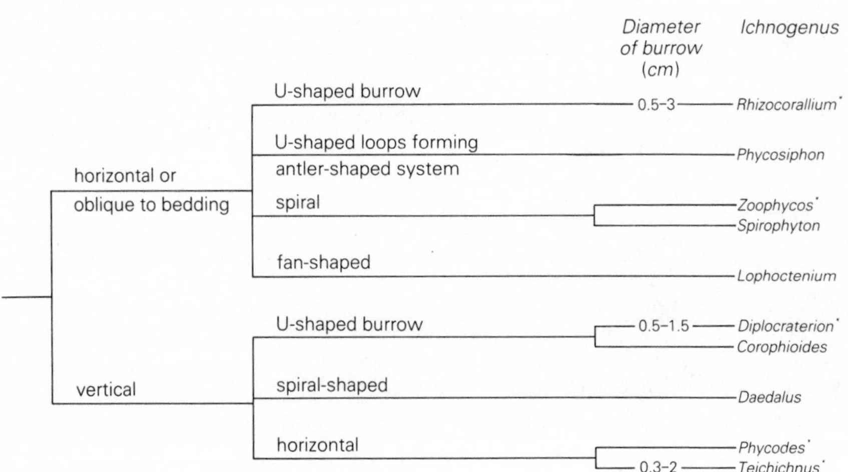

Figure 4.16 An identification key for traces with spreite.

4.4 Descriptions of common trace fossils

These descriptions are summarized mainly from those in Häntzschel (1975) and Chamberlain (1978).

4.4.1 *Arenicolites*

Position	Full relief
Shape	Simple vertical U-shaped burrow without spreite
Internal structure	Wall generally smooth, but in some cases lined or sculptured
Size	Distance between limbs of U, 1–10 cm; burrow diameter, 1–10 mm

Age Cambrian to Holocene
Function Dwelling burrow of suspension-feeding work or wormlike animal
Facies Littoral to bathyal

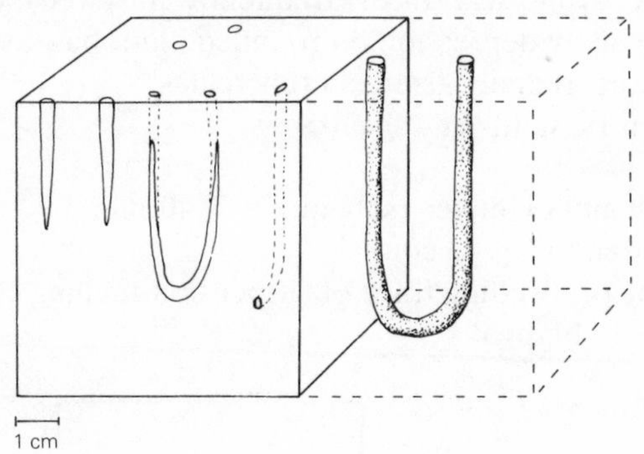

Figure 4.17 *Arenicolites.*

4.4.2 *Asterosoma*

Position Positive hyporelief
Shape Elongate bulbous oval rays that branch radially or in a fanlike manner from a central point; surface covered with longitudinal wrinkles
Internal structure Concentric laminae of sand and clay packed about a central tube
Size Patterns contain three to nine rays and are 14–30 cm across; individual rays are 15–30 mm across and 30–80 mm long
Age Devonian to Cretaceous
Function Burrows with radiating feeding trails made by decapod crustaceans
Facies Neritic (also tidal flat)

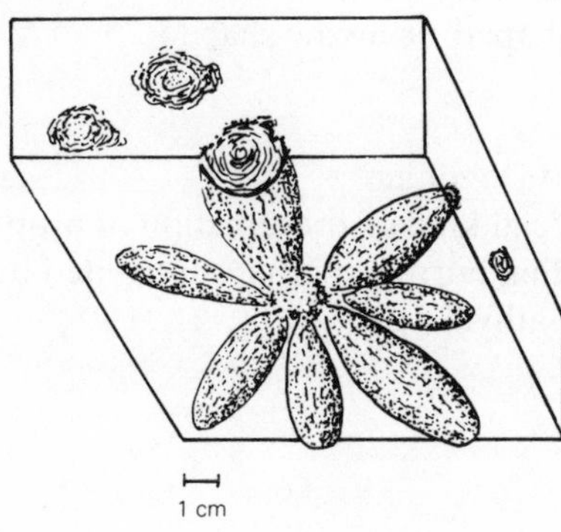

Figure 4.18 *Asterosoma.*

4.4.3 *Bergaueria*

Position	Full relief (generally exposed on sole of sandy beds)
Shape	Stubby, cylindrical traces (frequently clustered), commonly with shallow depression on rounded blunt base, surrounded by 6–8 short, radially arranged tubercules
Internal structure	Concentric sand–clay sheaths
Size	Length and diameter (subequal), 5–40 mm
Age	Cambrian to Cretaceous
Function	Resting or dwelling trace of suspension-feeding coelenterate
Facies	Neritic to bathyal

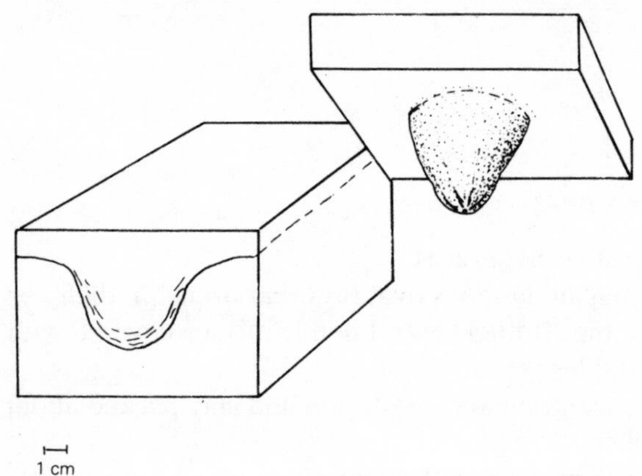

Figure 4.19 *Bergaueria.*

4.4.4 *Bifungites*

Position	Positive hyporelief
Shape	Dumbbell-shaped or arrow-shaped
Internal structure	None
Age	Cambrian to Devonian
Function	Possibly special kind of preservation of protrusive vertical U-shaped feeding burrow, perhaps inhabited by small trilobite
Facies	Littoral to bathyal

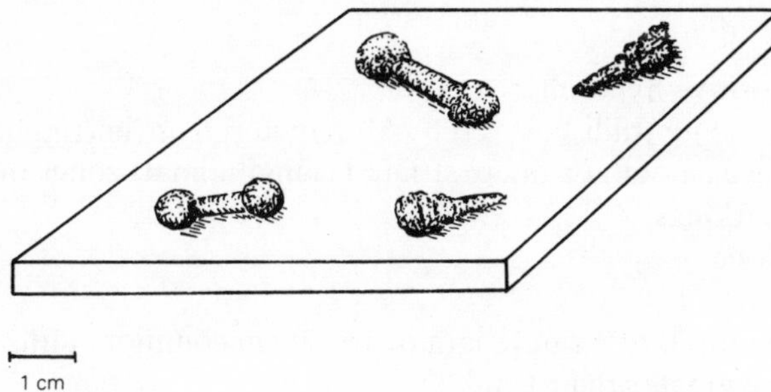

Figure 4.20 *Bifungites.*

4.4.5 Chondrites

Position Full relief
Shape Three-dimensional system of branching cylindrical tunnels; individual tunnel segments are generally straight
Internal structure None
Size Tunnel diameter, 0.5–5 mm
Age Ordovician to Holocene
Function Feeding burrow of sediment-eating worm or wormlike animal
Facies Littoral to abyssal

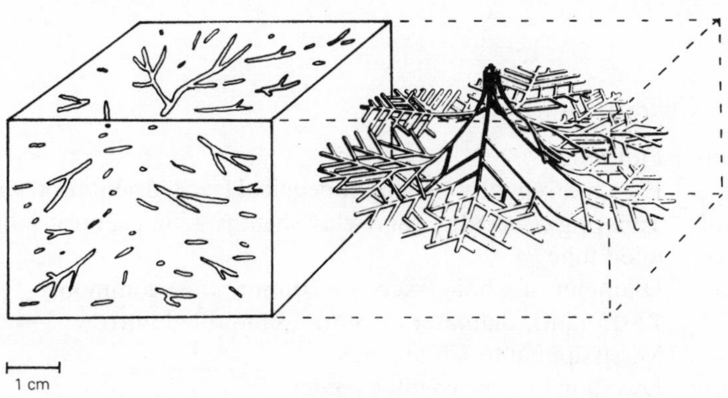

Figure 4.21 *Chondrites.*

4.4.6 Cruziana

Position	Positive hyporelief
Shape	Bilobate trails covered by V-shaped ridges (herringbone); may have smooth or finely striated (longitudinal) zones outside V markings
Internal structure	None
Size	Width, 0.5–8 cm; length of 10–20 cm common, although some are greater than 1 m
Age	Cambrian to Pennsylvanian
Function	Commonly thought to be trails made by furrowing or ploughing movement of trilobites or other similar arthropods
Facies	Neritic

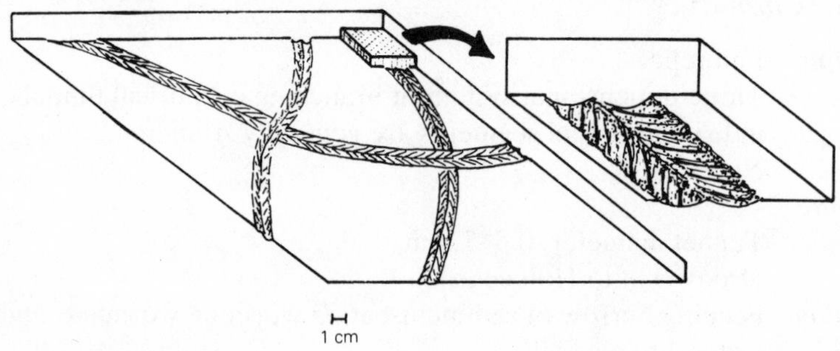

Figure 4.22 *Cruziana.*

4.4.7 Cylindrichnus

Position	Full relief
Shape	Elongate, slightly curving subconical trace; orientation variable
Internal structure	Tapering concentric sand–clay sheaths with a central sand-filled tube
Size	Diameter of whole trace, 10–20 mm (most commonly 12–15 mm); diameter of central sand-filled burrow, 2–4 mm
Age	Mississippian to Cretaceous
Function	Dwelling burrow of filter feeder

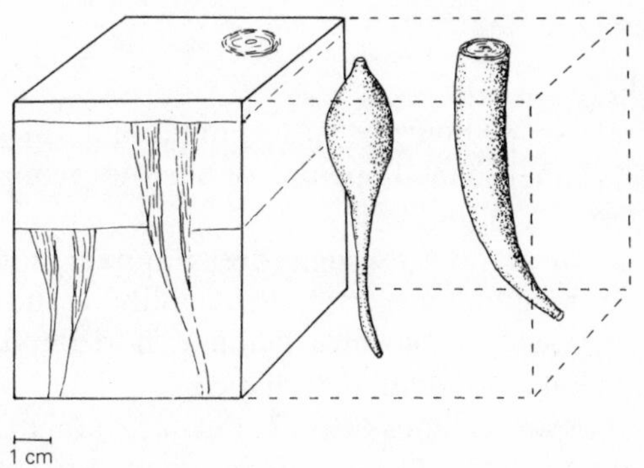

Figure 4.23 *Cylindrichnus.*

4.4.8 Diplichnites

Position	Semirelief
Shape	Simple track consisting of two parallel sets of fine ridges which are elongate oblique to track axis
Internal structure	None
Size	Track width, 1–2 cm; individual fine ridges are 1–5 mm long
Age	Cambrian to Permian
Function	Tracks produced by trilobite walking across muddy surface
Facies	Neritic

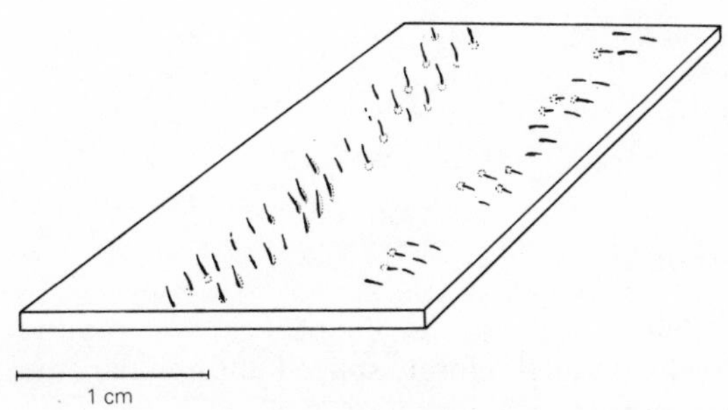

Figure 4.24 *Diplichnites.*

4.4.9 *Diplocraterion*

Position	Full relief
Shape	Vertical U-shaped burrow with spreite; limbs of U are parallel; funnel-shaped opening of burrows generally removed by erosion
Internal structure	Longitudinal sections through spreite appear as vertical meniscae; longitudinal section through the vertical burrow shows several thin concentric laminae; horizontal section on bedding planes are dumbbell shaped
Size	Distance between limbs of U, 3–15 cm (average 2–3 cm); depth of burrows, 2–60 cm; burrow diameter, 5–15 mm
Age	Cambrian to Cretaceous
Function	Dwelling burrow of suspension feeder
Facies	Littoral to neritic

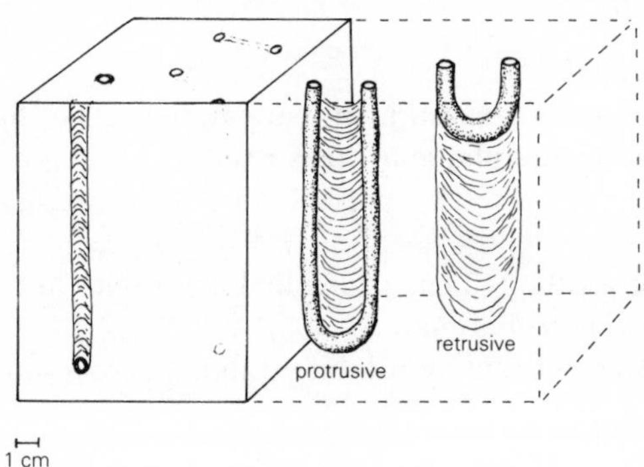

Figure 4.25 *Diplocraterion.*

4.4.10 *Helminthoida*

Position	Full relief
Shape	Generally parallel, closely spaced and regular, meandering tunnel trails
Internal structure	Commonly appear as horizontal paired tunnels with a halo between, around, and especially below the tunnels
Size	Tunnel 1–3 mm wide; width of the meander "belt" about 1 cm and length 10 cm
Age	Mississippian to Tertiary
Function	Internal grazing trails of wormlike animals
Facies	Neritic to abyssal

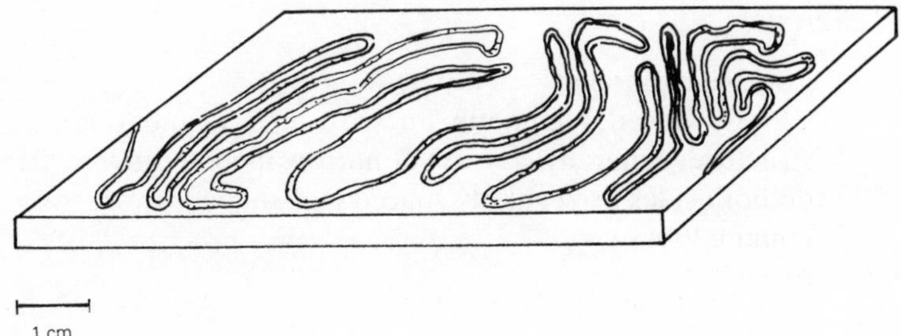

Figure 4.26 *Helminthoida.*

4.4.11 *Monocraterion*

Position	Full relief
Shape	Vertical funnel-shaped structure
Internal structure	Downward warping of surrounding laminae toward the central tube; transverse sections may show series of concentric rings
Size	Tube diameter, 5 mm; length commonly 8 cm (16 cm maximum); funnel diameter, 1–4 cm; funnel length, 2–4 cm
Age	Cambrian to Jurassic
Function	Dwelling burrow inhabited by gregarious, suspension-feeding wormlike animal
Facies	Littoral

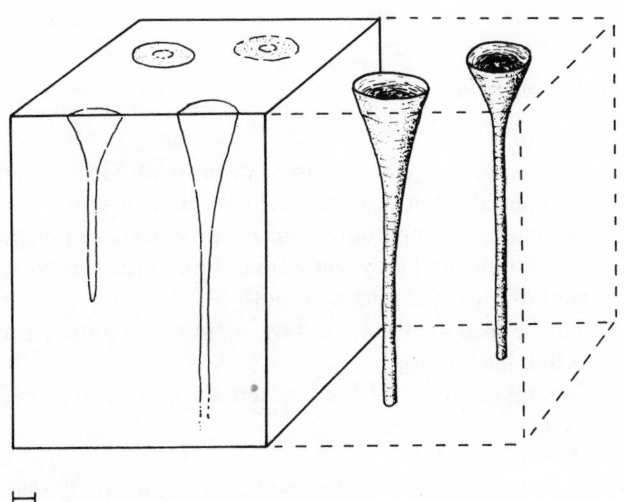

Figure 4.27 *Monocraterion.*

4.4.12 *Nereites*

Position	Positive hyporelief
Shape	Closely spaced, commonly finely striated meandering structure; generally consists of narrow median furrow, flanked on both sides by regularly spaced leaf-shaped, ovate, or pinnate lobes
Internal structure	None
Size	Width of trail, 1–2 cm
Age	Devonian to Cretaceous
Function	Internal grazing traces attributed to worms, gastropods, and crustaceans
Facies	Abyssal to bathyal

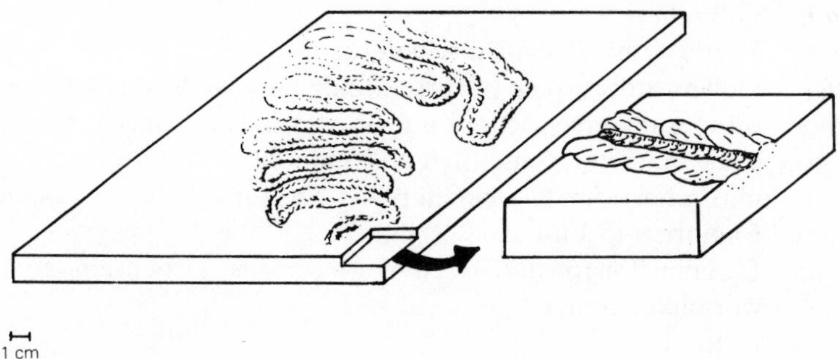

Figure 4.28 *Nereites.*

4.4.13 *Ophiomorpha*

Position	Full relief
Shape	Three-dimensional system of cylindrical, vertical, and horizontal tunnels, with local swelling, close to or at points of branching; bumpy outer surface produced by pellets which line the burrow and may show small longitudinal ridges; interior wall of burrow lining is smooth
Internal structure	The central gallery may show meniscate laminae produced by active back filling
Size	Tunnel diameter, 0.5–3 cm; length of vertical tunnels may exceed 1 m
Age	Permian to Holocene
Function	Dwelling burrows of decapod crustaceans (callianassids in modern sediments)
Facies	Littoral (also upper neritic)

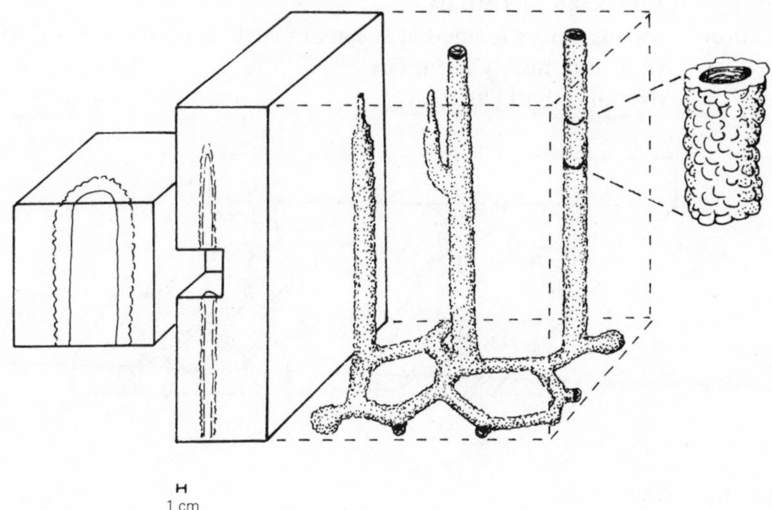

Figure 4.29 *Ophiomorpha.*

4.4.14 *Palaeophycus*

Position	Positive hyporelief
Shape	Cylindrical or subcylindrical burrows, usually sinuous; horizontal or slightly oblique to bedding and commonly intersecting one another
Internal structure	Distinct wall lining; infilling sediment introduced by passive, gravity-induced sedimentation and generally of the same composition as the surrounding matrix
Size	Diameter, 3–15 mm; length, 20 cm or more
Age	Precambrian to Holocene
Function	Open burrow constructed by a predaceous or suspension-feeding animal (Pemberton & Frey 1982)

4.4.15 *Paleodictyon*

Position	Positive hyporelief
Shape	Honeycomblike network of ridges consisting of regular polygons; generally hexagonal but four- to eight-sided polygons also occur
Internal structure	None
Size	Ridge width, 0.5–2 mm; size of mesh ranges from 1 to 50 mm, but is constant within individual networks

Age	Ordovician to Tertiary
Function	Grazing traces formed at sediment surface or at interface of sandy and muddy sediment
Facies	Abyssal to bathyal

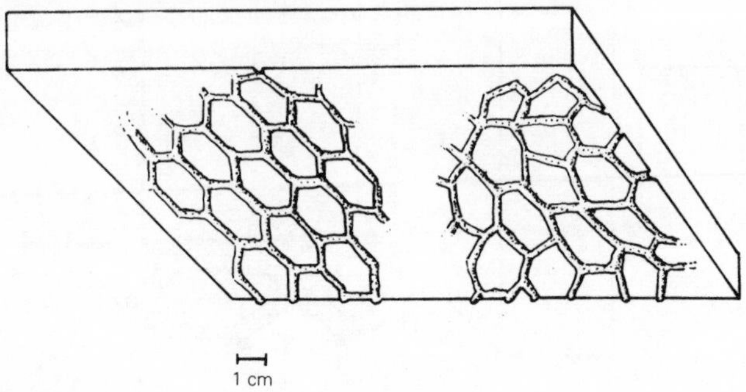

Figure 4.30 *Paleodictyon.*

4.4.16 Phycodes

Position	Positive hyporelief
Shape	Broomlike pattern of bundled horizontal tunnels
Internal structure	May show spreite
Size	Commonly 15 cm long
Age	Cambrian to Tertiary
Function	Feeding trace formed by wormlike sediment-eating animal
Facies	Neritic

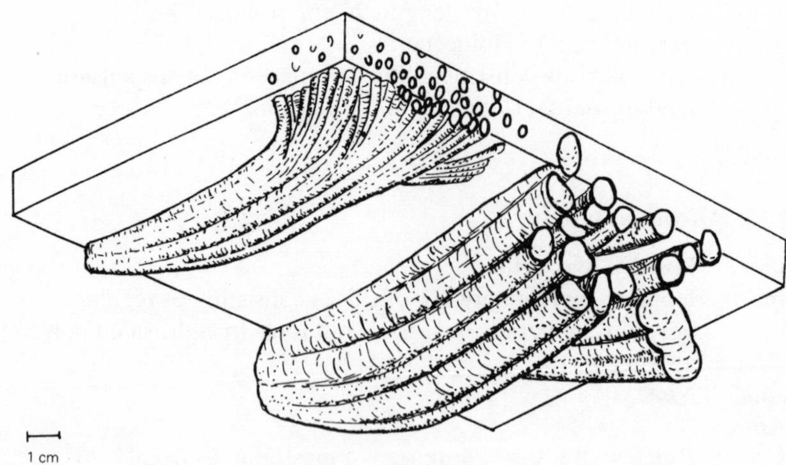

Figure 4.31 *Phycodes.*

4.4.17 *Planolites*

Position Full reliefs or positive hyporeliefs
Shape Generally unbranched cylindrical or subcylindrical infilled burrows, which are generally horizontal; they are straight to gently curved and commonly overlap one another
Internal structure Burrows unlined and filled with sediment (commonly pelleted) that differs from the surrounding matrix in terms of composition, color, texture, and fabric (Pemberton & Frey 1982)
Size Diameter, 0.5–20 mm
Age Precambrian to Holocene
Function Burrows of deposit-feeding animals

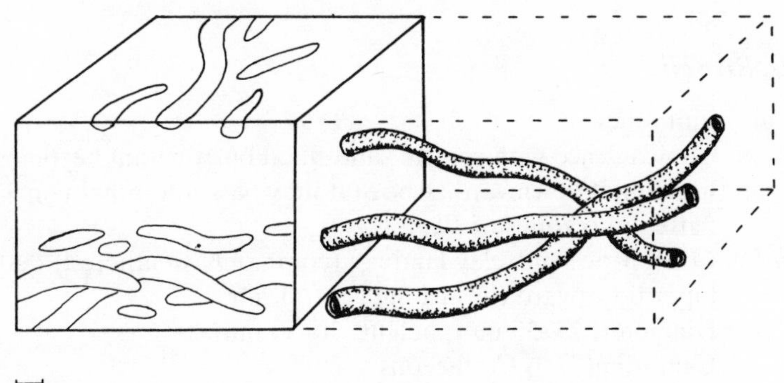

Figure 4.32 *Planolites.*

4.4.18 *Rhizocorallium*

Position Full relief
Shape U-shaped burrow (with spreite), generally oblique to bedding; commonly the upper portion is vertical, bending at depth to a subhorizontal orientation; the outer surface of tubes is commonly marked by numerous striae
Internal structure Longitudinal sections through burrows show long dark and light bands with parallel laminae or with spreite
Size Distance between the limbs of U, 2–15 cm; length of U may exceed 70 cm. Burrow diameter, 1–3 cm
Age Cambrian to Tertiary
Function Burrows of deposit-feeding animals (especially crustaceans) or dwelling burrows of filter feeders
Facies Littoral to neritic

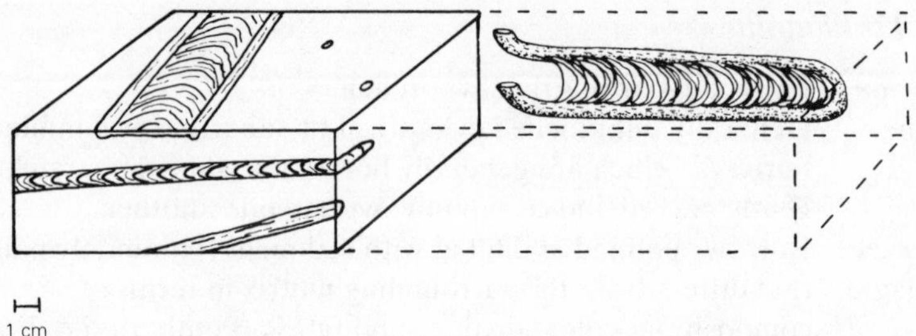

Figure 4.33 *Rhizocorallium.*

4.4.19 Rosselia

Position	Full relief
Shape	Conical trace with central sand-filled burrow that becomes horizontal downward. Above it may pass into other cones or flatten into zones of *Planolites*
Internal structure	Concentric sand–clay laminae (commonly weathered) that taper downward toward the central tube
Size	Diameter, 25–35 mm; height, 30–50 mm
Age	Cambrian(?) to Cretaceous
Function	Dwelling or feeding burrow
Facies	Neritic

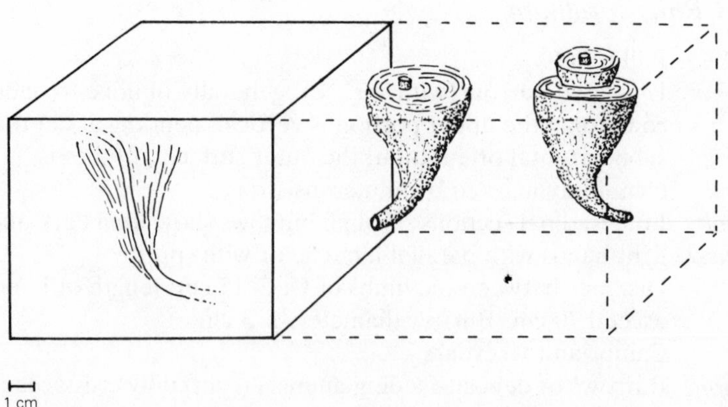

Figure 4.34 *Rosselia.*

4.4.20 *Scalarituba*

Position Full relief

Shape Subcylindrical sinuous burrows parallel, oblique, or normal to bedding

Internal structure The appearance of this trace depends on whether it is viewed on the upper or lower surface of a bed; on the lower surface it appears as a continuous series of bumps (trace on left side of Fig. 4.35) – this is commonly called the **Neonereites view**; on the upper surface it consists of a central furrow, sometimes with a distinct meniscate structure, with lateral lobes composed of oblique ridge furrows (trace in middle of Fig. 4.35) – this is called the **Phyllodicites view**; in some cases *Scalarituba* consists only of a meniscate furrow (trace on right side of Fig. 4.35)

Size Diameter, 2–10 mm; spacing between meniscae generally 2–3 mm

Age Ordovician to Permian

Function Burrow made by worm or wormlike deposit feeder

Facies Neritic to abyssal–bathyal

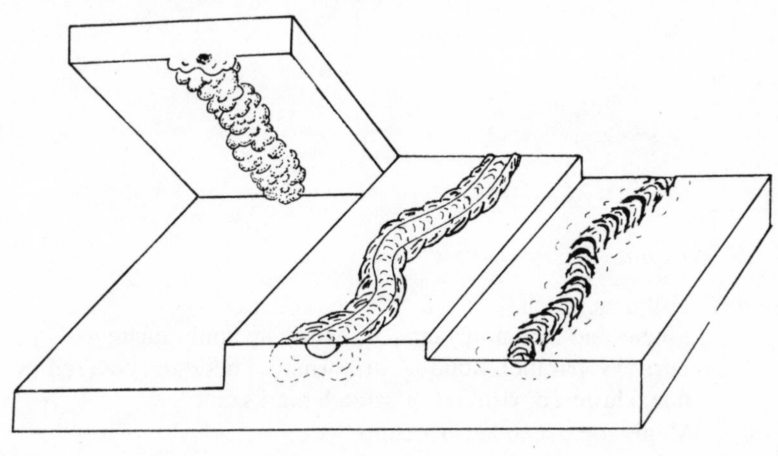

Figure 4.35 *Scalarituba.*

4.4.21 *Scolicia*

Position Semireliefs and full reliefs

Shape Bandlike horizontal, generally trilobate trails with varied

	sculpture; morphology varies depending on whether they were formed as surface trails or internal trails
Internal structure	None
Size	Width up to 4 cm; length up to 2 m
Age	Cambrian to Tertiary
Function	Creeping or feeding trails of gastropods
Facies	Neritic to abyssal–bathyal

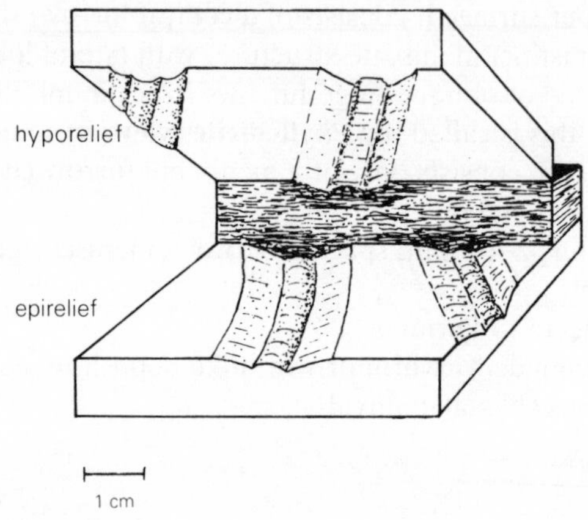

Figure 4.36 *Scolicia.*

4.4.22 *Scoyenia*

Position	Full or semireliefs
Shape	Linear and commonly curved, generally nonbranching burrows; parallel, oblique, or normal to bedding; covered by fine, clustered wrinkles or scratch marks
Internal structure	Meniscate backfilled structure
Size	Diameter, 1–10 mm
Age	Permian(?) to Holocene
Function	Burrows made by insect larvae, crustaceans or worms
Facies	Common in nonmarine deposits, especially red beds (also littoral to neritic)

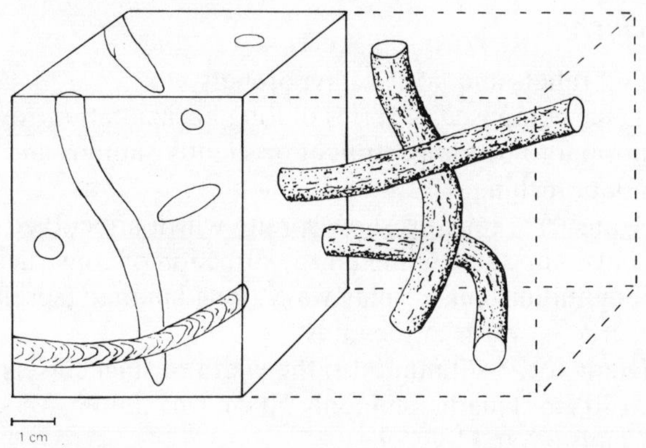

Figure 4.37 *Scoyenia.*

4.4.23 Skolithos

Position	Full reliefs
Shape	Straight, unbranched tubes perpendicular to bedding
Internal structure	None
Size	Diameter, 1–15 mm; length commonly up to 30 cm
Age	Precambrian to Cretaceous
Function	Dwelling burrow inhabited by gregarious suspension-feeding wormlike animal
Facies	Sandy littoral (also neritic to abyssal)

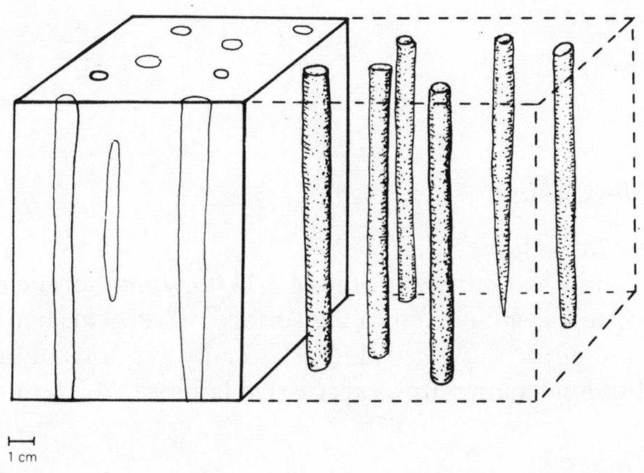

Figure 4.38 *Skolithos.*

4.4.24 Teichichnus

Position Full reliefs and positive hyporeliefs

Shape Trace composed of series of long horizontal burrows stacked normal to bedding; straight or slightly sinuous and generally nonbranching

Internal structure Transverse sections show spreite which are curved concave or convex-up, depending on the direction of construction: longitudinal cuts display wavy, long laminae (spreite) that merge upwards at the ends

Size Diameter, 3–20 mm (also the width of stacked sets); height up to 10 cm; length commonly 50 cm (maximum 135 cm)

Age Cambrian to Holocene

Function Burrows formed by deposit feeders

Facies Neritic

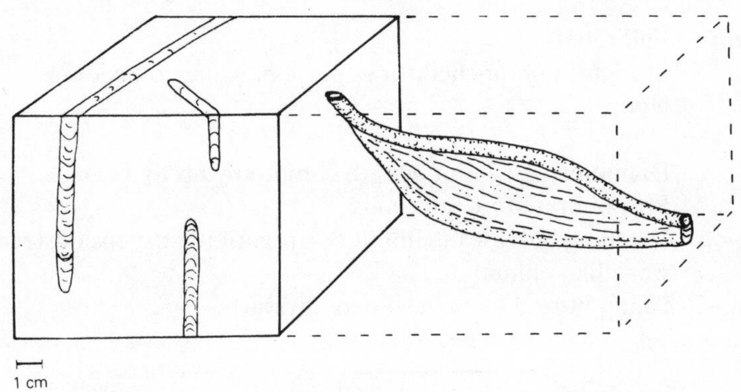

Figure 4.39 *Teichichnus.*

4.4.25 Thalassinoides

Position Full reliefs

Shape Cylindrical burrows forming 3-D horizontal branching networks connected to the surface by vertical shafts; commonly shows swelling, especially at points of branching

Internal structure Infilling commonly as successive laminae which thin upward

Size Diameter, 1–7 cm

Age Permian (?) Triassic to Holocene

Function Feeding and dwelling burrows or crustaceans (some associated with callianassid remains)

Facies Neritic

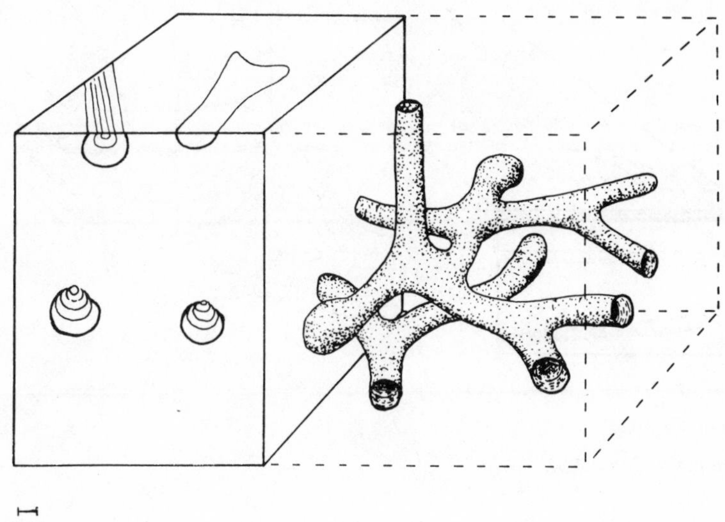

Figure 4.40 *Thalassinoides.*

4.4.26 Zoophycos

Position	Full reliefs
Shape	Trace consists of one or more broad spreite-filled loops or whorls; loops may by horizontal or inclined, commonly forming a spiral around a vertical axis, or they may be circular, arcuate, or lobate in outline
Internal structure	Vertical sections show spreite
Size	Loop diameter commonly to 60 cm (maximum 1.45 m); loop thickness, 1–7 mm
Age	Cambrian to Holocene
Function	Feeding or grazing trace made by wormlike animal (or possibly a sea pen or related form), produced by systematic helicoid mining and foraging through the sediment
Facies	Neritic to abyssal

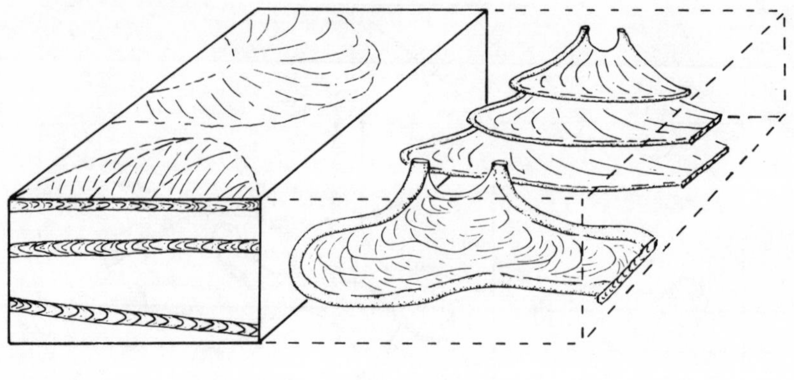

Figure 4.41 *Zoophycos.*

4.5 Behavioral classification

Although organizing traces by function is conceptually sound, its application is difficult. Many traces have served a dual function and therefore could be assigned to one of several categories. For example, of modern polychaete worms living in vertical burrows (*Skolithos* in the making), some are deposit feeders, some are filter feeders, and some are predators (Barnes 1963). Nevertheless, when studying traces, one should have some notion of behavioral classification. The following discussion is based mainly on Seilacher (1953), Simpson (1975), Frey (1978), and Frey and Pemberton (1984).

(a) *Resting traces (Cubichnia)*. Isolated shallow depressions made by animals that temporarily settled onto, or dug into, the substrate surface. Examples include *Rusophycus* and *Bergaueria* (Section 4.4.3).

(b) *Crawling traces (Repichnia)*. Trackways and trails made by animals traveling from one place to another. Examples include *Cruziana* (Section 4.4.6), *Diplichnites* (Section 4.4.8) and *Scolicia* (Section 4.4.21).

(c) *Feeding tracks (Fodinichnia)*. Burrows made by deposit feeders within the sediment. They may follow a complex behavior pattern (e.g. phobatictic sensitivity: avoidance of previously mined sediment) to achieve economical exploitation (Simpson 1975). Radial and U-shaped patterns predominate. Examples include *Chondrites* (Section 4.4.5), *Diplocraterion* (Section 4.4.9), *Phycodes* (Section 4.4.16), and *Rhizocorallium* (Section 4.4.18).

Table 4.1 Data on trace fossils.

Figures	Preservation*	Age	Location	Collection†
4.43a	PH	?	?	GW
4.43b	PH	Ordovician	Kentucky	SI
4.43c	PH	Jurassic	Wyoming	SI
4.43d	PH	Mississippian	Arkansas	SI
4.43e	PH	Silurian	Kentucky	SI
4.43f	PH	Cretaceous	Montana	SI
4.43h	PH	Devonian	New York	SI
4.44a	PH	Cambrian	Germany	SI
4.44b	PH	?	?	SI
4.44c	PH	Ordovician/Silurian	New York	SI
4.44d	FR	Ordovician/Devonian	Alabama	SI
4.44e	FR	Cretaceous	Bavaria	SI
4.44f	FR	Tertiary	California	GW
4.44g	FR	Triassic	Virginia	GW
4.45a	PH	Ordovician/Silurian	Saudi Arabia	SI
4.45b	PH	Cambrian	Montana	SI
4.45c	PH	?	?	GW
4.45d	FR	Tertiary	Maryland	GW

*PH = positive hyporelief; FR = full relief.
†GW = George Washington University; SI = Smithsonian Institution, Division of Paleobiology.

(d) *Grazing traces (Pascichnia)*. Grooves and furrows made by mobile deposit feeders on or near the substrate surface. These traces have a distinctive pattern produced by a biologic or genetic control (**thigmotaxis**: touch stimulus) that results in the most economical exploitation of nutrients in the sediment (Simpson 1975). Examples include *Helminthoida* (Section 4.4.10), *Nereites* (Section 4.4.12), *Paleodictyon* (Section 4.4.15), and *Zoophycos* (Section 4.4.26).
(e) *Dwelling traces (Domichnia)*. Burrows which provide relatively permanent homes, generally for suspension feeders or scavengers. These traces are mainly cylindrical with strengthened walls. Examples include *Arenicolites* (Section 4.4.1), *Monocraterion* (Section 4.4.11), *Ophiomorpha* (Section 4.4.13), and *Skolithos* (Section 4.4.23).
(f) *Escape structures (Fugichnia)*. Traces made in direct response to substrate erosion or aggradation.

4.6 Features that may be misidentified as trace fossils

A number of sedimentary features which may resemble trace fossils are produced by physical or chemical processes. These structures include: tool casts, flute casts, mudcracks, interference ripple marks, deformation structures, cone-in-cone, authigenic concretions, and crystals and molds of body fossils (Boyde 1975).

4.7 Value of trace fossils in sedimentology

4.7.1 Paleoenvironmental interpretation

Nonmarine deposits (especially red-bed sequences) contain an assemblage (Scoyenia association) of generally small traces with low diversity (see Chamberlain 1975, Frey *et al.* 1984). Most Paleozoic deposits contain few nonmarine traces because freshwater burrowing invertebrates were probably not present before the Permian (Miller 1984).

Some trace fossils are useful in the paleoenvironmental interpretation of marine deposits, but many occur in a broad range of facies. **Assemblages** of certain traces (ichnocoenose) characterize various bathymetric zones. These assemblages are largely controlled by depth-related parameters such as gradients in water temperature, salinity, dissolved oxygen, nutrient distribution, turbulence, sedimentation rates, and current activity (Rhoades 1975, Seilacher 1978). Each association is named for a characteristic ichnogenus.

Although this application of trace fossils has proven valuable, it must be used with caution. The presence of "shallow-water" traces in "deep-water" deposits is not uncommon (e.g. Hill 1981). "Deep-water" traces also occur in "shallow water". Keep in mind that the main controls of trace fossil distribution are substrate characteristics and available food rather than bathymetry *per se* (Crimes 1977). In some cases the necessary conditions for development of "shallow-water" traces may be met in relatively deep water (e.g. in some submarine fan deposits). However, in "deep-water" environments in which "shallow-water" traces occur, the ratio of "shallow-water" to "deep-water" trace fossils decreases with increasing depth (Crimes 1977).

(a) *Skolithos association.* Occurs in shallow marine environments (e.g. littoral) where sedimentation rates are relatively high and particulate food is kept in suspension by active currents. Shafts, occupied by suspension feeders, are common in this zone of low diversity.
(b) *Cruziana association.* Occurs in deeper water (e.g. shelf areas) where current action is less intense than in the littoral zone and particulate food settles to the bottom. Tracks, trails, and tunnels dominate in this zone of relatively high diversity where deposit feeders are abundant.
(c) *Nerites association.* With increasing depth (abyssal and bathyal) and distance from zones of food production, sediment feeders utilize

highly systematic grazing patterns. This association is characteristic of turbidite sequences and shows high diversity.

(d) *Zoophycos association*. Transitional between the *Cruziana* and *Nerites* associations.

4.7.2 Understanding conditions of deposition

Trace fossils can furnish valuable information concerning the conditions of sedimentation, especially whether it was rapid or slow, continuous, or discontinuous (Fig. 4.42). Intense **bioturbation** commonly occurs in areas of slow sedimentation and probably has more to do with the time available than with the abundance of trace makers (Howard 1975). In nearshore areas, where physical processes dominate and sediment rates are high, trace fossils are less abundant. Traces also provide evidence of periodic erosion, as manifest by burrow truncation and mucus-cemented burrow fragments forming an intraformational conglomerate.

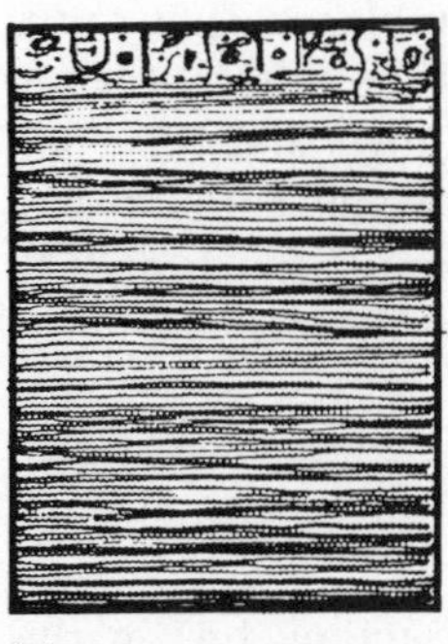
(a)

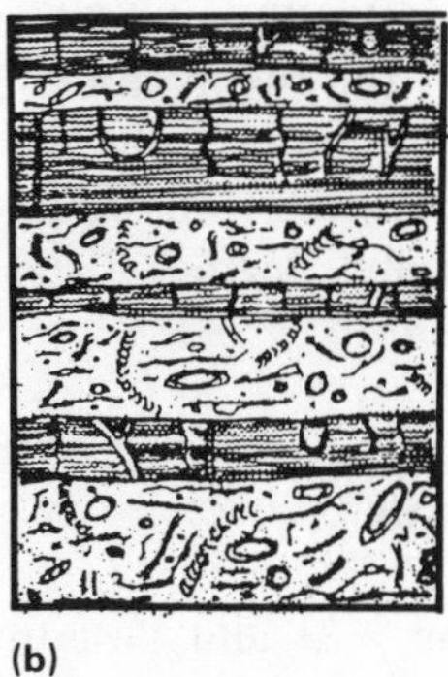
(b)

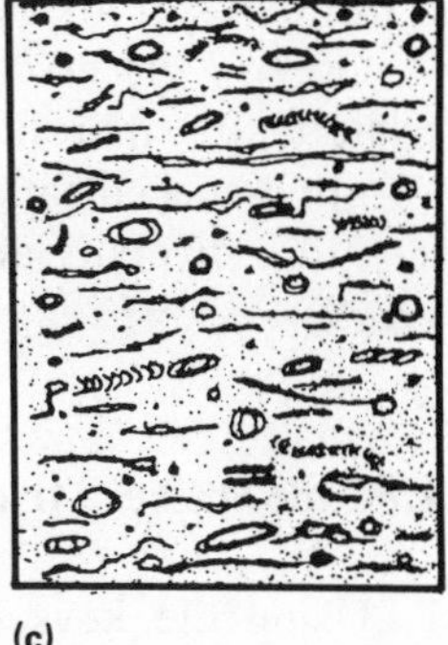
(c)

Figure 4.42 Bioturbation patterns developed under varying conditions of deposition (modified from Howard 1978).

(a) Rapid, continuous deposition. Trace fossils are absent or present as scattered escape structures. The upper portion of the bed may show intense bioturbation. Note that some laminated shale without trace fossils may indicate a hostile environment (e.g. anoxic) which excluded benthonic animals.

(b) Alternating periods of rapid and slow, continuous deposition. Trace fossil assemblages are commonly different in interbedded coarse-grained (rapid deposition) and fine-grained (slow deposition) deposits characteristic of turbidites. This may reflect differences in the organisms living in the coarser sediment and those living in the finer sediment. Alternatively the different assemblages may be caused by behavioral differences in response to the different sediment types.

(c) Slow, continuous deposition. Bioturbation is complete with no sedimentary structures preserved. The extensive infaunal reworking, which exceeds the rate of sedimentation, is mainly a function of the long time available for organic activity rather than a great abundance of organisms. Recognition of particular ichnogenera is difficult.

4.7.3 *Significance of sharp lithologic contacts*

Contacts between rock units can be interpreted in various ways. They may represent a short depositional hiatus or they may be major unconformities reflecting long periods of nondeposition or erosion. The types and character of trace fossils associated with such a contact may provide clues to its significance. The contact between the Lower Devonian Esopus Shale and the overlying sandstone (Carlisle Centre Formation) is a case in point. Although some workers have interpreted it as a major disconformity, the mode of formation and preservation of associated traces indicates that the contact reflects only a minor depositional break (Miller & Rehmer 1982).

4.7.4 *Biostratigraphy and evolution*

Because most ichnogenera are produced by a variety of organisms and therefore have long time ranges, they generally have little biostratigraphic value. There are cases, however, where traces are biostratigraphically useful in units with no body fossils. This is particularly true in some lower Paleozoic sequences (Seilacher 1970, Crimes 1975).

Comparison of neritic with abyssal–bathyal assemblages shows differences in the evolution of the two communities. These differences are related to environmental stability, which effects diversification and adaptive specialization. Deep-water environments (abyssal–bathyal) foster more diversity and a higher degree of specialization (Seilacher 1978: 198–9).

4.8 Exercises: trace fossils

1 Using the keys (Section 4.3) and descriptions (Section 4.4) in this book, together with the Treatise volume on trace fossils, name (ichnogenus) the traces shown in Figures 4.43, 4.44 a–e, and 4.45.
2 Indicate the probable function (e.g. "resting" trace – see Section 4.5) for the traces shown in Figures 4.43 a, d, f, g, 4.44 b, d, e, and 4.45 b, c, d.
3 Describe the wall character and filling (see Figure 4.2, I) of burrows shown in Figure 4.44 f and g.
4 Is the trace shown in Figure 4.45d protrusive or retrusive?
5 If the modern burrows shown in Figure 4.46 were fossilized, what ichnogeneric name might they be given?

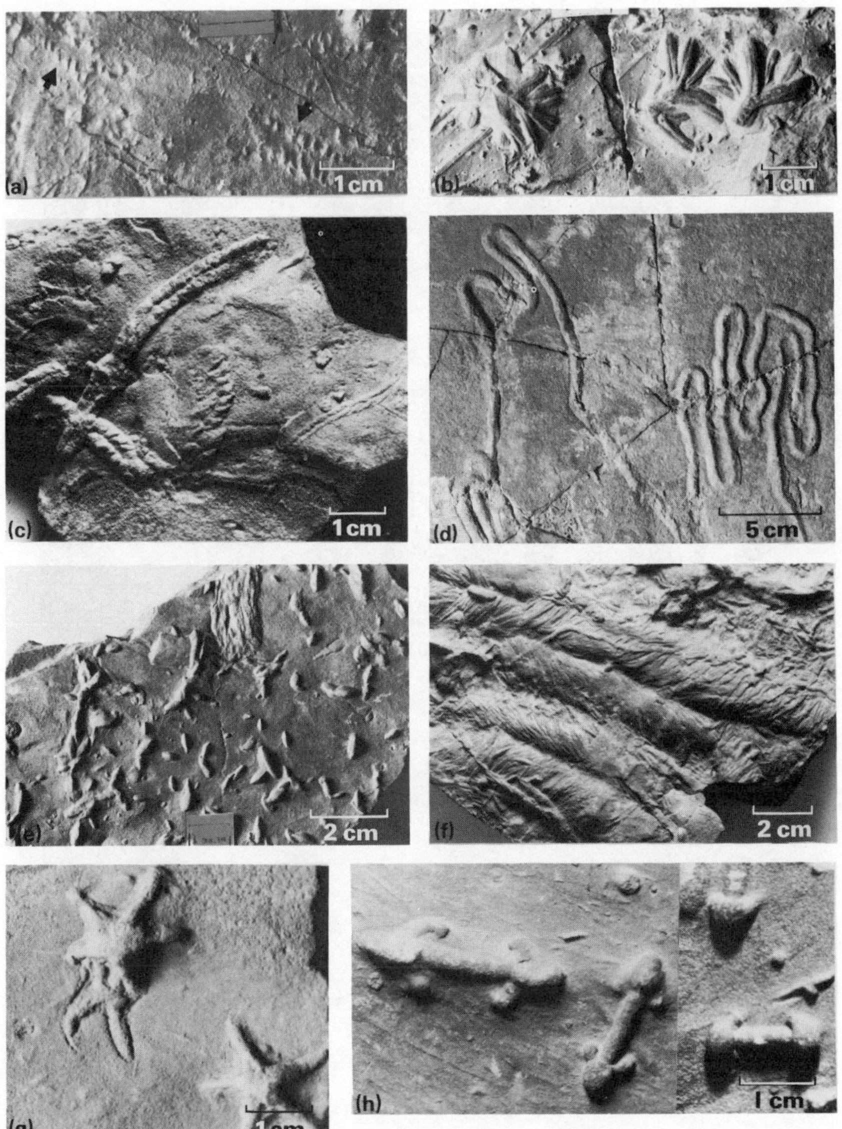

Figure 4.43 Trace fossils: see Table 4.1 for details.

Figure 4.44 More trace fossils: see Table 4.1 for details.

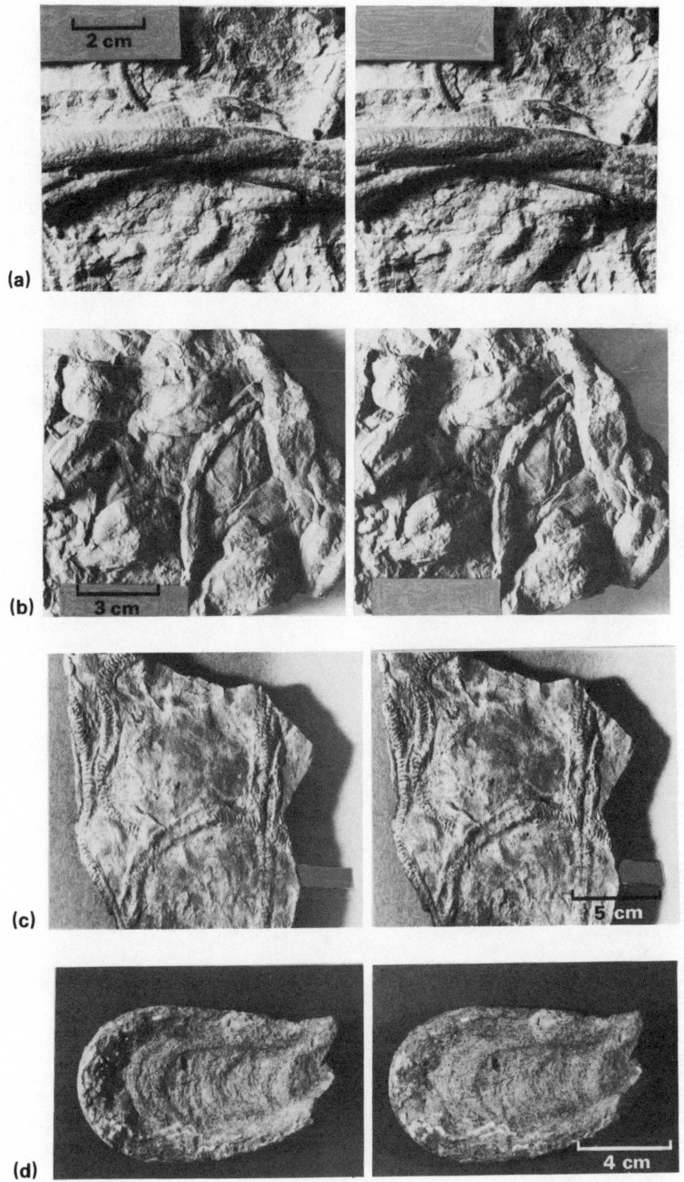

Figure 4.45 Stereograms of trace fossils: see Table 4.1 for details.

Figure 4.46 A stereogram of burrows from a low-energy marine environment near Assateague Island, Virginia.

5 Particle morphology

A number of quite distinct aspects, regarding sedimentary particles, are included under the broad heading of "morphology". They include sphericity, shape, roundness, and surface textures.

5.1 Definitions

5.1.1 Sphericity

This property describes how closely a grain resembles a sphere; indeed it has been defined in a variety of ways. Some definitions are based on the measurement of surface area, yet others on the measurement of grain volume. An easily understood definition involves the volume of the particle (V_p) and the volume of the smallest sphere (V_s) that will just enclose the particle. Sphericity thus defined is equal to $\sqrt[3]{(V_p/V_s)}$ (Wadell 1935). A perfect sphere has a sphericity of 1.0. Most sedimentary grains range between 0.6 and 0.7 (Folk 1980). More commonly used definitions involve three orthogonal axes where L, I, and S are the long, intermediate, and short axes respectively. One which approximates Wadell's sphericity is $\sqrt[3]{(IS/L^2)}$. Another, called the maximum projection sphericity, $\sqrt[3]{(S^2/LI)}$, is favoured by some because it relates better to the behavior of particles in a fluid (Sneed & Folk 1958).

5.1.2 Shape (also called form)

Particle shape is generally defined by two axial ratios, I/L and S/I (Zingg 1935). They define four shape classes as equant, bladed, discoidal, and rod-shaped. A diagram combining these classes with lines of equal sphericity illustrates how shape and sphericity are different (Fig. 5.1). For any numerical value of sphericity there are several shapes possible. For example, a grain with a sphericity of 0.5 may be bladed, discoidal, or rod-shaped.

5.1.3 Roundness

Roundness is geometrically independent of sphericity and shape (Fig. 5.2), although this fact is sometimes blurred by careless usage. This morphologic aspect is determined by the sharpness of edges or corners.

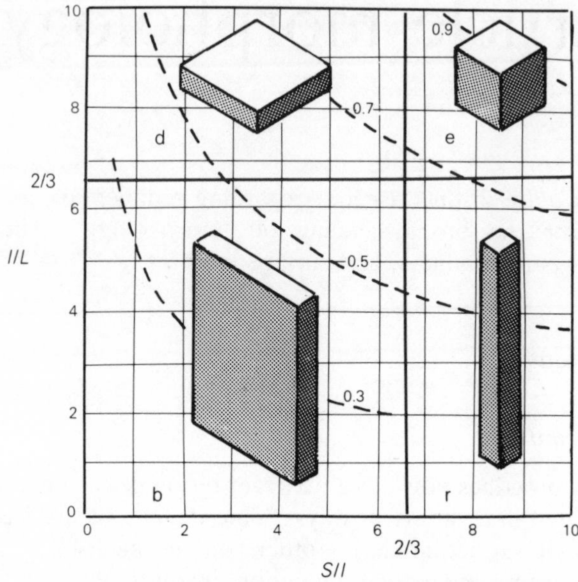

Figure 5.1 Grain shapes. Axial ratios (*I/L* and *S/I*) are based on length of long (*L*), intermediate (*I*) and short (*S*) axes. Four major shape categories are indicated as (d) discoidal, (e) equant, (b) bladed, and (r) rod-shaped. Dashed curves represent selected lines of equal sphericity. (Based on Zingg 1935.)

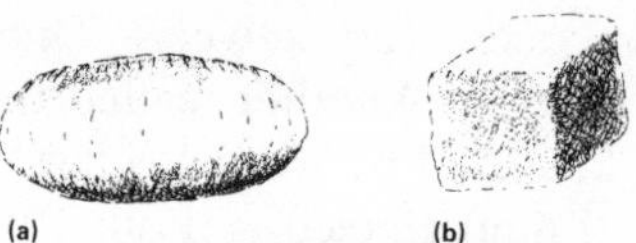

Figure 5.2 Two grains showing contrasting roundness and shape: (a) well rounded and nonequant (nonspherical) grain; (b) equant (high sphericity) but angular grain.

Roundness is defined as the average radius of curvature of the corners divided by the radius of the maximum inscribed circle for a two-dimensional image of the grain (Fig. 5.3). This can be expressed by the formula

$$\frac{\sum r/N}{R}$$

where r = the radius of curvature at the corners, N = the number of corners, and R = the radius of the largest inscribed circle.

Roundness classes commonly utilize a geometric scale, because small

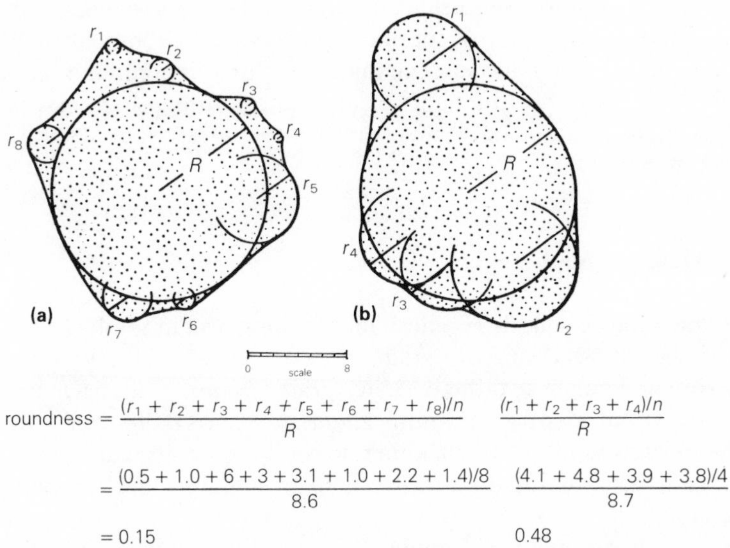

(a)
(b)
R
scale
0
8
roundness = $\frac{(r_1 + r_2 + r_3 + r_4 + r_5 + r_6 + r_7 + r_8)/n}{R}$ $\frac{(r_1 + r_2 + r_3 + r_4)/n}{R}$
= $\frac{(0.5 + 1.0 + 6 + 3 + 3.1 + 1.0 + 2.2 + 1.4)/8}{8.6}$ $\frac{(4.1 + 4.8 + 3.9 + 3.8)/4}{8.7}$
= 0.15 0.48

Figure 5.3 Two grain images showing method of roundness determination. Roundness based on two-dimensional outlines using the radius of curvature of the corners (r) and the radius of the maximum inscribed circle (R). (Modified from Krumbein 1940.)

differences between relatively angular grains are easier to identify than small differences between rounder grains. Unfortunately various classification systems use different class limits, which complicates comparison between studies.

5.1.4 Surface textures

The study of surface textures is generally confined to quartz grains and involves surface luster seen with the unaided eye and microrelief features viewed with the scanning electron microscope. Surface luster ranges from highly polished to "frosted," although neither extreme is common. Most grain surfaces show a luster intermediate between the two. Frosting, common in some sandstone (e.g. the Ordovician St Peter Sandstone), is attributed by some authors to wind abrasion. A more likely cause for frosted surfaces involves post-depositional processes. They include surface etching associated with calcite cementation as well as growth of minute crystal faces formed during the earliest stage of quartz cementation.

Use of the scanning electron microscope reveals a great variety of microrelief features (e.g. V-shaped pits and grooves) on loose sand grains. Some workers (e.g. Krinsley & Doornkamp 1973, Margolis &

Krinsley 1974) have suggested that particular combinations of these features are characteristic of specific depositional environments. Although this may be true for some surficial materials, use of microrelief features to study sedimentary environments of most ancient deposits is not possible because cementation and other diagenetic processes destroy primary surface textures.

5.2 Measurement

Determination of sphericity and shape is impractical in sand-size material, except in thin-section or grain mounts where sphericity can be approximated for a two-dimensional grain section. This is most easily done by visual comparison with silhouette charts (Fig. 5.4). In loose gravel or weakly lithified conglomerate the long, intermediate, and short axes can be measured directly, and sphericity and shape values calculated.

Direct measurement of roundness is so difficult and tedious that it is rarely done. Roundness is commonly determined using visual comparison charts (Fig. 5.5). This procedure is relatively fast and good enough for general descriptions. Its subjective nature may result in significant loss of accuracy and precision (Folk 1972) and is not useful for further rigorous analysis. As a result, subtile variations in roundness are not likely to be recognized. This problem is overcome by the use of Fourier analysis where a two-dimensional outline is broken up into a series of standard shapes ("harmonics") and the relative contribution ("amplitude") of each of these standard shapes to the two-dimensional outline is measured (Ehrlich & Weinberg 1970). The Fourier technique which allows rapid analysis is used in more rigorous studies of roundness and shape because of its precision and objectivity.

When studying any aspect of particle morphology, one should be aware of variations that are related to grain size and composition. It is generally best to study grains in a restricted size range and grains that are isotropic as regards abrasion and breaking (e.g. quartz). When working with loose sand grains (whether sieved or not), you will have to separate out a small subsample of several hundred grains from a sample containing thousands

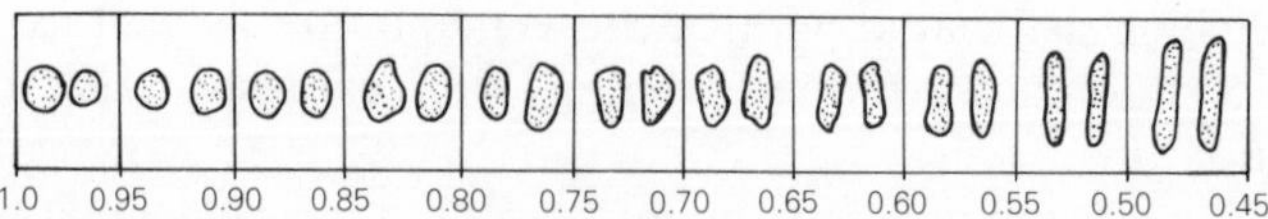

Figure 5.4 Grain images for visual determination of "projection sphericity" (modified from Rittenhouse 1943).

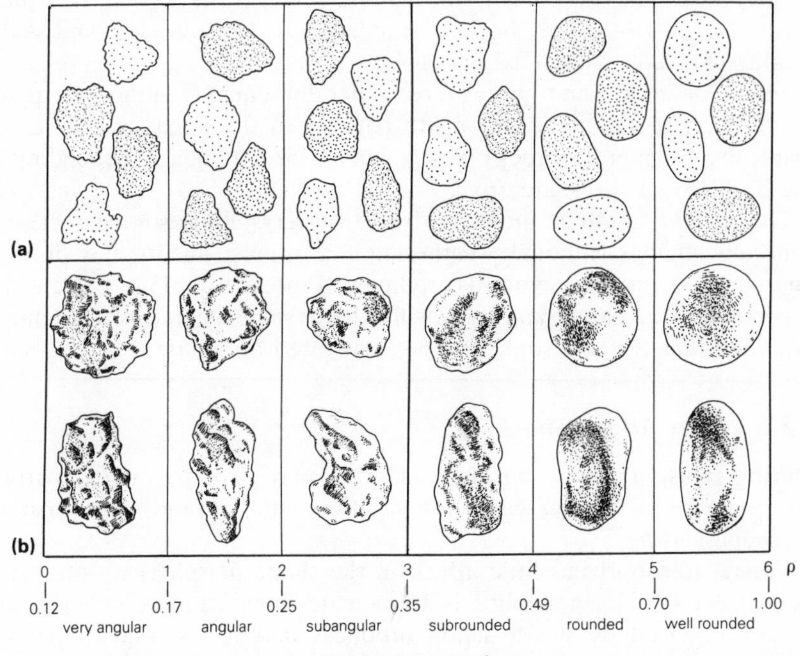

Figure 5.5 Grain images for the visual determination of roundness: (a) two-dimensional grain outlines (based on Krumbein 1941 and Shepard & Young 1961); (b) three-dimensional images (redrawn from Powers 1953). Class names and boundaries based on Powers (1953). ρ values from Folk (1955).

of grains. Careless separation may cause grains to be sorted according to differences in shape, and this results in a nonrepresentative subsample. For this reason, always use a sample splitter.

5.3 Factors that control particle morphology

Two factors determine the morphology of sedimentary particles. One is their initial morphology, which is inherited from the source rock. The other is mechanical alteration (abrasion, fracturing, and sorting) during transport.

5.3.1 Initial morphology

The initial shape of gravel depends on jointing and cleavage as well as on the rock type and the climate of the source area. Massive rocks (e.g.

granite and quartzite) begin their sedimentary lives as nearly equant clasts. In contrast, thinly bedded or foliated rocks (e.g. slate and shale) produce bladed or discoidal pebbles.

Monomineralic sand grains are generally equant, although quartz grains tend to be slightly elongate parallel to the *c*-axis. Lithic grains (sand-size fragments of rock) may be equant or nonequant, depending on the lithology of the source rock.

Gravel and sand-size grains derived from crystalline source rocks are generally angular, although weathering in a tropical climate may produce quartz grains that are somewhat rounded (Potter 1978: 433). Sand which originates from older sandstone will inherit some degree of roundness, provided that the sandstone was not cemented by quartz.

5.3.2 Effect of transport

During transport, abrasion and fracturing may strongly modify particle morphology. In some cases lateral variation within a sand body is caused by shape sorting.

Fluvial transport has little effect on the shape or sphericity of gravel. The effect on beach pebbes is less clear. Some studies indicate that abrasion caused by swash action produces flatter, less equant pebbles (sphericity < 0.65, according to Folk 1980) than are produced by fluvial processes. Other studies suggest that there is little difference between the morphology of beach pebbles and that of stream pebbles (for a review see Pettijohn 1975). Keep in mind that pebbles whose flatness is an inherited property (e.g. those derived from slate) have no environmental significance.

In contrast to shape and sphericity, numerous studies show that pebble roundness increases rapidly during fluvial transport (Pettijohn 1975, Folk 1980). "Soft" pebbles, such as limestone, which are initially angular to subangular, become rounded to well rounded within the first few kilometers of transport. More resistant pebbles may require several hundred kilometers of transport to achieve this degree of roundness, although the most rapid change occurs within the first 10 km.

Factors that effect the rate of abrasion, resulting in increased roundness, are particle size and composition as well as the mode of transportation (suspended versus traction) and the transporting medium (air versus water). Rounding of sand-size particles is much slower than for gravel. Fluvial transport has little effect on roundness in contrast to aeolian processes which are quite effective in producing rounded sand. Some studies suggest that beach processes may cause increased rounding, but their importance in the production of rounded sand is questioned.

Most sands have a simple history that involves weathering and erosion of crystalline rocks followed by transport to the site of deposition. In these sands the coarser-size grades are better rounded than the finer-size grades, regardless of the mean roundness for the whole sample. In contrast to the normal case, and of particular interest, are sands which show abnormal relationships between grain size and roundness, which Folk (1980: 14, 103–4) calls **textural inversions**. Examples include (1) sands with angular coarse grains and rounded fine grains and (2) sands with very angular grains and rounded grains within the same grade size (Fig. 8.5 c & d). Both situations may indicate a multiple source which contains sandstone (the source of the rounded grains) and crystalline rock (the source of the angular grains).

5.4 Reasons for studying particle morphology

Although a detailed analysis of particle morphology might be considered part of a standard lithologic description, the time and tedium involved demands that the results add significantly to the final interpretation. Because shape and sphericity are strongly controlled by particle composition, morphologic studies generally utilize quartz grains. The value of gross grain shape in provenance interpretation is illustrated by studies of surficial sand on the South Texas continental shelf (Mazzullo & Withers 1984) and the southern New England shelf (Mazzullo *et al.* 1984).

Roundness studies, although severely limited as a basis for paleocurrent interpretation, may provide valuable data for paleoenvironmental interpretation. Use of textural inversions as a guide to interpreting complex source areas has been discussed (Section 5.3.2). The study of the St Peter Sandstone by Mazzullo and Ehrlich (1983) is an example of how analysis of quartz-grain morphology may aid in paleoenvironmental interpretation. They determined that stratigraphic variation in grain roundness was related to transport from coastal aeolian and fluvial–deltaic sources into deeper waters of the inner shelf.

5.5 Sample statistical analysis using the chi-square test

5.5.1 Introduction

The statistical test used to evaluate grain morphology data depends on the method used to collect the data. Sphericity and shape are commonly measured on an interval scale, amenable to a variety of parametric (e.g. the t test) and nonparametric tests. Roundness is usually determined by visual comparison with grain images and the observations assigned to roundness classes that are ranked in a numerical sequence. The nonparametric chi-square test is well suited to this sort of grouped data and is used in the example that follows.

5.5.2 The problem

Consider two sand samples collected from a coastal area. One is from the beach and the other from an adjacent dune. Using a binocular microscope, the roundness of 373 grains was determined. Inspection of the data (Table 5.1) indicates that the dune sand contains a greater proportion of rounded and well rounded grains, but let us go a bit further in describing the difference. A simple histogram (Fig. 5.6) is a useful graphic, but you will note that the modal class (the one with the greatest number of observations) is the same for both samples. Thus far our efforts to illustrate the difference in grain roundness between the dune and beach sands have not been very successful. Calculating the mean roundness (Table 5.2) is far more effective. We can now tell the interested listener that the beach sand has a mean roundness of 2.8 compared to the dune sand's 3.2, and that the beach sand is more angular. Some listeners are skeptical by nature and will question whether or not this represents a real difference between the two samples. What these doubters really want to know is whether the observed difference is caused by random variability within the coastal sands from which the samples were collected, and how much difference there is between two samples from the same population of sand grains? To determine this we will use a test statistic (the one that we will use is called "chi-square") that allows us to evaluate whether the two samples came from a single population of sand grains or whether they came from two different populations. Let us take the statistical analysis of this problem step by step.

Table 5.1 Grain counts for roundness of two sand samples.

Roundness	Observed frequency	
	Beach	Dune
very angular	6	6
angular	26	18
subangular	65	70
subrounded	50	60
rounded	17	45
well rounded	2	8

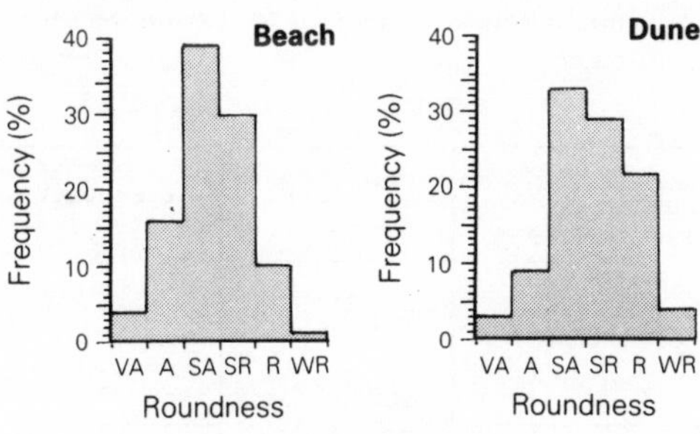

Figure 5.6 Histograms showing the roundness of two sand samples.

5.5.3 The chi-square test

(1) Set up the **null hypothesis** (H_0) that states that there is *no difference* between the two samples, i.e. they are taken from the same population. The "no difference" aspect is a structural feature of the null hypothesis and must be stated this way.

(2) Put the observed frequencies (in this example the number of grains of given roundness) into tabular form (Table 5.3a). Each entry is referred to as a **cell**. A vertical sequence of cells is called a **column** and a horizontal sequence is called a **row**. In our example there are two columns, six rows, and twelve cells.

(3) Calculate the **expected frequency** (designated as E, which in our example is the number of grains expected to occur in each cell purely by chance) for each of the twelve cells (Table 5.3b) by the following formula:

$$E = (n_R \times n_C)/N$$

where n_R is the total number of grains in the row containing the cell in question, n_C is the total number of grains in the column containing that cell, and N is the total number of grains in both samples.

In our example the expected frequency for the first cell (very angular – beach) would be

$$(12 \times 166)/373 = \mathit{5.34}$$

(4) For each cell square the difference between the observed (O) and expected (E) frequencies and divide by the expected frequency (E). In Table 5.3c, these values are listed under the heading "Chi-square

Table 5.2 Tally sheet for computing mean roundness for (a) the beach sand and (b) the dune sand.

(a)

Beach	Class interval (ρ)	Midpoint (ρ) M	Frequency F	Product $M \times F$
very angular	0–1	0.5	6	3.0
angular	1–2	1.5	26	39.0
subangular	2–3	2.5	65	162.5
subrounded	3–4	3.5	50	175.0
rounded	4–5	4.5	17	76.5
well rounded	5–6	5.5	2	11.0
			166	467

$$\text{Mean roundness} = \frac{\Sigma\,(M \times F)}{\Sigma\ F} = \frac{467}{166} = 2.8$$

(b)

Dune	Class interval (ρ)	Midpoint (ρ) M	Frequency F	Product $M \times F$
very angular	0–1	0.5	6	3.0
angular	1–2	1.5	18	27.0
subangular	2–3	2.5	70	175.0
subrounded	3–4	3.5	60	210.0
rounded	4–5	4.5	45	202.5
well rounded	5–6	5.5	8	44.0
			207	661.5

$$\text{Mean roundness} = \frac{\Sigma\,(M \times F)}{\Sigma\ F} = \frac{661.5}{207} = 3.2$$

Table 5.3 Analysis of roundness data using the chi-square test.

	(a) Observed frequency		n	(b) Expected frequency		(c) Chi-square contribution	
	Beach	Dune		Beach	Dune	Beach	Dune
very angular	6	6	12	5.34	6.66	0.082	0.065
angular	26	18	44	19.58	24.42	2.104	1.687
subangular	65	70	135	60.08	74.92	0.403	0.323
subrounded	50	60	110	48.95	61.05	0.022	0.018
rounded	17	45	62	27.59	34.41	4.066	3.261
well rounded	2	8	10	4.45	5.55	1.349	1.082
n	166	207	373			8.026	6.436
						$\chi^2 = 14.462$	

contribution" because the summation of them is chi-square according to the formula:

$$\text{chi-square} = \Sigma(O - E)^2/E$$

Returning to the first cell in our example (very angular – beach) where $O = 6$ and $E = 5.34$, the chi-square contribution is

$$(6 - 5.34)^2/5.34 = 0.44/5.34 = \mathit{0.082}$$

(5) Summation of the chi-square contributions (Table 5.3c) gives a *chi-square value of 14.46*. The larger this value, the greater the difference between the two samples. Is 14.46 large enough to allow us to reject the null hypothesis? We cannot answer that question quite yet. We first need to determine the degrees of freedom, pick a significance level, and determine the critical value for chi-square.

(6) To determine the degrees of freedom (*df*) in this form of the chi-square test we use

$$df = (c - 1)(r - 1)$$

where c is the number of cells in a column (vertical) and r is the number of cells in row (horizontal). In our example

$$df = (2 - 1)(6 - 1) = 5$$

(7) We now need to determine the **critical value for chi-square** that will allow rejection or acceptance of the null hypothesis. This depends on the *df* and the significance level. The *df* are set by the data base, but you must pick the significance level. A significance level of 0.05 means that a particular chi-square value that would lead to a wrong decision regarding rejection or acceptance of the null hypothesis could occur by chance 5 times out of 100. The 0.05 level is commonly chosen as a realistic value for geologic problems and that is the one we will use. A much abbreviated list of critical chi-square values is given below (more complete lists can be found in any statistics book). The critical value for 5 degrees of freedom and a significance level of 0.05 is 11.07. This is less than our computed value of 14.46. Remembering that the greater the chi-square value the greater the difference between the samples, it should be clear that the null hypothesis, which states that there is *no* difference, must be *rejected*. The general rule for the chi-square test is:

reject if the computed value is greater than the critical value;
accept if the computed value is less than the critical value.

Partial list of critical chi-square values.

df	0.1	0.05	0.01
1	2.71	3.84	6.64
2	4.60	5.99	9.21
3	6.25	7.82	11.34
4	7.78	9.49	13.28
5	9.24	*11.07*	15.09
6	10.64	12.59	16.81
7	12.02	14.07	18.48
8	13.36	15.51	20.09
9	14.68	16.92	21.67

(8) Think about the alternate hypothesis. Although we have not stated it, the **alternate hypothesis** (which we accepted by rejecting the null hypothesis) indicates that *there is a difference* in the roundness of grains in the beach sand compared to the dune sand. Does this statistical analysis indicate that wind transport is a more effective rounding agent than is water moving over a beach? The answer is an

emphatic "no"! There is no causative interpretation built into statistical tests such as the chi-square test. It is possible that wind action did a better job rounding the dune sand than the water did on the beach sand. Although our results are compatible with this interpretation, they do not prove it. Indeed several field studies which have shown beach sand to be more angular than sand in adjacent coastal dunes suggest that the variation in roundness is not a function of abrasion at all (Beal & Shepard 1956). The reason seems to be related to a shape-sorting process where the wind preferentially transports spherical, well rounded sand grains and leaves behind a deflation lag of elongate, angular grains. This example demonstrates that great care must be taken when using the results of a statistical test to aid in making a geologic interpretation.

5.5.4 *Restrictions on this form of the chi-square test*

(a) The data must be in the form of **absolute frequencies** rather than percentages.
(b) The number of observations should be greater than 50 (some books say 40).
(c) No more than one cell in five (i.e. 20% of the total number of cells) should have an expected frequency of less than 5. Adjacent cells should be combined if possible and realistic until this condition is met. In the example presented above, only one cell (well rounded/beach) had an expected frequency of less than 5. As this is one in 12 we are safe. If two more cells (e.g. very angular/beach and very angular/dune) had been less than 5, they would have been combined with the "angular" cells. Obviously that would have changed the final chi-square value. It would also have lowered the degrees of freedom to 4, because the number of rows would have been reduced from 6 to 5, thereby resulting in a different critical value.

5.6 Exercises: roundness and chi-square

Evaluate one of the data sets given in Table 5.4 (your instructor will indicate which one to do). Each set contains data from a single sand sample that was sieved to separate grains into discrete size groups. The roundness of two size fractions (fine sand with a size range of 0.125–0.25 mm and coarse sand with a size range of 0.50–1.00 mm) was determined. Your job is to do the following.

Table 5.4 Problem sets for analysis of roundness. Use only the one set assigned by your instructor.

(a)	Observed frequency	
	Fine	Coarse
very angular	10	6
angular	15	11
subangular	38	20
subrounded	53	72
rounded	27	33
well rounded	7	14

(b)	Observed frequency	
	Fine	Coarse
very angular	14	3
angular	20	13
subangular	50	40
subrounded	28	37
rounded	7	15
well rounded	2	14

(c)	Observed frequency	
	Fine	Coarse
very angular	18	4
angular	32	37
subangular	50	43
subrounded	21	35
rounded	19	31
well rounded	8	17

1 Make a roundness histogram for each size fraction.
Modal roundness class for:

fine sand fraction = ______

coarse sand fraction = ______

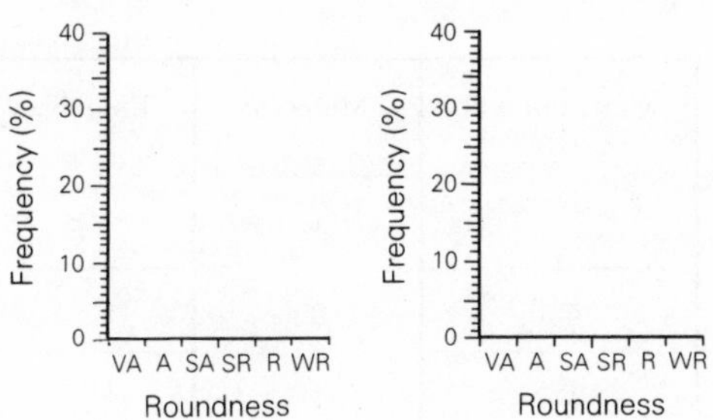

Figure 5.7 A diagram for use in plotting a roundness histogram.

2 Determine the mean roundness for each size fraction.

Table 5.5 Table to use in calculating mean roundness.

____________	Class interval (ρ)	Midpoint (ρ)	Frequency	Product
		M	F	$M \times F$
very angular	0–1	0.5		
angular	1–2	1.5		
subangular	2–3	2.5		
subrounded	3–4	3.5		
rounded	4–5	4.5		
well rounded	5–6	5.6		
			_____	_____

$$\text{Mean roundness} = \frac{\Sigma\ (M \times F)}{\Sigma\ \ F} = \_\_\_\_\_ = \_\_\_\_\_$$

(continued over)

Table 5.5 *continued*

____________	Class interval (ϱ)	Midpoint (ϱ) M	Frequency F	Product $M \times F$
very angular	0–1	0.5		
angular	1–2	1.5		
subangular	2–3	2.5		
subrounded	3–4	3.5		
rounded	4–5	4.5		
well rounded	5–6	5.5		
			_____	_____

$$\text{Mean roundness} = \frac{\Sigma\ (M \times F)}{\Sigma\ \ F} = \_\_\_\_\_ = \_\_\_\_\_$$

3 Use the chi-square test to determine whether or not there is a significant difference in the roundness of the two size fractions.

Table 5.6 Table to use in calculating chi-square.

	Observed frequency		n	Expected frequency		Chi-square contribution	
very angular							
angular							
subangular							
subrounded							
rounded							
well rounded							
n							
						$\chi^2 =$	

Statement of null hypothesis: ____________________

____

____

Computed value of chi-square = _____

Degrees of freedom (*df*) = _____

Critical value of chi-square (at 0.05 level) = __________

Accept or reject the null hypothesis: __________

4 Briefly give the geologic significance of your results.

____

____

____

5 *Optional.* Determine the roundness of at least 50 grains in each of two sand samples using a binocular microscope and the grain images shown in Figure 5.5b. The choice of samples is yours, but be sure that you have thought about the geologic problem that you are trying to solve. Before mounting the grains use a sample splitter to obtain a manageable sample size. Mount the grains on a recessed cardboard slide that has a numbered grid (the kind used to study forams). After your grain count is complete evaluate the data using the chi-square test. Remember that you use the number of grains counted rather than frequency in percent.

6 Mineral identification using X-ray diffraction

X-ray diffraction is a valuable tool in determining the mineralogy of sedimentary rocks. Not only can the mineral species be identified, but in some cases a semi-quantitative determination of mineral substance can also be made. This is especially important for mudrock where petrographic methods are of limited utility. Indeed it is the most important technique in evaluating the chemical composition in some solid-solution series, such as mole-percent MgO in dolomite and magnesian calcite.

I should stress that it is an adjunct to petrographic study, not a substitute. Although in some cases X-ray diffraction is a superior method for mineral identification, it indicates nothing about textural paragenetic relationships within a rock. For this one must rely on petrographic analysis.

6.1 Introduction

A monochromatic beam of X-rays passing through a mineral grain is scattered by the atoms that compose the mineral. At specific angles of incidence, the scattered X-rays are in phase producing an intensified secondary beam. This phenomenon is known as **diffraction**. W. L. Bragg, working with his father L. H. Bragg, noted that diffraction could be pictured as a reflection of the X-ray beams by planes of atoms.

Diffraction occurs when the distance traveled by one scattered beam is different, by a length equal to the X-ray wavelength, from the distance traveled by another beam scattered by an adjacent plane of atoms (Fig. 6.1a). This diffracted beam is called a **first-order reflection**. Diffraction also occurs when the difference in distance traveled by X-rays scattered from two adjacent layers of atoms equals two wavelengths (Fig. 6.1b). The resultant beam is called a **second-order reflection**. Higher-order reflections occur each time the path difference is a whole-number multiple of the wavelength. The general relationship is expressed by the **Bragg equation**:

$$n\lambda = 2d \sin \theta$$

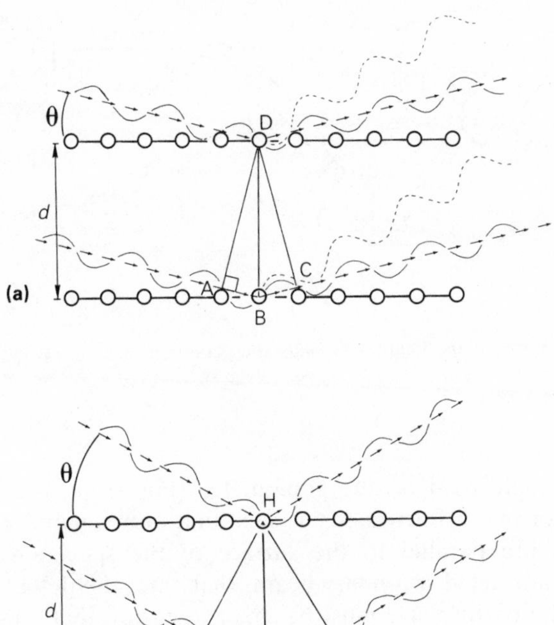

Figure 6.1 Diffraction of X-rays by layers of atoms.
(a) **First-order reflections** occur when the path difference (AB + BC) between X-ray beams scattered by adjacent planes of atoms equals *one* X-ray wavelength. These beams are in phase and combine to form a secondary beam. Other scattered beams (e.g. those shown as dashed lines), which do not meet this condition, are out of phase and are destroyed. Note that θ = angles ADB and BDC and that side BD = *d*.
(b) **Second-order reflections** occur when the path difference (EF + FG) equals *two* wavelengths. Note that θ = angles EHF and FHG and that side FH = *d*.

where n = a whole number, λ = the X-ray wavelength, d = the distance between planes of atoms (Å), and θ = the angle of incidence.

Powder diffractometry is the method generally used to study sedimentary materials. After a sample is ground to a fine powder (1–50 μm) it is placed in the diffractometer. The direction of the primary X-ray beam remains constant as the sample rotates around an axis normal to the primary beam. Diffracted beams that arrive at the detector tube, attached to a goniometer, are recorded as peaks on a strip chart. The diffractometer is designed so that the goniometer arm and the attached detector tube rotate at twice the rate of the sample. Thus, as the sample rotates through an angle of θ, the detector tube rotates through **2θ**,

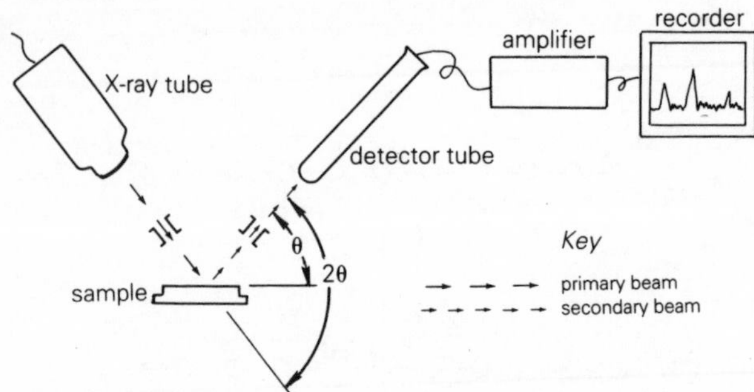

Figure 6.2 A schematic diagram showing the geometry of an X-ray diffractometer.

which is the angle read on the goniometer (Fig. 6.2). The geometrical arrangement of the diffractometer is such that *only* mineral grains whose lattice planes are parallel to the surface of the specimen holder will contribute to diffracted secondary beams that enter the detector tube. For this reason, the particle size must be small to ensure that a large number of correctly positioned grains are present.

6.2 Mineral identification (exclusive of clays)

When a powdered monomineralic sample is analyzed, diffraction occurs for each angle of incidence that satisfies the Bragg equation. Each angle is related to a set of lattice planes with a characteristic *d* spacing. Because every mineral has a number of distinctive sets of lattice parameters, X-ray diffraction produces a unique series of reflections (peaks) on the strip chart, which is known as a **diffractogram**. This unique character is based on the position of each reflection as measured by 2θ and on the intensity of each reflection. The **relative intensity** equals the intensity of a particular reflection given as a ratio of the strongest reflection (Fig. 6.3).

Generally, samples of unknown mineralogy are run on an X-ray diffractometer through a range of 2θ from 2 or 3° to 40°. The 2θ of each major reflection is measured and compared with analyses of standards, such as those found in Table 6.6 or in the ASTM Powder Diffraction File (see Phillips & Phillips 1980: 304–5). Note that an exact correspondence does not occur in the example shown in Figure 6.3 (also see Table 6.1). For most of the reflections there is some difference between the measured values for the unknown and the published values for the standard. Very weak reflections commonly do not show up, even in monomineralic samples. This problem is worse in samples composed of several different

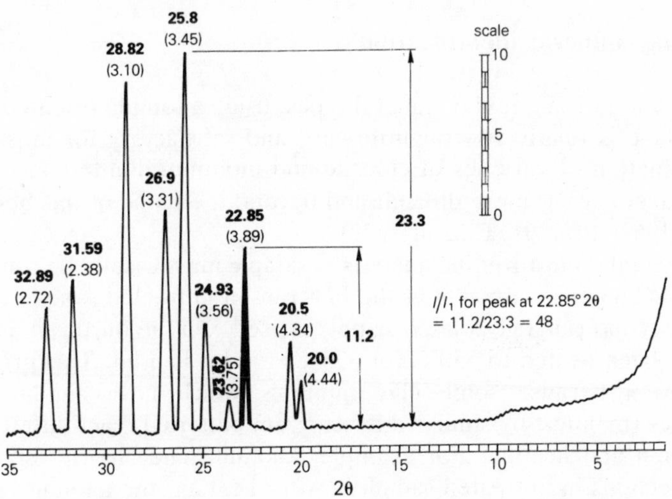

Figure 6.3 An indexed diffractogram of unknown mineral specimen. Numbers (not in parentheses) are measured 2θ values; numbers in parentheses are calculated *d* values (Å). Example of method for calculating the relative intensity (for reflection at 22.85° 2θ) is shown. For comparison with data from the barite standard, see Table 6.1.

Table 6.1 Comparison of XRD data for unknown mineral specimen (Fig. 6.1) and barite standard (from Table 6.6).

Calculated for unknown sample			Data from barite standard		
2θ	d(Å)	I/I_1	2θ	d(Å)	I/I_1
20.00	4.40	13	20.00	4.40	20
20.50	4.30	24	20.46	4.34	40
22.85	3.89	48	22.80	3.90	60
23.62	3.75	8	23.60	3.77	10
24.93	3.56	28	24.90	3.58	30
25.80	3.45	100	25.88	3.44	100
26.90	3.31	60	26.88	3.32	70
28.82	3.10	94	28.79	3.10	100
31.59	2.83	40	31.57	2.83	50
32.89	2.72	33	32.85	2.73	50

minerals. The signal for weak reflections may not be strong enough to be recorded on the diffractogram, or weak reflections of one mineral may be masked by stronger reflections of another mineral.

6.3 Clay mineral identification

Identification of major clay mineral types, using a sample oriented on the (001) plane is relatively straightforward and satisfactory for most work. Determination of varieties of chlorite and montmorillonite (smectite) or mixed-layer clays is more difficult and beyond the scope of this book (see Müller 1967: 197–201, Carroll 1970).

For even the most routine analysis, a sample must usually be run on the diffractometer three times. On the first run an untreated sample is used. On the second run a glycolated sample is used. On the third run a sample that has been heated to 550°C (or 425°C) for 1 h is used. This procedure is followed because some clay minerals which have similar lattice structures (manifest by similar diffractogram patterns) react differently to glycolation and heating. For example, kaolinite and chlorite both have 7 Å reflections in untreated samples. After heating, the kaolinite goes to mullite and its 7 Å reflection disappears. Chlorite is little affected by heating and its 7 Å peak remains. Thus a 7 Å reflection produced by an untreated sample may be interpreted as being of either kaolinite or chlorite. If this peak remains unchanged after heating, it can only be interpreted as a product of chlorite. The results of glycolation and heating of oriented samples are shown graphically in Figure 6.4 and described in more detail in Table 6.2.

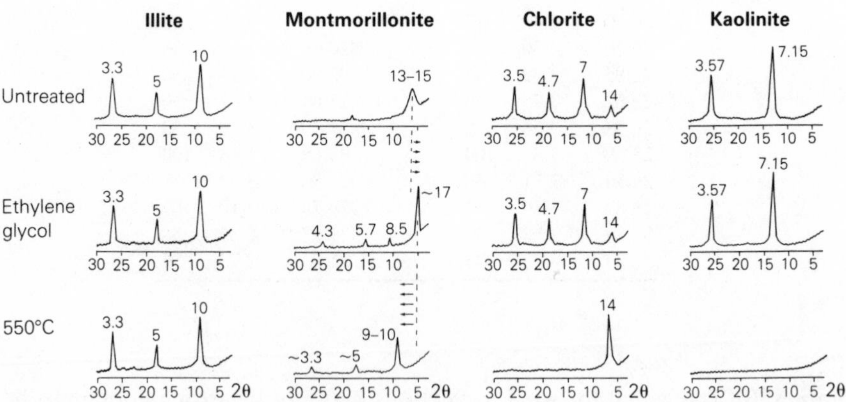

Figure 6.4 X-ray diffraction patterns for clay minerals, prepared using oriented mounts: see Table 6.2 for additional details.

Table 6.2 Data for identification of **clay minerals** in an oriented mount using X-ray diffraction (based on Carroll 1970). See Figure 6.4 for typical diffractograms.

Clay mineral	Untreated	Ethylene glycol	Heated to 550°C
illite	generally broad (001) reflection at approximately 8.8° 2θ (10 Å) with integral series of basal reflections including 17.7° 2θ (5 Å) and 26.75° 2θ (3.3 Å)	no change	(001) may be more intense
montmorillonite	(001) reflection variable from 6.80 to 5.89° 2θ (13–15 Å); higher-order basal reflections irrational	(001) increases to approximately 5.2° 2θ (17 Å) with integral series of basal reflections including 10.4° 2θ (8.5 Å) and 15.5° 2θ (5.7 Å)	(001) collapses to between 9.83 and 8.84° 2θ (between 9 and 10 Å) with corresponding integral series of higher-order basal reflections
chlorite	(001) reflection at approximately 6.3° 2θ (14+ Å) with an integral series of basal reflections including 12.62° 2θ (7 Å), 18.92° 2θ (4.7 Å), and 25.45° 2θ (3.5 Å).	no change	(001) reflection intensified; higher-order basal reflections disappear
kaolinite	(001) reflection at 12.38° 2θ (7.15 Å) and (002) reflection at 24.94° 2θ (3.57 Å); higher-order reflections generally too weak for recognition in samples composed of several clay minerals; disordered (poorly crystallized) kaolinite shows broader and less intense basal reflections	no change	Structure collapses to an X-ray amorphous mineral metakaolin (peaks disappear)

6.4 Chemical composition in solid-solution series

Determining the chemical composition of minerals in which solid solution occurs is important to sedimentologists. Substitution of calcium for magnesium in dolomite and magnesian calcite increases certain cell parameters, causing a shift in the angular position (2θ) of the strongest dolomite reflection (104). Accurate measurement of the position of this reflection allows one to determine the calcium content in dolomite (Fig. 6.5). Similarly, substitution of magnesium for calcium in calcite, which reduces the cell dimensions, can be determined by measuring the position of the strongest calcite reflection (104) (Goldsmith & Joensuu 1955, Goldsmith & Graf 1958). Other examples are summarized by Zussman (1967: 320–7).

6.5 Quantification of mineral content

The abundance of minerals in sediment and sedimentary rock can be determined by comparing the intensities of their strongest reflections. In

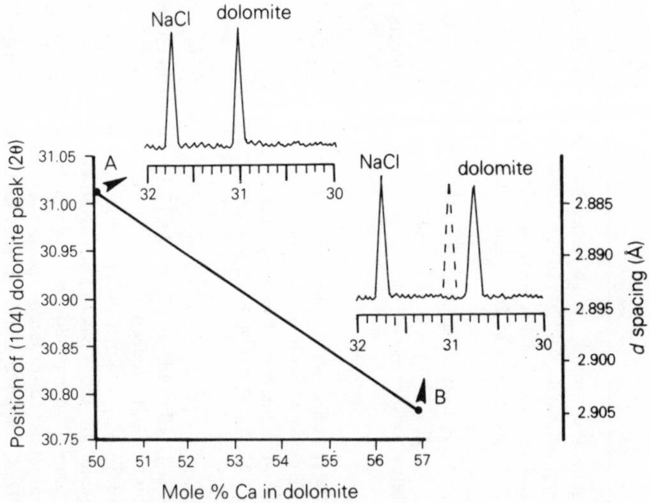

Figure 6.5 A calibration curve to determine the calcium content of dolomite. A and B show X-ray diffractograms representative of minimum and maximum calcium substitution. For the (104) dolomite peak, I/I_1 = 100; for the (200) halite peak (NaCl), I/I_1 = 100, d = 2.82 Å, 2θ = 31.72, which is used as an internal standard to fix the position of the (104) dolomite peak accurately. Note that increased calcium substitution, going from A to B, is accompanied by an increase in the *d* spacing and a shift in the (104) dolomite peak to lower 2θ values. (Based on data in Blatt *et al.* 1980: Fig. 14.10.)

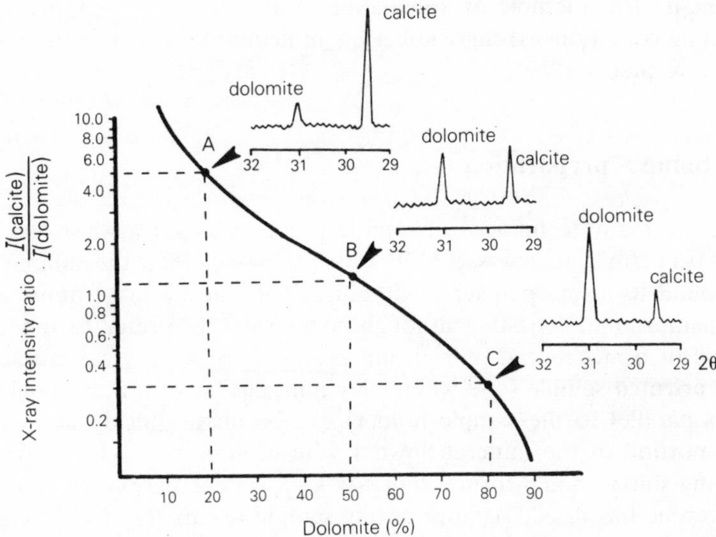

Figure 6.6 A calibration curve used to determine the relative proportions of mixtures of calcite and dolomite using X-ray diffraction. A, B, and C show representative diffractograms. For the (104) calcite peak, $I/I_1 = 100$, $d = 3.03$ Å, $2\theta = 29.48$; for the (104) dolomite peak, $I/I_1 = 100$, $d = 2.88$ Å, $2\theta = 30.99$. The X-ray intensity ratio is determined using intensity values for these reflections. (After Tennant & Berger 1957).

the case of calcite and dolomite, this method works very well because the absolute intensity of their strongest reflections is nearly equal. Thus an analysis of a sample of 50% calcite and 50% dolomite will produce a diffractogram with the strongest calcite and dolomite reflections that have nearly the same intensity (Fig. 6.6,B). Standards of known composition can be used to establish a curve that relates the reflection intensity to mineral abundance. These curves can then be used to estimate the relative abundance of calcite and dolomite in samples of unknown composition. More complex systems (e.g. one containing low-magnesium calcite, high-magnesium calcite and aragonite) can also be analyzed by this method (Taft & Harbaugh 1964).

A number of factors complicate the use of X-ray diffraction as a routine method of quantifying mineral content. One is the fact that the strongest reflection of some minerals is more intense than that for other minerals. For instance, a sample containing equal amounts of illite, montmorillonite, and kaolinite will produce a diffractogram in which the (001) kaolinite reflection is one and a half times to twice as intense as the (001) illite reflection and the (001) montmorillonite reflection is three to four times as intense as the (001) illite peak (Weaver 1958, Griffin & Goldberg 1963). In addition, the methods of sample preparation and treatment, the method of calculating peak intensity, and instrument operating conditions strongly affect quantification of clay mineral content (Pierce & Siegal 1969).

6.6 Sample preparation

There are many techniques of sample preparation for analysis by X-ray diffraction (for a review see Müller 1967: 184–6). First the sample must be ground to a fine powder (1–50 μm,). This can be done quite simply with a mortar and pestle, although some workers prefer to use a wet ballmill or a mechanical mortar and pestle.

An **oriented sample** (one where clay minerals lie with their basal (001) planes parallel to the sample holder) can be made quickly by mixing a small portion of the mineral powder with acetone on a glass slide. The resulting slurry should form a *thin and uniform* coating on the slide after the acetone has dried. A more lasting sample results if quick-drying glue (acetone base) is added to the slurry. Alternatively, suspended sediment may be allowed to settle through a column of water onto the glass slide either by gravity or in a centrifuge. Some workers prefer to mount suspended sediment on porcelain filters under suction (Gibbs 1965). A quite different method involves pressing the powder into a tablet using a hydraulic press.

Unoriented samples are made by dusting the powder onto a glass slide coating with a fast-drying, sticky fluid (e.g. glue mixed with acetone, nail polish, etc.). Other methods involve mixing the mineral powder with cork powder in a ratio of 10 : 1 (Müller 1967: 186) or *gently* packing the mineral powder into a hollow which has been cut into an aluminum sample holder (Carroll 1970: 61).

6.7 Exercises: X-ray diffraction

1 Calculate the *d* spacing for the following 2θ values using the Bragg equation.

(a) 8.93° 2θ =_____ Å

(b) 28.97° 2θ =_____ Å

(c) 36.70° 2θ =_____ Å

Note. You will use the Bragg equation in the following form:

$$d = n\lambda/2 \sin \theta, \quad \text{where } \lambda = 1.5418 \text{ and } n = 1$$

Remember that $2\theta \neq 2 \sin \theta$.

2 Use Table 6.3 to determine the mineral that produced the 2θ values given in (1) above.

Mineral is ______________________

3 Compare the calculated *d* spacing from (1) above with those for the standard found in Table 6.6.

Calculated	*d from Table 6.6*
____	____
____	____
____	____

4 Measure the 2θ values for the reflections shown in Figures 6.7, 6.8, 6.9, and 6.10. Also label each reflection (peak) with a letter to indicate the mineral associated with it (e.g. Q for quartz, C for calcite, etc.) based on comparison of values in Tables 6.3–6.6. Do this in *pencil*, because you may want to change your mind before the job is completed. *List* the minerals below.

(a) Figure 6.7 (use Tables 6.3 & 6.6) ______________________

____

(b) Figure 6.8 (use Tables 6.3 & 6.6) ______________________

____

(c) Figure 6.9 (use Tables 6.4 & 6.6) ______________________

____

(d) Figure 6.10 (use Fig. 6.4 & Table 6.2) ____________________

____

5 Calculate the relative intensity of peaks A and B in Figure 6.7. See Figure 6.3 for an example of the method to be used.

A = ____________ I/I_1; B = ____________ I/I_1

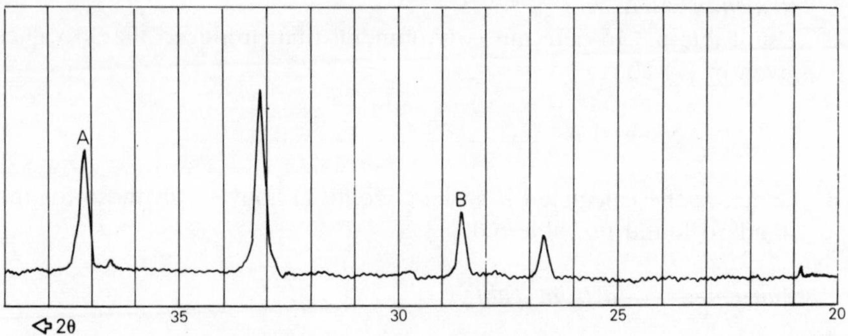

Figure 6.7 The diffractogram of a mineral associated with carbonized wood: Potomac Group (Lower Cretaceous) sandstone from northern Virginia.

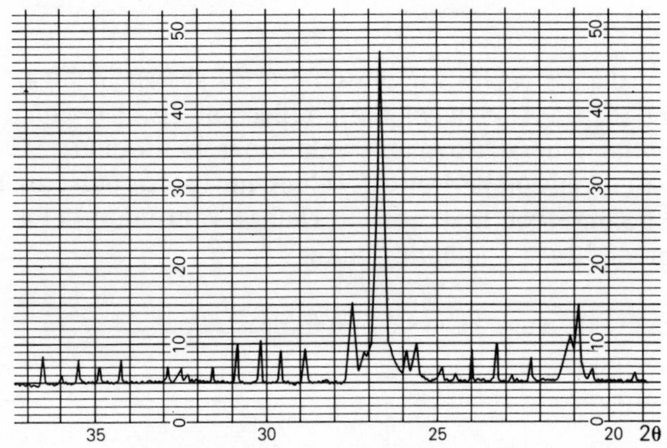

Figure 6.8 The diffractogram of a bulk sample of Pennsylvanian sandstone from Colorado.

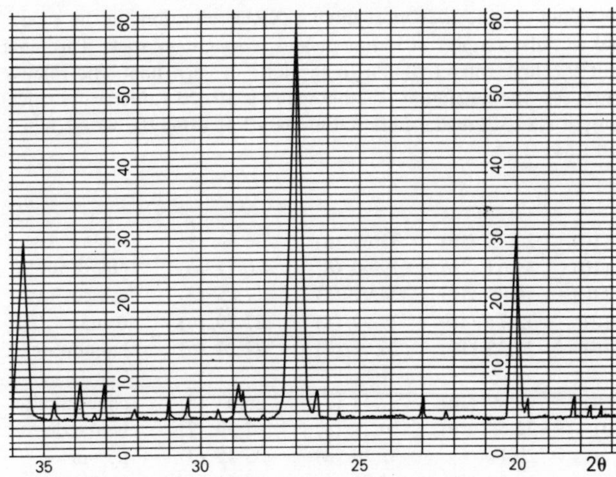

Figure 6.9 The diffractogram of a heavy mineral sample from modern river sand.

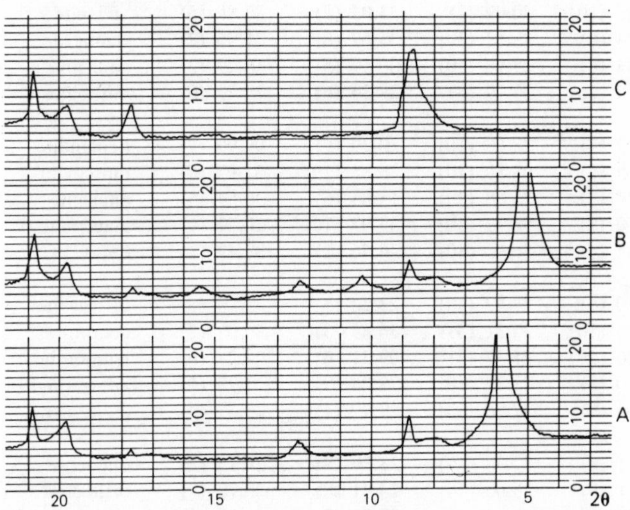

Figure 6.10 Diffractograms of bulk samples of saprolite below the Potomac Group (Lower Cretaceous) sandstone in northern Virginia: A, untreated sample (air dried); B, sample treated with ethylene glycol; C, sample heated to 550°C.

Table 6.3 2θ values for the four most intense XRD reflections in the range 2–40° 2θ for minerals found in bulk samples of sediment and sedimentary rock. The table is arranged sequentially for the first entry (column to the left) of each line. The relative intensity is given in parentheses; the maximum possible value is 10. 2θ values were calculated from *d* values given in the ASTM Powder Diffraction Data File using the wavelength of Cuk alpha radiation (λ = 1.5418).

8.75 (10)	26.45 (10)	33.69 (8)	36.68 (8)	biotite
8.75 (10)	34.67 (10)	19.60 (8)	26.77 (6)	glauconite
8.89 (10)	26.85 (10)	34.97 (5)	17.85 (3)	muscovite
8.95 (6)	33.71 (10)	28.99 (8)	27.79 (6)	trona
9.31 (6)	21.36 (10)	25.37 (8)	27.27 (6)	laumontite
9.84 (9)	22.39 (10)	22.74 (7)	26.07 (5)	clinoptilolite
9.99 (9)	22.68 (10)	30.29 (8)	17.39 (7)	heulandite
11.71 (10)	29.19 (6)	31.20 (3)	33.45 (3)	gypsum
12.33 (10)	12.36 (10)	27.79 (10)	28.52 (10)	phillipsite
12.36 (10)	12.33 (10)	27.79 (10)	28.52 (10)	phillipsite
12.56 (10)	25.30 (10)	35.63 (9)	37.47 (4)	chamosite
13.02 (10)	30.09 (7)	33.05 (7)	27.88 (5)	vivianite
14.24 (8)	28.52 (10)	33.69 (8)	31.96 (7)	glauberite
15.83 (6)	25.98 (10)	30.54 (5)	18.29 (2)	analcime
16.14 (10)	27.79 (8)	27.36 (6)	28.70 (6)	mirabilite
17.39 (7)	22.68 (10)	30.29 (9)	09.99 (9)	heulandite
17.85 (3)	08.89 (10)	26.85 (10)	34.97 (5)	muscovite
18.29 (2)	25.98 (10)	15.83 (6)	30.54 (5)	analcime
19.60 (8)	08.75 (10)	34.67 (10)	26.77 (6)	glauconite
20.85 (4)	26.66 (10)	36.56 (1)	39.49 (1)	quartz
21.10 (6)	27.49 (10)	23.22 (5)	25.60 (5)	microcline
21.25 (10)	33.31 (3)	36.65 (3)	36.07 (2)	goethite
21.36 (10)	25.37 (8)	09.31 (6)	27.27 (6)	laumontite
22.06 (8)	27.79 (10)	28.06 (9)	23.73 (6)	albite (high)
22.06 (9)	27.96 (10)	27.79 (7)	23.53 (4)	albite (low)
22.11 (8)	27.88 (10)	23.79 (8)	28.15 (8)	oligoclase
22.11 (9)	28.06 (10)	23.41 (8)	26.77 (7)	orthoclase
22.39 (10)	09.84 (9)	22.74 (7)	26.07 (5)	clinoptilolite
22.68 (10)	30.29 (9)	09.99 (8)	17.39 (7)	heulandite
22.74 (7)	22.39 (10)	09.84 (9)	26.07 (5)	clinoptilolite
22.80 (6)	25.88 (10)	28.79 (10)	26.88 (7)	barite
22.98 (1)	25.46 (10)	31.40 (3)	36.88 (2)	anhydrite
23.09 (3)	25.48 (10)	39.45 (2)	36.00 (1)	calcite
23.22 (5)	27.49 (10)	21.10 (6)	25.60 (5)	microcline
23.41 (8)	28.06 (10)	22.11 (9)	26.77 (7)	orthoclase

23.48 (8)	26.79 (10)	27.68 (8)	27.13 (6)	sanidine
23.53 (4)	27.96 (10)	22.06 (9)	27.79 (7)	albite (low)
23.73 (6)	27.79 (10)	28.06 (9)	22.06 (8)	albite (high)
23.79 (8)	27.88 (10)	22.11 (8)	28.15 (8)	oligoclase
24.32 (3)	33.31 (10)	35.77 (5)	—	hematite
24.70 (7)	26.84 (10)	30.49 (10)	29.40 (7)	carnallite
24.80 (6)	32.08 (10)	38.30 (5)	35.05 (1)	siderite
25.19 (10)	25.82 (7)	36.56 (4)	37.18 (3)	strontianite
25.30 (10)	12.56 (10)	35.63 (9)	37.47 (4)	chamosite
25.37 (8)	21.36 (10)	09.31 (6)	27.27 (6)	laumontite
25.46 (10)	31.40 (3)	38.68 (2)	22.98 (1)	anhydrite
25.60 (5)	27.49 (10)	21.10 (6)	23.22 (5)	microcline
25.79 (7)	33.32 (10)	37.34 (4)	38.97 (3)	marcasite
25.82 (7)	25.19 (10)	36.56 (4)	37.18 (3)	strontianite
25.88 (10)	28.79 (10)	26.88 (7)	22.80 (6)	barite
25.88 (4)	31.96 (10)	32.92 (6)	33.15 (6)	fluorapatite
25.98 (10)	15.83 (6)	30.54 (5)	18.29 (2)	analcime
26.07 (5)	22.39 (10)	9.84 (9)	22.74 (7)	clinoptilolite
26.19 (7)	32.34 (10)	33.34 (7)	34.40 (7)	apatite (carbonate)
26.24 (10)	27.25 (6)	33.18 (5)	37.93 (4)	aragonite
26.45 (10)	08.75 (10)	33.69 (8)	36.68 (8)	biotite
26.66 (10)	20.85 (4)	36.56 (1)	39.49 (1)	quartz
26.77 (6)	8.75 (10)	34.67 (10)	19.60 (8)	glauconite
26.77 (7)	28.06 (10)	22.11 (9)	23.41 (8)	orthoclase
26.79 (10)	23.48 (8)	27.68 (8)	27.13 (6)	sanidine
26.84 (10)	30.49 (10)	24.70 (7)	29.40 (7)	carnallite
26.85 (10)	8.89 (10)	34.97 (5)	17.85 (3)	muscovite
26.88 (7)	25.88 (10)	28.79 (10)	22.80 (6)	barite
27.06 (10)	30.07 (10)	28.09 (6)	32.79 (6)	celestite
27.13 (6)	26.79 (10)	23.48 (8)	27.68 (8)	sanidine
27.25 (6)	26.24 (10)	33.18 (5)	37.93 (4)	aragonite
27.27 (6)	21.36 (10)	25.37 (8)	9.31 (6)	laumontite
27.36 (6)	16.14 (10)	27.79 (8)	28.70 (6)	mirabilite
27.37 (1)	31.72 (10)	45.49 (6)	—	halite
27.49 (10)	21.10 (6)	23.22 (5)	25.60 (5)	microcline
27.68 (8)	26.79 (10)	23.48 (8)	27.13 (6)	sanidine
27.79 (10)	12.33 (10)	12.36 (10)	28.52 (10)	phillipsite
27.79 (10)	28.06 (9)	22.06 (8)	23.73 (6)	albite (high)
27.79 (6)	33.71 (10)	28.99 (8)	8.95 (6)	trona
27.79 (7)	27.96 (10)	22.06 (9)	23.53 (4)	albite (low)
27.79 (8)	16.14 (10)	27.36 (6)	28.70 (6)	mirabilite
27.88 (10)	22.11 (8)	23.79 (8)	28.15 (8)	oligoclase
27.88 (5)	13.02 (10)	30.09 (7)	33.05 (7)	vivianite
27.96 (10)	22.06 (9)	27.79 (7)	23.53 (4)	albite (low)
28.06 (10)	22.11 (9)	23.41 (8)	26.77 (7)	orthoclase
28.06 (9)	27.79 (10)	22.06 (8)	23.73 (6)	albite (high)

(continued)

Table 6.3 *continued*

28.09 (6)	27.06 (10)	30.07 (10)	32.79 (6)	celestite
28.15 (8)	27.88 (10)	22.11 (8)	23.79 (8)	oligoclase
28.30 (9)	47.06 (10)	—	—	fluorite
28.52 (10)	12.33 (10)	12.36 (10)	27.79 (10)	phillipsite
28.52 (10)	14.24 (8)	33.69 (8)	31.96 (7)	glauberite
28.54 (4)	33.07 (10)	37.10 (6)	—	pyrite
28.70 (6)	16.14 (10)	27.79 (8)	27.36 (6)	mirabilite
28.79 (10)	25.88 (10)	26.88 (7)	22.80 (6)	barite
28.99 (8)	33.71 (10)	8.95 (6)	27.79 (6)	trona
29.19 (6)	11.71 (10)	31.20 (3)	33.45 (3)	gypsum
29.40 (7)	26.84 (10)	30.49 (10)	24.70 (10)	carnallite
29.48 (10)	23.09 (3)	39.45 (2)	36.00 (1)	calcite
30.07 (10)	27.06 (10)	28.09 (6)	32.79 (6)	celestite
30.09 (7)	13.02 (10)	33.05 (7)	27.88 (5)	vivianite
30.29 (9)	22.68 (10)	9.99 (8)	17.39 (7)	heulandite
30.49 (10)	26.84 (10)	24.70 (7)	29.40 (7)	carnallite
30.54 (5)	25.98 (10)	15.83 (6)	18.29 (2)	analcime
30.99 (10)	41.18 (3)	35.34 (1)	33.56 (1)	dolomite
31.20 (3)	11.71 (10)	29.19 (6)	33.45 (3)	gypsum
31.31 (3)	21.25 (10)	36.65 (3)	36.07 (2)	goethite
31.40 (3)	25.46 (10)	38.68 (2)	22.99 (1)	anhydrite
31.72 (10)	45.49 (6)	27.37 (1)	—	halite
31.96 (10)	32.92 (6)	33.15 (6)	25.88 (4)	fluorapatite
31.96 (7)	28.52 (10)	14.24 (8)	33.69 (8)	glauberite
32.08 (10)	24.80 (6)	38.30 (5)	35.05 (1)	siderite
32.34 (10)	26.19 (7)	33.34 (7)	34.40 (7)	apatite (carbonate)
32.66 (10)	43.03 (4)	35.88 (2)	38.85 (<5)	magnesite
32.79 (6)	27.06 (10)	30.07 (10)	28.09 (6)	celestite
32.92 (6)	31.96 (10)	33.15 (6)	25.88 (4)	fluorapatite
33.05 (7)	13.02 (10)	30.09 (7)	27.88 (5)	vivianite
33.07	37.10 (6)	28.54 (4)	—	pyrite
33.15 (6)	31.96 (10)	32.92 (6)	25.88 (4)	fluorapatite
33.18 (5)	26.24 (10)	27.25 (6)	37.93 (5)	aragonite
33.31 (10)	35.77 (5)	24.32 (3)	—	hematite
33.32 (10)	25.79 (7)	37.34 (4)	38.97 (3)	marcasite
33.34 (7)	32.34 (10)	26.19 (7)	34.40 (7)	apatite (carbonate)
33.45 (3)	11.71 (10)	29.19 (6)	31.20 (3)	gypsum
33.56 (1)	30.99 (10)	41.18 (3)	35.34 (1)	dolomite
33.69 (8)	28.52 (10)	14.24 (8)	31.96 (7)	glauberite
33.69 (8)	8.75 (10)	26.45 (10)	36.68 (8)	biotite

33.71 (10)	28.99 (8)	8.95 (6)	27.79 (6)	trona
34.40 (7)	32.34 (10)	26.19 (7)	33.34 (7)	apatite (carbonate)
34.67 (10)	8.75 (10)	19.60 (8)	26.77 (6)	glauconite
34.97 (5)	8.89 (10)	26.85 (10)	17.85 (3)	muscovite
35.05 (1)	32.08 (10)	24.80 (6)	38.30 (5)	siderite
35.34 (1)	30.99 (10)	41.18 (3)	33.56 (1)	dolomite
35.63 (9)	12.56 (10)	25.30 (10)	37.47 (4)	chamosite
35.77 (5)	33.31 (10)	24.32 (3)	—	hematite
35.88 (2)	32.66 (10)	43.03 (4)	38.85 (<5)	magnesite
36.00 (1)	29.48 (10)	23.09 (3)	39.45 (2)	calcite
36.07 (2)	21.25 (10)	33.31 (3)	36.65 (3)	goethite
36.56 (1)	26.66 (10)	20.85 (4)	39.46 (1)	quartz
36.56 (4)	25.19 (10)	25.82 (7)	37.18 (3)	strontianite
36.65 (3)	22.25 (10)	33.31 (3)	36.07 (2)	goethite
36.68 (8)	8.75 (10)	26.45 (10)	33.69 (8)	biotite
37.10 (6)	33.07 (10)	28.54 (4)	—	pyrite
37.18 (3)	25.19 (10)	25.82 (7)	36.56 (4)	strontianite
37.34 (4)	33.32 (10)	25.79 (7)	38.97 (3)	marcasite
37.47 (4)	12.56 (10)	25.30 (10)	35.63 (9)	chamosite
37.93 (4)	26.24 (10)	27.25 (6)	33.18 (5)	aragonite
38.30 (5)	32.08 (10)	24.80 (6)	35.05 (1)	siderite
38.68 (2)	25.46 (10)	31.40 (3)	22.98 (1)	anhydrite
38.97 (3)	33.32 (10)	25.79 (7)	37.34 (4)	marcasite
39.45 (2)	29.48 (10)	23.09 (3)	36.00 (1)	calcite
39.49 (1)	26.66 (10)	20.85 (4)	36.56 (1)	quartz

Table 6.4 2θ values for the four most intense XRD reflections in the range 2–40° 2θ for minerals found in heavy mineral separations. The table is arranged sequentially for the first entry (column to the left) of each line. The relative intensity is given in parentheses; the maximum possible value is 10. 2θ values were calculated from *d* values given in the ASTM Powder Diffraction Data File using the wavelength of Cuk alpha radiation (λ = 1.5418).

6.14 (6)	12.38 (10)	24.80 (7)	36.30 (6)	chlorite
8.75 (10)	26.45 (10)	33.69 (8)	36.68 (8)	biotite
8.75 (10)	34.67 (10)	19.60 (8)	26.77 (6)	glauconite
10.51 (7)	33.05 (10)	28.70 (8)	26.37 (7)	actinolite
10.53 (10)	28.80 (7)	27.36 (2)	33.34 (2)	hornblende
10.56 (10)	28.60 (10)	33.12 (9)	27.29 (8)	tremolite
10.75 (10)	33.28 (6)	29.28 (5)	19.95 (3)	glaucophane
10.94 (4)	33.27 (10)	31.12 (7)	22.06 (5)	zoisite
12.38 (10)	24.80 (7)	6.14 (6)	36.30 (6)	chlorite
16.00 (10)	19.60 (9)	32.32 (9)	22.68 (7)	andalusite
17.70 (4)	31.00 (10)	29.45 (4)	32.09 (4)	clinozoisite
17.99 (3)	27.59 (10)	29.89 (9)	34.56 (9)	sphene
18.18 (10)	31.14 (9)	36.01 (5)	26.99 (4)	enstatite
18.29 (4)	35.48 (10)	30.13 (7)	37.17 (1)	magnetite
18.41 (5)	35.63 (10)	30.30 (6)	37.47 (1)	chromite
18.64 (5)	30.27 (10)	36.18 (6)	23.79 (5)	wolframite
19.17 (1)	28.06 (10)	35.63 (4)	38.30 (4)	kyanite
19.60 (8)	8.75 (10)	34.67 (10)	26.77 (6)	glauconite
19.60 (9)	16.00 (10)	32.32 (9)	22.68 (7)	andalusite
19.73 (10)	19.95 (10)	36.53 (9)	30.09 (8)	chloritoid
19.95 (10)	19.73 (10)	36.53 (9)	30.09 (8)	chloritoid
19.95 (3)	10.75 (10)	33.28 (6)	29.28 (5)	glaucophane
20.02 (5)	27.00 (10)	35.66 (5)	38.54 (1)	zircon
20.85 (4)	26.66 (10)	36.56 (1)	39.49 (1)	quartz
21.05 (7)	34.83 (10)	22.28 (9)	30.18 (9)	tormaline
21.25 (10)	33.31 (3)	36.65 (3)	36.07 (2)	goethite
22.06 (5)	33.27 (10)	31.12 (7)	10.94 (4)	zoisite
22.28 (9)	34.83 (10)	30.18 (9)	21.05 (7)	tourmaline
22.68 (7)	16.00 (10)	19.60 (9)	32.32 (9)	andalusite
22.80 (6)	25.88 (10)	28.79 (10)	26.88 (7)	barite
23.22 (9)	26.90 (10)	25.37 (9)	28.93 (6)	wollastonite
23.79 (5)	30.27 (10)	36.18 (6)	18.64 (5)	wolframite
23.86 (5)	32.68 (10)	35.34 (9)	—	ilmenite
24.10 (6)	30.43 (10)	24.10 (6)	38.12 (5)	topaz
24.32 (3)	33.31 (10)	35.77 (5)	—	hematite

24.80 (6)	32.08 (10)	38.30 (5)	35.05 (1)	siderite
24.80 (7)	12.38 (10)	6.14 (6)	36.30 (6)	chlorite
25.02 (6)	29.66 (10)	33.27 (10)	27.93 (8)	staurolite
25.30 (10)	37.83 (2)	36.98 (1)	38.61 (1)	anatase
25.37 (10)	30.83 (9)	25.67 (8)	36.28 (3)	brookite
25.37 (8)	26.90 (10)	23.22 (9)	28.93 (6)	wollastonite
25.60 (9)	43.40 (10)	35.16 (8)	37.81 (4)	corundum
25.67 (8)	25.37 (10)	30.83 (9)	36.28 (3)	brookite
25.79 (7)	33.32 (10)	37.34 (4)	38.97 (3)	marcasite
25.88 (10)	28.79 (10)	26.88 (7)	22.80 (6)	barite
25.88 (4)	31.96 (10)	32.92 (6)	33.15 (6)	fluorapatite
26.13 (9)	26.53 (10)	35.48 (9)	33.56 (8)	sillimanite
26.19 (7)	32.34 (10)	33.34 (7)	34.40 (7)	apatite (carbonate)
26.24 (10)	27.25 (6)	33.18 (5)	37.93 (4)	aragonite
26.37 (7)	33.05 (10)	28.70 (8)	10.51 (7)	actinolite
26.45 (10)	8.75 (10)	33.69 (8)	36.68 (8)	biotite
26.53 (10)	35.48 (9)	26.13 (9)	33.56 (8)	sillimanite
26.61 (10)	33.90 (8)	37.98 (3)	39.01 (1)	cassiterite
26.66 (10)	20.85 (4)	36.56 (1)	39.49 (1)	quartz
26.77 (6)	8.75 (10)	34.67 (10)	19.60 (8)	glauconite
26.88 (7)	25.88 (10)	28.79 (10)	22.80 (6)	barite
26.90 (10)	23.22 (9)	25.37 (8)	28.93 (6)	wollastonite
26.99 (4)	18.18 (10)	31.14 (9)	36.01 (5)	enstatite
27.00 (10)	20.02 (5)	35.66 (5)	38.54 (1)	zirzon
27.25 (6)	26.24 (10)	33.18 (5)	37.93 (4)	aragonite
27.29 (8)	10.56 (10)	28.60 (10)	33.12 (9)	tremolite
27.36 (2)	10.53 (10)	28.80 (7)	33.34 (2)	hornblende
27.49 (10)	36.09 (4)	41.26 (2)	39.22 (1)	rutile
27.59 (10)	29.89 (9)	34.56 (9)	17.99 (3)	sphene
27.62 (3)	29.78 (10)	35.51 (4)	30.30 (3)	diopside
27.88 (10)	30.94 (8)	35.19 (5)	36.22 (5)	hypersthene
27.92 (7)	30.43 (10)	24.10 (6)	38.12 (5)	topaz
28.06 (10)	35.63 (4)	38.30 (4)	19.17 (1)	kyanite
28.30 (9)	47.06 (10)	—	—	fluorite
28.54 (4)	33.07 (10)	37.10 (6)	—	pyrite
28.60 (10)	10.56 (10)	33.12 (9)	27.29 (8)	tremolite
28.70 (8)	33.05 (10)	10.51 (7)	26.37 (7)	actinolite
28.79 (10)	25.88 (10)	26.88 (7)	22.80 (6)	barite
28.80 (7)	10.53 (10)	27.36 (2)	33.34 (2)	hornblende
28.89 (10)	31.16 (7)	27.07 (5)	21.31 (3)	monazite
28.93 (10)	26.90 (10)	23.22 (9)	25.37 (8)	wollastonite

(continued)

Table 6.4 *continued*

29.28 (5)	10.75 (10)	33.28 (5)	19.95 (3)	glaucophane
29.45 (4)	31.00 (10)	17.70 (4)	32.09 (4)	clinozoisite
29.66 (10)	33.27 (10)	37.93 (8)	25.02 (6)	staurolite
29.87 (10)	33.51 (4)	27.62 (3)	30.30 (3)	diopside
29.88 (10)	35.05 (9)	35.77 (9)	30.40 (8)	augite
29.89 (9)	27.59 (10)	34.56 (9)	17.99 (3)	sphene
30.09 (8)	19.73 (10)	19.95 (10)	36.53 (9)	chloritoid
30.13 (7)	35.48 (10)	18.29 (4)	37.17 (1)	magnetite
30.18 (9)	34.83 (10)	22.28 (9)	21.05 (7)	tourmaline
30.20 (3)	33.86 (10)	37.20 (2)	38.80 (2)	grossularite garnet
30.27 (10)	36.18 (6)	18.64 (5)	23.79 (5)	wolframite
30.30 (3)	29.87 (10)	35.51 (4)	27.62 (3)	diopside
30.30 (6)	35.63 (10)	18.41 (5)	37.47 (1)	chromite
30.40 (8)	29.88 (10)	35.05 (9)	35.77 (9)	augite
30.43 (10)	27.92 (7)	24.10 (6)	38.12 (5)	topaz
30.62 (9)	34.22 (10)	37.63 (9)	39.17 (6)	garnet (Fe, Mn)
30.83 (10)	37.54 (7)	33.47 (6)	34.59 (6)	epidote
30.83 (9)	25.37 (10)	25.67 (8)	36.28 (3)	brookite
30.94 (8)	27.88 (10)	35.19 (5)	36.22 (5)	hypersthene
30.99 (10)	41.18 (3)	35.34 (1)	33.56 (1)	dolomite
31.00 (10)	17.70 (4)	29.45 (4)	32.09 (4)	clinozoisite
31.05 (6)	34.77 (10)	36.53 (3)	38.30 (3)	pyrope garnet
31.12 (7)	33.27 (10)	22.06 (5)	10.94 (4)	zoisite
31.14 (9)	18.18 (10)	36.01 (5)	26.99 (4)	enstatite
31.30 (4)	36.90 (10)	—	—	spinel
31.31 (3)	21.25 (10)	36.65 (3)	36.07 (2)	goethite
31.96 (10)	32.92 (6)	33.15 (6)	25.88 (4)	fluorapatite
32.08 (10)	24.80 (6)	38.30 (5)	35.05 (1)	siderite
32.09 (4)	31.00 (10)	17.70 (4)	29.45 (4)	clinozoisite
32.32 (9)	16.00 (10)	19.60 (9)	22.68 (7)	andalusite
32.34 (10)	26.19 (7)	33.34 (7)	34.40 (7)	apatite (carbonate)
32.66 (10)	43.03 (4)	35.88 (2)	38.85 (<5)	magnesite
32.68 (10)	35.34 (9)	23.86 (5)	—	ilmenite
32.92 (6)	31.96 (10)	33.15 (6)	25.88 (4)	fluorapatite
33.05 (10)	28.70 (8)	10.51 (7)	26.37 (7)	actinolite
33.07 (10)	37.10 (6)	28.54 (4)	—	pyrite
33.12 (9)	10.56 (10)	28.60 (10)	27.29 (8)	tremolite
33.15 (6)	31.96 (10)	32.92 (6)	25.88 (4)	fluorapatite
33.18 (5)	26.24 (10)	27.25 (6)	37.93 (5)	aragonite
33.27 (10)	29.66 (10)	37.93 (8)	25.02 (6)	staurolite
33.27 (10)	31.12 (7)	22.06 (5)	10.94 (4)	zoisite
33.28 (6)	10.75 (10)	29.28 (5)	19.95 (3)	glaucophane

33.31 (10)	35.77 (5)	24.32 (3)	—	hematite
33.32 (10)	25.79 (7)	37.34 (4)	38.97 (3)	marcasite
33.34 (2)	10.53 (10)	28.80 (6)	27.36 (2)	hornblende
33.34 (7)	32.34 (10)	26.19 (7)	34.40 (7)	apatite (carbonate)
33.47 (6)	30.83 (10)	37.54 (7)	34.59 (6)	epidote
33.56 (1)	30.99 (10)	41.18 (3)	35.34 (1)	dolomite
35.56 (8)	26.53 (10)	35.48 (9)	26.13 (8)	sillimanite
33.69 (8)	8.75 (10)	26.45 (10)	36.68 (8)	biotite
33.86 (10)	30.20 (3)	37.20 (2)	38.80 (2)	grossularite garnet
33.90 (8)	26.61 (10)	37.98 (3)	39.01 (1)	cassiterite
34.22 (10)	30.62 (9)	37.63 (9)	39.17 (6)	garnet (Fe, Mn)
34.40 (7)	32.34 (10)	26.19 (7)	33.34 (7)	apatite (carbonate)
34.56 (9)	27.59 (10)	29.89 (9)	17.99 (3)	sphene
34.59 (6)	30.83 (10)	37.54 (7)	33.47 (6)	epidote
34.67 (10)	8.75 (10)	19.60 (8)	26.77 (6)	glauconite
34.77 (10)	31.05 (6)	36.53 (5)	38.30 (3)	pyrope garnet
34.83 (10)	22.28 (9)	30.18 (9)	21.05 (7)	tourmaline
35.05 (1)	32.08 (10)	24.80 (6)	38.30 (5)	siderite
35.05 (9)	29.88 (10)	35.77 (9)	30.40 (8)	augite
35.16 (9)	43.40 (10)	25.60 (8)	37.81 (4)	corundum
35.19 (5)	27.88 (10)	30.94 (8)	36.22 (5)	hypersthene
35.34 (1)	30.99 (10)	41.18 (3)	33.56 (1)	dolomite
35.34 (9)	32.68 (10)	23.86 (5)	—	ilmenite
35.48 (10)	30.13 (7)	18.29 (4)	37.17 (1)	magnetite
35.48 (9)	26.53 (10)	26.13 (9)	33.56 (8)	sillimanite
35.51 (4)	29.87 (10)	27.62 (3)	30.30 (3)	diopside
35.63 (10)	30.30 (6)	18.41 (5)	37.47 (1)	chromite
35.63 (4)	28.06 (10)	38.30 (4)	19.17 (1)	kyanite
35.66 (5)	27.00 (10)	20.02 (5)	38.54 (1)	zircon
35.77 (5)	33.31 (10)	24.32 (3)	—	hematite
35.77 (9)	29.88 (10)	35.05 (9)	30.40 (8)	augite
36.01 (5)	18.18 (10)	31.14 (9)	26.99 (4)	enstatite
36.07 (2)	21.25 (10)	33.31 (3)	36.65 (3)	goethite
36.09 (4)	27.49 (10)	41.26 (2)	39.22 (1)	rutile
36.18 (6)	30.27 (10)	18.64 (5)	23.79 (5)	wolframite
36.22 (5)	27.88 (10)	30.94 (8)	35.19 (5)	hypersthene
36.28 (3)	25.37 (10)	30.83 (9)	25.67 (8)	brookite
36.30 (6)	12.38 (10)	24.80 (7)	56.14 (6)	chlorite
36.53 (3)	34.77 (10)	31.05 (6)	38.30 (3)	pyrope garnet
36.53 (9)	19.73 (10)	19.95 (10)	30.09 (8)	chloritoid
36.56 (1)	26.66 (10)	20.85 (4)	39.46 (1)	quartz

(continued)

Table 6.4 *continued*

36.65 (3)	22.25 (10)	33.31 (3)	36.07 (2)	goethite
36.68 (8)	08.75 (10)	24.45 (10)	33.69 (8)	biotite
36.90 (10)	31.30 (4)	—	—	spinel
36.98 (1)	25.30 (10)	37.83 (1)	38.61 (1)	anatase
37.10 (6)	33.07 (10)	28.54 (4)	—	pyrite
37.17 (1)	35.48 (10)	30.13 (7)	18.29 (4)	magnetite
37.20 (2)	33.86 (10)	30.20 (3)	38.80 (2)	grossularite garnet
37.34 (4)	33.32 (10)	25.79 (7)	38.97 (3)	marcasite
37.47 (1)	35.63 (10)	30.30 (6)	18.41 (5)	chromite
37.54 (7)	30.83 (10)	33.47 (6)	34.59 (6)	epidote
37.63 (9)	34.22 (10)	30.62 (9)	39.17 (6)	garnet (Fe, Mn)
37.81 (4)	43.40 (10)	35.16 (9)	25.60 (8)	corundum
37.83 (2)	25.30 (10)	38.61 (1)	36.98 (1)	anatase
37.93 (4)	26.24 (10)	27.25 (6)	33.18 (5)	aragonite
37.93 (8)	29.66 (10)	33.27 (10)	25.02 (6)	staurolite
37.98 (3)	26.61 (10)	33.90 (3)	39.01 (1)	cassiterite
38.12 (5)	30.43 (10)	27.92 (7)	24.10 (6)	topaz
38.30 (3)	34.77 (10)	31.05 (6)	36.53 (3)	pyrope garnet
38.30 (4)	28.06 (10)	35.63 (4)	19.17 (1)	kyanite
38.30 (5)	32.08 (10)	24.80 (6)	35.05 (1)	siderite
38.54 (1)	27.00 (10)	20.02 (5)	35.66 5)	zircon
38.61 (1)	25.30 (10)	37.83 (1)	36.98 (1)	anatase
38.80 (2)	33.86 (10)	30.20 (3)	37.20 (2)	grossularite garnet
38.97 (3)	33.32 (10)	25.79 (7)	37.34 (4)	marcasite
39.01 (1)	26.61 (10)	33.90 (8)	37.98 (3)	cassiterite
39.17 (6)	34.22 (10)	30.62 (9)	37.63 (9)	garnet (Fe, Mn)
39.22 (1)	27.49 (10)	36.09 (4)	41.26 (2)	rutile
39.49 (1)	26.66 (10)	20.85 (4)	36.56 (1)	quartz
41.18 (3)	30.99 (10)	35.34 (1)	33.56 (1)	dolomite
41.26 (2)	27.49 (10)	36.09 (2)	39.22 (1)	rutile
43.40 (10)	35.16 (9)	25.60 (8)	37.81 (4)	corundum

Table 6.5 2θ values for the four most intense XRD reflections in the range 2–40° 2θ for minerals found in sediment and sedimentary rock (exclusive of clays). The table is arranged in alphabetical order. The relative intensity is given in parentheses; the maximum possible value is 10. Values decrease from left to right. 2θ values were calculated from *d* values given in the ASTM Powder Diffraction Data File using the wavelength of Cuk alpha radiation (λ = 1.5418).

33.05 (10)	28.70 (8)	10.51 (7)	26.37 (7)	actinolite
27.79 (10)	28.06 (9)	22.06 (8)	23.73 (6)	albite (high)
27.96 (10)	22.06 (9)	27.79 (7)	23.53 (4)	albite (low)
25.98 (10)	15.83 (6)	30.54 (5)	18.29 (2)	analcime
25.30 (10)	37.83 (2)	36.98 (1)	38.61 (1)	anatase
16.00 (10)	19.60 (9)	32.32 (9)	22.68 (7)	andalusite
25.46 (10)	31.40 (3)	38.68 (2)	22.98 (1)	anhydrite
32.34 (4)	26.19 (7)	33.34 (7)	34.40 (7)	apatite (carbonate)
26.24 (10)	27.25 (6)	33.18 (5)	37.93 (4)	aragonite
29.88 (10)	35.05 (9)	35.77 (9)	30.40 (8)	augite
25.88 (10)	28.79 (10)	26.88 (7)	22.80 (6)	barite
8.75 (10)	26.45 (10)	33.69 (8)	36.68 (6)	biotite
25.37 (10)	30.83 (9)	25.67 (8)	36.28 (3)	brookite
29.48 (10)	23.09 (3)	39.45 (2)	36.00 (1)	calcite
26.84 (10)	30.49 (10)	24.70 (7)	29.40 (7)	carnallite
26.61 (10)	33.90 (8)	37.98 (3)	39.01 (1)	cassiterite
27.06 (10)	30.07 (10)	28.09 (6)	32.79 (6)	celestite
12.56 (10)	25.30 (10)	35.63 (9)	34.47 (4)	chamosite
12.38 (10)	24.80 (7)	6.14 (6)	36.30 (6)	chlorite
19.73 (10)	19.95 (10)	36.53 (9)	30.09 (8)	chloritoid
35.63 (10)	30.30 (6)	18.41 (5)	37.47 (1)	chromite
22.39 (3)	9.84 (9)	22.74 (7)	26.07 (5)	clinoptilolite
31.00 (10)	17.70 (4)	29.45 (4)	32.09 (4)	corundum
29.87 (10)	35.51 (9)	27.62 (3)	30.30 (5)	diopside
30.99 (10)	41.18 (3)	35.34 (1)	33.56 (1)	dolomite
18.18 (10)	31.14 (9)	36.01 (5)	26.99 (4)	enstatite
30.83 (10)	37.54 (7)	33.47 (6)	34.59 (6)	epidote
31.96 (10)	32.92 (6)	33.15 (6)	25.88 (4)	fluorapatite
28.30 (9)	47.06 (10)	—	—	fluorite
34.22 (10)	30.62 (9)	37.63 (9)	39.17 (6)	garnet (Fe, Mn)
28.52 (10)	14.24 (8)	33.69 (8)	31.96 (7)	glauberite
8.85 (10)	34.67 (10)	19.60 (8)	26.77 (6)	glauconite
10.75 (10)	33.28 (6)	29.28 (5)	19.95 (3)	glaucophane
21.25 (10)	33.31 (3)	36.65 (3)	36.07 (2)	goethite
33.86 (10)	30.20 (3)	37.30 (2)	38.80 (2)	grossularite garnet
11.71 (10)	29.19 (6)	31.20 (3)	33.45 (3)	gypsum

(continued)

Table 6.5 *continued*

31.72 (10)	45.49 (6)	27.37 (1)	—	halite
33.31 (10)	35.77 (5)	24.32 (2)	—	hematite
22.68 (10)	30.29 (9)	9.99 (8)	17.39 (7)	heulandite
10.53 (10)	28.80 (7)	27.36 (2)	33.34 (2)	hornblende
27.88 (10)	30.94 (8)	35.19 (5)	36.22 (5)	hypersthene
32.68 (10)	35.34 (9)	23.86 (5)	—	ilmenite
28.06 (10)	35.63 (4)	38.30 (4)	19.17 (1)	kyanite
21.36 (10)	25.37 (8)	9.31 (6)	27.27 (6)	laumontite
32.66 (10)	43.03 (4)	35.88 (2)	38.55 (<5)	magnesite
35.48 (10)	30.13 (7)	18.29 (4)	37.17 (1)	magnetite
33.32 (10)	25.79 (7)	37.34 (4)	38.97 (3)	marcasite
27.49 (10)	21.10 (6)	23.22 (5)	25.60 (5)	microcline
16.14 (10)	27.79 (8)	27.36 (6)	28.70 (6)	mirabilite
28.89 (10)	31.16 (7)	27.07 (5)	21.31 (3)	monazite
8.89 (10)	26.85 (10)	34.97 (5)	17.85 (3)	muscovite
27.88 (10)	22.11 (8)	23.79 (8)	28.15 (8)	oligoclase
28.06 (10)	22.11 (9)	23.41 (8)	26.77 (7)	orthoclase
12.33 (10)	12.36 (10)	27.79 (10)	28.52 (10)	phillipsite
33.07 (10)	37.10 (6)	28.54 (4)	—	pyrite
34.77 (10)	31.05 (6)	36.53 (3)	38.30 (3)	pyrope garnet
26.66 (10)	20.85 (4)	36.56 (1)	39.49 (1)	quartz
27.49 (10)	36.09 (4)	41.26 (2)	39.22 (1)	rutile
26.79 (10)	23.48 (8)	27.68 (8)	27.13 (6)	sanidine
32.08 (10)	24.80 (6)	38.30 (5)	35.05 (1)	siderite
26.53 (10)	35.48 (9)	26.13 (9)	33.56 (8)	sillimanite
27.59 (10)	29.89 (9)	34.56 (9)	17.99 (3)	sphene
36.90 (10)	31.30 (4)	—	—	spinel
29.66 (10)	33.27 (10)	37.93 (8)	25.02 (6)	staurolite
25.19 (10)	25.82 (7)	36.56 (4)	37.18 (3)	strontianite
30.43 (10)	27.92 (7)	24.10 (6)	38.12 (5)	topaz
34.83 (10)	22.28 (9)	30.18 (9)	21.05 (7)	tourmaline
10.56 (10)	28.60 (10)	33.12 (9)	27.29 (8)	tremolite
33.71 (10)	28.99 (8)	8.95 (6)	27.79 (6)	trona
13.02 (10)	30.09 (7)	33.05 (7)	27.88 (5)	vivianite
30.27 (10)	36.18 (6)	18.64 (5)	23.79 (5)	wolframite
26.90 (10)	23.22 (9)	25.37 (8)	28.93 (6)	wollastonite
27.00 (10)	20.02 (5)	35.66 (5)	38.54 (1)	zircon
33.27 (10)	31.12 (7)	22.06 (5)	10.94 (4)	zoisite

Table 6.6 2θ values for XRD reflections in the range 2–40° 2θ for minerals found in sediment and sedimentary rock. 2θ values were calculated from *d* values given in the ASTM Powder Diffraction Data File using the wavelength of Cuk alpha radiation (λ = 1.5418).

Actinolite

2θ	d(Å)	I/I_1
9.72	9.060	40
10.51	8.420	70
17.32	5.120	30
18.18	4.880	50
19.64	4.520	50
22.98	3.870	50
26.37	3.380	70
27.27	3.270	60
28.70	3.110	80
30.40	2.940	60
33.05	2.710	100
34.63	2.590	50
35.48	2.530	60
38.64	2.330	40
39.71	2.270	20

Albite (high)[†]

2θ	d(Å)	I/I_1
13.75	6.440	20
22.06	4.030	80
22.92	3.880	20
23.73	3.750	60
24.52	3.630	30
26.44	3.370	20
27.79	3.210	100
28.06	3.180	90
28.52	3.130	30
30.31	2.949	20
30.52	2.929	20
31.56	2.835	20
35.66	2.518	20

Albite (low)[†]

2θ	d(Å)	I/I_1
13.86	6.440	10
22.06	4.030	90
23.10	3.850	20
23.53	3.780	40
24.18	3.680	20
24.25	3.670	20
24.32	3.660	40
25.37	3.510	20
26.45	3.370	20
27.79	3.210	70
27.96	3.190	100
28.14	3.170	40
28.33	3.150	40

Albite (low)[†]

2θ	d(Å)	I/I_1
30.14	2.965	30
30.23	2.956	20
30.53	2.928	20
32.25	2.862	20
35.02	2.562	20

Analcime*

2θ	d(Å)	I/I_1
15.83	5.600	60
18.29	4.850	20
24.25	3.670	10
26.98	3.430	100
30.54	2.927	50
31.93	2.803	10
33.27	2.693	20
35.83	2.506	10
37.04	2.427	10

Anatase

2θ	d(Å)	I/I_1
25.30	3.520	100
36.98	2.431	10
37.83	2.378	20
38.61	2.332	10

Andalusite

2θ	d(Å)	I/I_1
16.00	5.540	100
19.60	4.530	90
22.68	3.920	70
25.30	3.520	60
25.52	3.490	40
32.20	2.780	20
32.32	2.770	90
36.13	2.486	20
36.19	2.482	20
36.43	2.466	50
37.83	2.378	20
38.25	2.353	20
39.65	2.273	40
39.98	2.255	40

Anhydrite

2θ	d(Å)	I/I_1
22.98	3.870	10
25.45	3.498	100
28.36	3.118	<5

Anhydrite

2θ	d(Å)	I/I_1
31.40	2.849	30
32.00	2.797	<5
36.33	2.473	10
38.68	2.328	20

Apatite (carbonate)

2θ	d(Å)	I/I_1
21.57	4.120	40
24.09	3.694	10
26.19	3.402	70
28.44	3.138	10
32.34	2.768	100
33.34	2.687	70
34.40	2.607	70
35.85	2.505	10

Aragonite

2θ	d(Å)	I/I_1
26.24	3.396	100
27.25	3.273	60
31.16	2.870	10
32.78	2.732	10
33.18	2.700	50
36.16	2.484	30
36.21	2.481	10
37.31	2.410	20
37.93	2.372	40
38.45	2.341	20
38.66	2.329	20

Augite

2θ	d(Å)	I/I_1
26.94	3.310	50
27.36	3.260	50
27.88	3.200	60
29.88	2.990	100
30.40	2.940	80
31.27	2.860	60
32.32	2.770	50
35.05	2.560	90
35.77	2.510	90
38.13	2.360	30
39.34	2.290	50

Barite*

2θ	d(Å)	I/I_1
20.00	4.440	20
20.46	4.340	40

(continued)

Table 6.6 *continued*

Barite*

2θ	d(Å)	I/I_1
22.80	3.900	60
23.60	3.770	10
24.90	3.576	30
25.88	3.442	100
26.88	3.317	70
28.79	3.101	100
28.34	3.834	50
31.57	2.83	50
32.76	2.734	20
32.85	2.726	50
36.21	2.481	10
38.78	2.322	20
39.11	2.303	10

Biotite

2θ	d(Å)	I/I_1
8.75	10.10	100
19.34	4.590	20
26.45	3.370	100
28.24	3.160	20
30.62	2.920	20
33.69	2.660	80
35.63	2.520	40
36.68	2.450	80
39.52	2.280	20

Brookite

2θ	d(Å)	I/I_1
25.37	3.510	100
25.67	3.470	80
30.83	2.900	90
36.28	2.476	30
37.33	2.409	20
37.96	2.370	10
39.24	2.296	10

Calcite

2θ	d(Å)	I/I_1
23.09	3.852	30
29.48	3.030	100
31.57	2.834	<5
36.00	2.495	10
39.45	2.945	20

Carnallite

2θ	d(Å)	I/I_1
18.56	4.780	20
18.92	4.690	40

Carnallite

2θ	d(Å)	I/I_1
19.09	4.650	20
23.01	3.865	30
23.71	3.753	50
24.70	3.604	70
25.05	3.555	60
26.84	3.322	100
27.19	3.280	40
29.40	3.038	70
30.04	2.975	30
30.49	2.932	100
31.34	2.854	40
33.29	2.691	30
37.60	2.392	40
38.37	2.346	50
38.75	2.342	20

Cassiterite

2θ	d(Å)	I/I_1
26.61	3.350	100
33.90	2.644	80
37.98	2.369	30
39.01	2.309	10

Celestite

2θ	d(Å)	I/I_1
21.00	4.230	10
23.60	3.770	40
25.95	3.433	30
27.06	3.295	100
28.09	3.177	60
30.07	2.972	100
32.79	2.731	60
33.51	2.674	50
34.74	2.582	10
37.67	2.388	10
37.84	2.377	20

Chamosite

2θ	d(Å)	I/I_1
12.56	7.050	100
19.00	4.670	20
19.38	4.580	20
20.75	4.280	10
22.80	3.900	10
25.30	3.520	100
31.96	2.800	?
33.43	2.680	40
35.63	2.520	90
37.47	2.400	40

Chamosite

2θ	d(Å)	I/I_1
38.47	2.340	10
39.71	2.270	10

Chlorite

2θ	d(Å)	I/I_1
6.14	14.40	60
12.38	7.150	100
18.52	4.790	40
19.17	4.630	40
24.80	3.590	70
31.16	2.870	30
33.43	2.680	40
34.36	2.610	20
35.19	2.550	10
36.30	2.475	60
37.63	2.390	10
39.34	2.290	10

Chloritoid

2θ	d(Å)	I/I_1
18.68	4.750	10
19.13	4.640	10
19.73	4.500	100
19.95	4.450	100
23.35	3.810	30
24.66	3.610	10
27.44	3.250	60
30.09	2.970	80
30.62	2.920	20
32.32	2.770	40
33.18	2.700	70
33.69	2.660	30
35.77	2.510	10
36.53	2.460	90
37.47	2.400	50
37.96	2.370	30
38.81	2.320	10
39.17	2.300	50
39.89	2.260	30

Chromite

2θ	d(Å)	I/I_1
18.41	4.820	50
30.30	2.950	60
35.63	2.520	100
37.47	2.400	10

Clinoptilolite†

2θ	d(Å)	I/I_1
9.84	8.990	90
11.19	7.910	40
17.32	5.120	30
19.07	4.654	30
22.39	3.971	100
22.74	3.910	70
25.09	3.549	20
26.07	3.418	50
26.34	3.383	30
28.19	3.165	40
28.59	3.122	30
29.05	3.074	20
22.36	3.970	70
32.03	2.794	70
32.77	2.733	30

Clinozoisite†

2θ	d(Å)	I/I_1
11.07	7.990	30
17.70	5.010	40
22.25	3.996	30
25.62	3.477	30
28.04	3.182	20
29.45	3.033	40
31.00	2.885	100
32.09	2.789	40
33.58	2.669	30
34.04	2.634	20
34.67	2.587	30
36.85	2.439	20
37.52	2.387	20
37.77	2.382	30

Corundum

2θ	d(Å)	I/I_1
25.60	3.479	80
35.16	2.552	90
37.81	2.379	40
43.40	2.085	100

Diopside*

2θ	d(Å)	I/I_1
26.61	3.350	10
27.62	3.230	30
29.87	2.991	100
30.30	2.950	30
30.91	2.893	30
34.98	2.566	20
35.51	2.528	40
35.66	2.518	30
39.10	2.304	20

Dolomite

2θ	d(Å)	I/I_1
22.06	4.030	<5
24.12	3.690	10
30.99	2.886	100
33.56	2.670	10
35.34	2.540	10
37.39	2.405	10
41.18	2.192	30

Enstatite

2θ	d(Å)	I/I_1
20.13	4.410	10
26.99	3.303	40
28.28	3.167	100
29.39	2.941	40
31.14	2.872	90
31.67	2.825	20
33.10	2.706	30
35.42	2.534	40
36.01	2.494	50
36.36	2.471	30
38.17	2.358	10
39.52	2.280	10

Epidote*

2θ	d(Å)	I/I_1
11.09	7.980	10
17.67	5.018	40
22.24	3.997	40
25.51	3.492	40
26.43	3.372	10
27.91	3.197	20
30.83	2.900	100
31.86	2.809	50
33.47	2.677	60
34.59	2.593	60
35.55	2.525	10
36.70	2.449	10
37.54	2.396	70
39.36	2.289	30

Fluorapatite*

2θ	d(Å)	I/I_1
10.90	8.120	10
21.92	4.055	10
22.97	3.872	10
25.88	3.422	40
28.18	3.167	10
29.12	3.067	20
31.96	2.800	100
32.92	2.772	60
33.15	2.702	60

Fluorapatite*

2θ	d(Å)	I/I_1
34.17	2.624	30
35.67	2.517	10
39.36	2.289	10

Fluorite

2θ	d(Å)	I/I_1
28.30	3.153	90
47.06	1.931	100

Garnet (grossularite)

2θ	d(Å)	I/I_1
30.20	2.959	30
33.86	2.647	100
33.57	2.524	10
37.20	2.417	20
38.80	2.321	20

Garnet (iron, manganese)

2θ	d(Å)	I/I_1
30.62	2.920	90
34.22	2.620	100
37.63	2.390	90
39.17	2.300	60

Garnet (pyrope)

2θ	d(Å)	I/I_1
31.05	2.880	60
34.77	2.580	100
36.53	2.460	30
38.30	2.350	30
39.89	2.260	30

Glauberite

2θ	d(Å)	I/I_1
14.24	6.220	80
19.00	4.670	50
20.27	4.380	60
22.62	3.930	60
23.60	3.770	30
25.52	3.490	40
28.52	3.130	100
29.78	3.000	60
31.50	2.840	60
31.96	2.800	70
33.69	2.660	80
35.05	2.560	10
36.37	2.470	70
38.64	2.330	70

(continued)

Table 6.6 *continued*

Glauconite

2θ	d(Å)	I/I_1
8.75	10.10	100
17.81	4.980	?
19.60	4.530	80
20.42	4.350	20
21.57	4.120	10
24.52	3.630	40
26.77	3.330	60
28.89	3.090	40
30.94	2.890	10
33.56	2.670	10
34.67	2.587	100
37.54	2.396	60
39.83	2.263	20

Goethite

2θ	d(Å)	I/I_1
17.81	4.980	10
21.25	4.180	100
26.37	3.380	10
33.31	2.690	30
34.77	2.580	10
35.63	2.520	<5
36.07	4.900	20
36.65	2.452	30

Gypsum

2θ	d(Å)	I/I_1
11.71	7.560	100
20.80	4.270	50
23.47	3.790	20
28.30	3.153	<5
29.19	3.059	60
31.20	2.867	30
32.13	2.786	10
33.45	2.679	30
34.62	2.591	<5
36.00	2.495	10
36.68	2.450	<5
37.47	2.400	<5

Halite

2θ	d(Å)	I/I_1
27.37	3.258	10
31.72	2.821	100
45.49	1.994	60

Hematite

2θ	d(Å)	I/I_1
24.32	3.660	30
33.31	2.690	100
35.77	2.510	50
39.43	2.285	<5

Heulandite†

2θ	d(Å)	I/I_1
9.99	8.850	80
11.34	7.800	70
13.35	6.630	60
16.79	5.280	50
17.39	5.100	70
19.09	4.650	60
22.68	3.920	100
26.05	3.420	70
27.97	3.190	50
28.52	3.130	40
30.20	2.959	90
31.90	2.805	70
32.40	2.730	40
36.99	2.430	30

Hornblende*

2θ	d(Å)	I/I_1
9.87	8.960	10
10.53	8.400	100
19.73	4.500	10
27.36	3.260	20
28.80	3.100	70
30.41	2.939	10
32.09	2.789	10
33.34	2.697	20
34.67	2.587	10
35.38	2.537	10
38.73	2.325	10

Hypersthene

2θ	d(Å)	I/I_1
26.53	3.360	30
27.88	3.200	100
2.980	2.980	20
30.94	2.890	80
32.80	2.730	30
35.19	2.550	50
36.22	2.480	50

Ilmenite

2θ	d(Å)	I/I_1
23.86	3.730	50
32.68	2.740	100
35.34	2.540	90
40.45	2.230	70

Kyanite*

2θ	d(Å)	I/I_1
19.77	4.490	10
20.51	4.330	10
23.60	3.770	10
26.62	3.350	10
28.06	3.180	100
33.18	2.700	10
35.63	2.520	40
38.30	2.350	40

Laumontite†

2θ	d(Å)	I/I_1
9.31	9.500	60
12.94	6.480	40
19.77	4.490	30
21.36	4.160	100
21.32	3.660	40
25.37	3.510	80
26.53	3.360	30
27.27	3.270	60
27.88	3.200	30
29.48	3.030	30
31.05	2.880	30
31.99	2.798	30
34.78	2.579	30
36.82	2.441	30

Magnesite

2θ	d(Å)	I/I_1
32.66	2.742	100
35.88	2.503	20
38.85	2.318	<5
43.03	2.102	20

Magnetite

2θ	d(Å)	I/I_1
18.29	4.850	40
30.13	2.966	70
35.48	2.530	100
37.17	2.419	10

Marcasite

2θ	d(Å)	I/I_1
25.79	3.431	70
31.18	2.868	<5
33.09	2.707	30
33.32	2.689	100
37.34	2.408	40
38.97	2.311	30

Microcline†

2θ	d(Å)	I/I_1
13.71	6.460	20
21.10	4.210	60
22.34	3.980	30
23.22	3.830	50
23.99	3.710	40
24.94	3.570	20
25.60	3.480	50
26.48	3.366	50
27.10	3.290	40
27.49	3.244	100
29.53	3.025	40
30.15	2.964	50
30.81	2.902	50
32.45	2.759	20
34.22	2.620	30
34.88	2.572	20
35.47	2.531	30

Mirabilite*

2θ	d(Å)	I/I_1
16.14	5.490	100
16.66	5.320	30
18.18	4.880	20
18.60	4.770	50
20.56	4.320	20
22.51	3.950	20
23.22	3.830	40
27.36	3.260	60
27.79	3.210	80
28.70	3.110	60
31.40	2.847	20
31.95	2.801	30
35.68	2.516	40
36.15	2.485	20
36.77	2.444	30

Muscovite

2θ	d(Å)	I/I_1
8.89	9.950	100
17.85	4.970	30
19.86	4.470	20
20.66	4.300	<5
21.62	4.110	<5
22.51	3.950	10
22.91	3.882	10
23.85	3.731	20
25.53	3.489	20
26.67	3.342	20
26.85	3.320	100
27.89	3.199	30
29.91	2.987	30
31.29	2.859	20
32.09	2.789	20
34.55	2.596	20
34.97	2.566	50
37.80	2.384	30

Oligoclase

2θ	d(Å)	I/I_1
13.77	6.430	50
18.92	4.690	60
22.11	4.020	80
22.52	3.880	50
23.79	3.740	80
24.18	3.680	30
24.52	3.630	70
25.75	3.460	40
26.13	3.410	30
26.53	3.360	60
27.36	3.260	30
27.88	3.200	100
28.15	3.170	80
28.61	3.120	70
29.68	3.010	60
30.40	2.940	70
30.72	2.910	60
33.82	2.650	50
35.63	2.520	70

Orthoclase

2θ	d(Å)	I/I_1
13.75	6.440	60
15.12	5.860	20
20.90	4.250	30
22.11	4.020	90
23.41	3.800	80
25.52	3.490	20
26.77	3.330	70
28.06	3.180	100
29.78	3.000	70
30.51	2.930	70
31.61	2.830	60
33.82	2.650	60
35.48	2.530	70
36.37	2.470	60
37.63	2.390	60
39.34	2.290	70

Philippsite†

2θ	d(Å)	I/I_1
12.33	7.180	100
12.36	7.160	100
13.77	6.430	60
16.48	5.380	60
17.49	5.070	60
17.96	4.940	70
20.66	4.300	60
21.57	4.120	80
21.84	4.070	60
27.19	3.280	80
27.79	3.210	100
28.52	3.130	100
30.51	2.930	70
32.51	2.754	80
33.01	2.706	100
33.18	2.700	100
33.27	2.693	80
33.33	2.688	80

Pyrite

2θ	d(Å)	I/I_1
28.54	3.128	40
33.07	2.709	100
37.10	2.423	60
40.79	2.212	40

Quartz (alpha)

2θ	d(Å)	I/I_1
20.85	4.260	40
26.66	3.343	100
36.56	2.458	10
39.49	2.282	10

Rutile

2θ	d(Å)	I/I_1
27.49	3.245	100
36.09	2.489	40
39.22	2.297	10
41.26	2.188	20

Sanidine

2θ	d(Å)	I/I_1
13.31	6.650	10
13.60	6.510	10

(continued)

Table 6.6 *continued*

Sanidine

2θ	d(Å)	I/I_1
15.10	5.869	10
20.95	4.241	50
22.53	3.947	20
23.48	3.789	80
24.57	3.623	20
25.03	3.557	10
25.76	3.459	50
26.79	3.328	100
27.13	3.287	60
27.37	3.258	40
27.68	3.223	80
29.83	2.995	50
30.78	2.905	20
32.37	2.766	20
34.39	2.608	10
34.74	2.582	30

Siderite

2θ	d(Å)	I/I_1
24.80	3.590	60
32.08	2.790	100
35.05	2.560	10
38.30	2.350	50

Sillimanite

2θ	d(Å)	I/I_1
16.57	5.350	70
19.47	4.560	30
23.86	3.730	50
26.13	3.410	90
26.53	3.360	100
27.97	3.190	10
30.51	2.930	10
31.05	2.880	70
33.56	2.670	80
35.48	2.530	90
37.15	2.420	60
37.97	2.370	10
39.17	2.300	30
39.52	2.280	60

Sphene

2θ	d(Å)	I/I_1
17.99	4.930	30
27.59	3.233	100
29.89	2.989	90
31.49	2.841	10
34.56	2.595	90

Sphene

2θ	d(Å)	I/I_1
38.10	2.362	10
39.65	2.273	30

Spinel

2θ	d(Å)	I/I_1
19.00	4.670	<5
31.30	2.858	40
36.90	2.436	100
38.59	2.333	<5

Staurolite

2θ	d(Å)	I/I_1
19.65	8.310	10
12.44	7.116	30
21.40	4.152	40
25.02	3.559	60
29.17	3.061	30
29.66	3.012	100
31.27	2.860	30
31.60	2.831	50
32.31	2.771	50
33.27	2.693	100
35.16	2.552	30
37.47	2.400	60
37.93	2.372	80
38.18	2.357	40
39.78	2.266	20

Strontianite

2θ	d(Å)	I/I_1
20.33	4.367	10
21.12	4.207	10
25.19	3.535	100
25.82	3.450	70
29.64	3.014	20
31.29	2.859	10
31.52	2.838	20
34.55	2.596	10
35.14	2.554	20
37.18	2.481	30
36.56	2.458	40
36.66	2.451	30
39.80	2.265	10

Sylvite

2θ	d(Å)	I/I_1
28.37	3.146	100
40.56	2.224	60

Tourmaline*

2θ	d(Å)	I/I_1
13.88	6.380	30
17.81	4.980	30
19.30	4.600	20
21.05	4.220	70
22.28	3.990	90
26.60	3.480	60
26.37	3.380	20
28.70	3.110	10
29.68	3.010	10
30.18	2.961	90
30.86	2.897	10
34.20	2.622	10
34.83	2.576	100
37.54	2.396	20
37.86	2.376	20
38.44	2.342	20
39.17	2.300	10

Tremolite†

2θ	d(Å)	I/I_1
9.85	8.980	20
10.56	8.380	100
17.49	5.070	20
18.64	4.760	20
19.68	4.510	20
21.15	4.200	40
22.98	3.870	20
26.40	3.376	40
27.29	3.268	80
28.60	3.121	100
30.42	2.938	40
31.90	2.805	50
32.80	2.730	20
33.12	2.705	90
34.60	2.592	30
35.50	2.529	40
37.80	2.380	30
38.56	2.335	30
38.80	2.321	40

Trona

2θ	d(Å)	I/I_1
8.95	9.880	60
10.03	4.920	40
21.57	4.120	10
22.22	4.000	20
25.98	3.430	20
27.79	3.210	60

Trona

2θ	d(Å)	I/I_1
28.99	3.080	80
32.00	2.790	10
32.44	2.760	30
33.71	2.659	100
34.67	2.587	20
35.77	2.510	30
36.15	2.485	10
36.73	2.447	60
37.06	2.426	20
39.91	2.259	40

Vivianite†

2θ	d(Å)	I/I_1
11.06	8.000	30
13.02	6.800	100
18.07	4.910	40
23.16	3.840	40
27.88	3.200	50
30.08	2.970	70
33.05	2.710	70
35.63	2.520	30
37.05	2.420	40
38.99	2.310	30

Wolframite

2θ	d(Å)	I/I_1
15.60	5.680	10
18.64	4.760	50

Wolframite

2θ	d(Å)	I/I_1
23.79	3.740	50
24.40	3.648	50
30.27	2.953	100
31.41	2.848	20
36.18	2.483	60
37.72	2.385	20

Wollastonite

2θ	d(Å)	I/I_1
11.54	7.670	30
16.26	5.540	10
23.22	3.830	90
25.37	3.510	80
26.90	3.314	100
27.51	3.242	10
28.93	3.086	60
30.02	2.977	30
31.96	2.800	10
32.92	2.721	30
35.11	2.556	50
36.27	2.477	30
39.13	2.302	30

Zircon

2θ	d(Å)	I/I_1
20.02	4.434	50

Zircon

2θ	d(Å)	I/I_1
27.00	3.302	100
33.82	2.650	10
35.66	2.518	50
38.54	2.336	10

Zoisite†

2θ	d(Å)	I/I_1
10.94	8.090	40
17.70	5.010	30
19.00	4.670	20
22.06	4.030	50
24.41	3.646	20
24.67	3.609	20
27.28	3.269	20
28.34	3.149	20
28.69	3.111	20
28.76	3.104	30
29.12	3.068	30
31.12	2.874	70
32.07	2.790	30
33.27	2.693	100
33.97	2.639	30
36.12	2.487	20
37.31	2.410	20
38.52	2.337	20

* Most of all the reflections with relative intensity less than 10 have been deleted.
† Most of all the reflections with relative intensity less than 20 have been deleted.

7 Grain size

Grain size is studied for a variety of reasons. First it is a fundamental descriptive measure of sediment and sedimentary rock. It is also important in understanding the mechanisms operative during transportation and deposition, as well as the distance of sediment transport. Grain size is commonly related to other properties (e.g. permeability) which have major economic implications. These reasons have made and continue to make size analysis an important aspect of sedimentologic research.

7.1 Grain-size classification

7.1.1 Size grades

Sediment particle size is measured in metric units. Size grades (**grade** = sizes intermediate between two defined points on a size scale) are based on a geometric scale in which class limits increase from a base of 1 mm by a factor of 2 or decrease by a factor of 0.5. The size grades most commonly used by geologists were devised by J. A. Udden and modified by C. K. Wentworth (1922). It is commonly known as the Udden–Wentworth Grade Scale (Table 7.1).

7.1.2 ϕ notation

Krumbein (1934) proposed that grain size should be expressed as **phi** (ϕ), which is the negative logarithm to the base 2 of the particle diameter in millimeters. Thus ϕ is a dimensionless quantity and Udden–Wentworth size grades are separated by ϕ values which are whole numbers (Table 7.1). Conversion between ϕ units and metric units can be done graphically (Table 7.1).

Phi notion simplified calculations used to derive grain-size parameters (e.g. mean size and standard deviation) and gained some popularity among sedimentologists for nearly five decades. The current availability of electronic calculators and computers has largely negated this advantage. In addition, calculation of grain-size parameters using graphical methods, which require the ϕ notation, is inferior to the method of moments where the ϕ notation is unnecessary (see Section 7.5.3a).

Table 7.1 Udden–Wentworth size classes. Nomogram used to convert millimeters to φ or φ to millimeters shown to left. (Modified from Folk 1980: 23.)

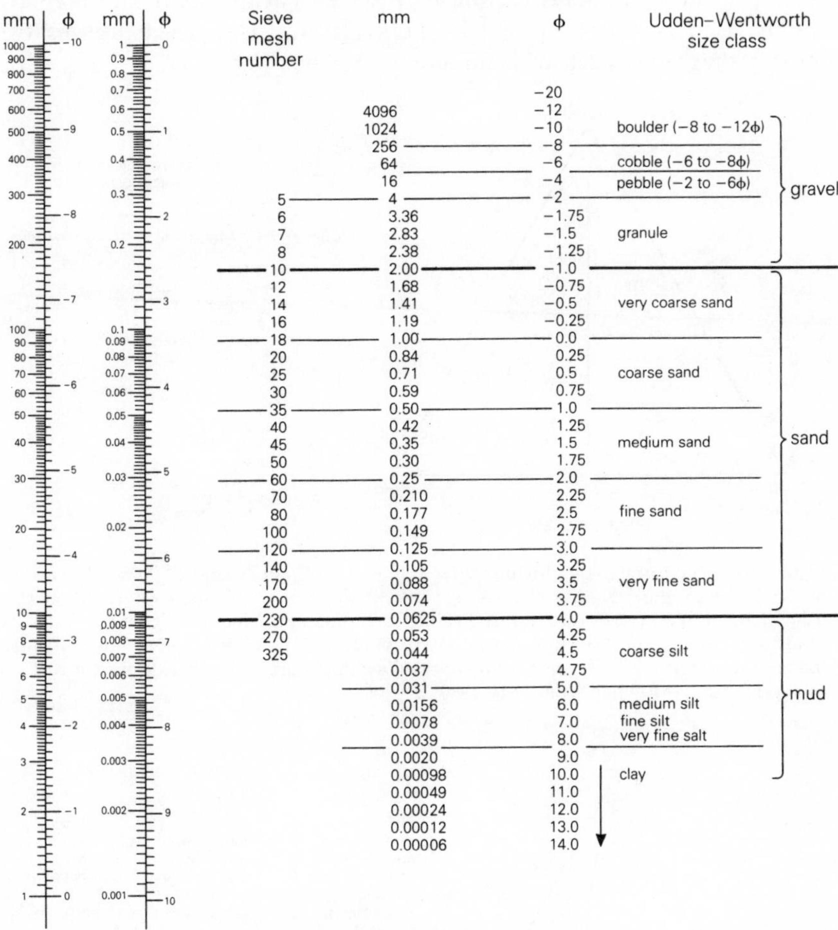

Sieve mesh number	mm	φ	Udden–Wentworth size class	
		−20		
	4096	−12		
	1024	−10	boulder (−8 to −12φ)	
	256	−8		
	64	−6	cobble (−6 to −8φ)	
	16	−4	pebble (−2 to −6φ)	gravel
5	4	−2		
6	3.36	−1.75		
7	2.83	−1.5	granule	
8	2.38	−1.25		
10	2.00	−1.0		
12	1.68	−0.75		
14	1.41	−0.5	very coarse sand	
16	1.19	−0.25		
18	1.00	0.0		
20	0.84	0.25		
25	0.71	0.5	coarse sand	
30	0.59	0.75		
35	0.50	1.0		
40	0.42	1.25		
45	0.35	1.5	medium sand	sand
50	0.30	1.75		
60	0.25	2.0		
70	0.210	2.25		
80	0.177	2.5	fine sand	
100	0.149	2.75		
120	0.125	3.0		
140	0.105	3.25		
170	0.088	3.5	very fine sand	
200	0.074	3.75		
230	0.0625	4.0		
270	0.053	4.25		
325	0.044	4.5	coarse silt	
	0.037	4.75		
	0.031	5.0		
	0.0156	6.0	medium silt	mud
	0.0078	7.0	fine silt	
	0.0039	8.0	very fine salt	
	0.0020	9.0		
	0.00098	10.0	clay	
	0.00049	11.0		
	0.00024	12.0		
	0.00012	13.0		
	0.00006	14.0		

Finally, the φ scale which is familiar to sedimentologists "is often meaningless to most biologists, archaeologists and engineers who report grain sizes in metric units, as measured" (Pierce & Graus, 1981: 1349). This is equally true for many geologists. These are all good reasons to suggest that grain-size data be reported in metric units and that *the φ notation be abandoned*. Unfortunately this will not happen until a comprehensive and geologically significant system of nomenclature for size parameters, based on metric units, is established.

7.1.3 *Nomenclature*

Although there are many classification systems available, one of the most widely used is that proposed by Folk (1954, 1980) which utilizes two ternary diagrams, each with three end-member classes (Figs 7.1 & 7.2).

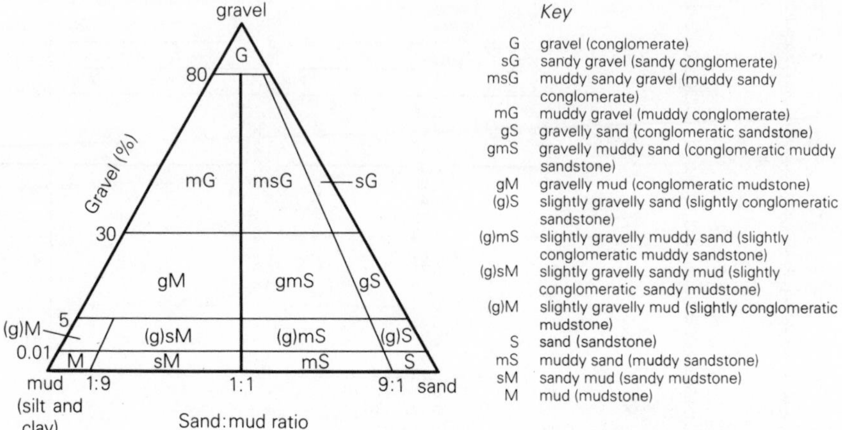

Figure 7.1 The terminology for mixtures of gravel (> 2 mm), sand (0.0625–2.0 mm) and mud (< 0.0625 mm). Specify the average size of the gravel and sand where practicable, using Udden–Wentworth size terms (Table 7.1). Examples include "granular very fine sandstone" for gS and "slightly pebbly coarse sandy claystone" for (g)sM. For gravel-free material use Figure 7.2. Terms for unindurated sediment are given first; terms for rock are in parentheses. (Modified from Folk 1980: 26–7.)

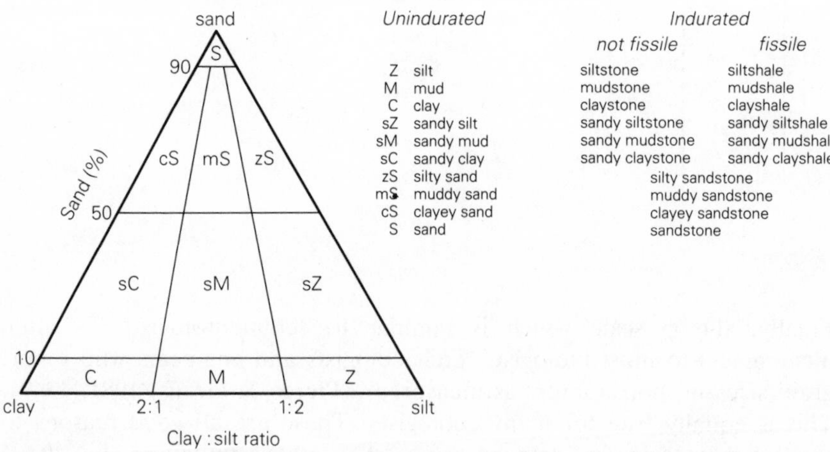

Figure 7.2 The terminology for mixtures of sand and mud. Specify the average size of the sand where practicable, using Udden–Wentworth size terms (Table 7.1). Examples include "medium sandy siltstone" for sZ and "clayey fine sand" for cS. Fissile rock names are given without hyphen as done by Potter *et al.* (1980: 14). (Modified from Folk 1980: 26–7.)

When naming a specimen, first determine the gravel content. Even a "trace" (0.01%) of gravel is reflected by using "slightly gravelly" as part of the name (Fig. 7.1). Next determine the proportion of sand to mud, using the ratios 9 : 1, 1 : 1, and 1 : 9 to establish the appropriate grain-size name.

If possible, indicate the average size of each fraction considered independently of any other fraction that may be present by using the appropriate Udden–Wentworth size terms (Table 7.1). For example, a rock containing 88% sand which ranges in size between 0.25 and 0.5 mm and 12% gravel which ranges in size between 1 and 2 cm would be called a "cobbly medium sandstone".

If mud is abundant, try to determine the proportion of silt and clay, using silt-to-clay ratios of 2 : 1 and 1 : 2 (Fig. 7.2) to establish the textural name. For indurated material the name is further modified by indicating whether or not the rock is fissile (characterized by a closely spaced parting parallel to the bedding). When practical, include the Udden–Wentworth size term that best describes the sand and gravel that may be present. Examples include "pebbly siltshale" and "slightly bouldery coarse sandy claystone." **Mudrock** is used for fine-grained rock whose silt–clay content is unknown, and **shale** is used for fissile mudrock whose silt–clay content is unknown.

7.2 Grain-size analysis of unconsolidated sediment

The procedures for analyzing sand, mud (silt and clay), and gravel are all different and are briefly described below. Some samples (e.g. one composed of clay and sand) may require that several methods be used.

7.2.1 Sand

Sieving is commonly used in determining the grain-size distribution of sand. A dry sample is placed in the uppermost sieve in a set of stacked sieves (Fig. 7.3). The stack of sieves, arranged in order so that the coarsest sieve is at the top with finer ones below (with a pan at the bottom to catch any sediment that passes through the lowest and finest sieve), is placed on a shaking machine. After ten minutes of shaking, the sand that has collected on each sieve and the pan is removed and weighed.

At this point one should ask "What do these numbers mean?" Referring to the example shown in Figure 7.3, we might say that 12.59 g, or 28.45% (wt.%), of the total sample is composed of grains with a diameter between 0.25 and 0.5 mm. Unfortunately this is not an accurate statement because sand grains are not spheres and a "true" diameter does

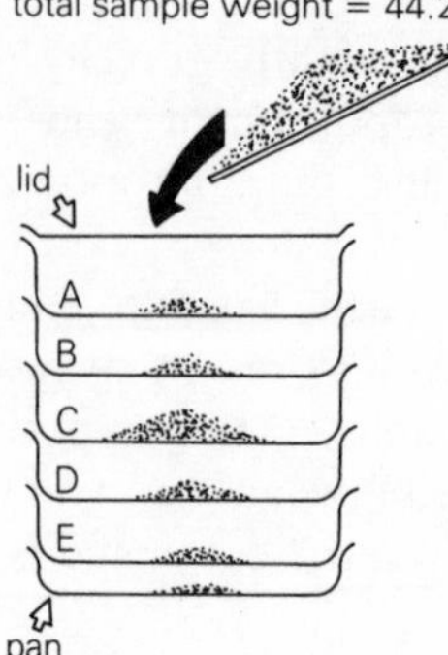

Sieve	Screen size (mm)	Weight of sieve (g)
A	1.0	5.31
B	0.5	8.70
C	0.25	12.59
D	0.125	9.13
E	0.0625	6.03
pan	<0.0625	2.49

Figure 7.3 An example of data collected by sieving.

not exist. The property measured is really the smallest cross-section of a grain, which is a function of shape as well as of the absolute dimensions. Thus rod-shaped grains of a certain mass may pass through a sieve which retains equant grains of the same mass.

A more serious problem with sieve analysis involves technique and how it affects the segregation of grains into discrete size groups. If we analyzed ten subsamples of the sand illustrated in Figure 7.3, would we always end up with 28.45% of the subsample on the 0.25 mm sieve? Unless our procedure was exactly the same for all ten analyses, we probably would not. Indeed the results might be very different. Some of the contributing factors include:

(a) The sample size. Too large a sample will inhibit the passage of grains through the sieves, and too small a sample will affect the precision of weight measurements (unless a chemical balance is used). Folk (1980) suggests that the sample should weigh between 30 and 70 g.
(b) The sieving time. Ten minutes is generally considered optimum; less time may result in incomplete sieving.
(c) The condition of the wire mesh in each sieve. If the mesh is damaged or severely clogged, accurate results are impossible.
(d) The size interval between sieves in each stack. If too few sieves are used, too much sand may accumulate on sieves near the modal size.
(e) The number of grain aggregates present. Ideally there should be none.
(f) The amount of clay in the sample. Too much clay will tend to clog the sieves.
(g) Failure to use a sample splitter when obtaining the subsample to be sieved.

(h) The care taken when removing the sample from the sieve prior to weighing.
(i) The care taken in weighing the sample.

Settling tubes or **sedimentation tubes** provide an increasingly popular alternative to sieving as a means of determining grain-size distribution of sand (Zeigler *et al.* 1960, Gibbs 1974, Taira & Scholle 1977). They utilize the fact that larger particles fall through water faster than smaller particles. The rate at which sediment passes through the column of water in the tube and collects at the lower end is measured and used to calculate the relative abundance of the various size fractions. Although settling tubes generate relatively precise data in a short period of time, they have some drawbacks. The most serious problem involves smaller grains being dragged down by larger ones or, in some cases, settling being inhibited by too high a sediment concentration.

Automated measurement of the nominal section grain diameters using a microprocessor-controlled image analysis system has several advantages over the other methods. This technique (1) allows rapid analysis, (2) utilizes small samples, (3) uses the same technique for all grains regardless of size, and (4) eliminates error introduced by material wear or personal choice of axes to be measured (Mazzullo & Kennedy 1985).

7.2.2 Silt and clay

Sedimentation methods based on particle settling velocity are generally used to analyze sediment composed of silt and/or clay. The size parameter measured, called the **equivalent diameter** (the diameter of a quartz sphere having the same settling velocity as the particle), is related to settling velocity by **Stoke's law**, generally written as

$$w = \frac{(\varrho_s - \varrho)g}{18\mu} d^2$$

where w = settling velocity, ϱ_s = density of the particle, ϱ = density of the water, g = acceleration due to gravity, μ = dynamic viscosity of the water, and d = equivalent diameter of the particle.

The **pipette method** is generally used by sedimentologists. First, any sediment coarser than 62 μm is removed by sieving (wet sieving for clay-rich material). The sample (5–15 g) is then added to distilled water to produce a 1 l dilute suspension of uniform concentration. A specified volume of the suspension (20 ml) is then withdrawn from prescribed depths (generally 5, 10, or 20 cm) on a time schedule determined by calculations based on Stoke's law. At these times all particles of a given size will have settled below that depth, and only finer particles remain in

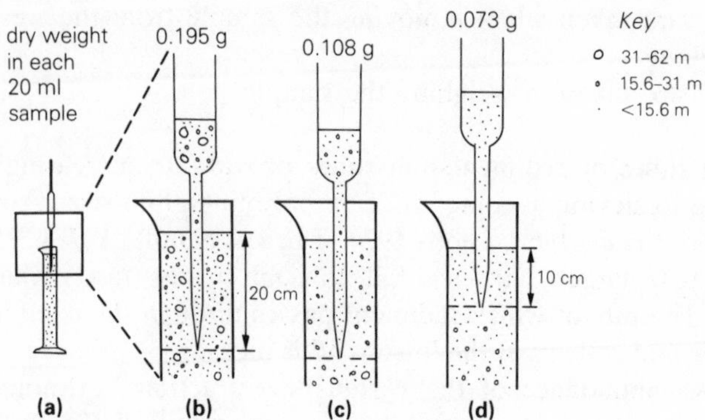

Figure 7.4 The pipette method for studying silt and clay.
(a) General setup with pipette and 1 l graduated cylinder.
(b) After 20 s a 20 ml sample is withdrawn from a depth of 20 cm. Because no appreciable settling has occurred in this sample, all grain sizes are present in the proportions found in the original sample. This sample is one-fiftieth of the total volume of the suspension. If the dry weight of the suspended sediment is 0.195 g, the total weight of the original sample is 0.195 × 50 = 9.75 g.
(c) After 1 m 45 s a 20 ml sample is withdrawn from a depth of 20 cm. By this time all the particles coarser than 31 μm have settled below the depth of 20 cm. If the dry weight of this sample is 0.108 g, the weight of the whole sample finer than 31 μm is 0.108 g × 50 = 5.40 g. The total weight of particles in the range 31–62 μm is 9.75 g (from (b) above) − 5.40 g = 4.35 g. This is 45% of the total sample (4.35/9.75).
(d) After 6 m 58 s a 20 ml sample is withdrawn from a depth of 10 cm. If the dry weight of this sample is 0.073 g, the weight of that part of the sample finer than 15.6 μm is 0.073 g × 50 = 3.64 g. The total weight of particles in the range 15.6–31 μm is 5.40 g (from (c) above) − 3.64 g = 1.76 g. This is 18% of the total sample (1.76/9.75).

Note. This example is based on data in Folk (1980: 37). The withdrawal times were calculated using Stoke's law (for water at 20°C and solids with a density of 2.65) in the form

$$T = D/1500 \times A \times d^2$$

where T = time in minutes, D = depth in cm, and d = particle diameter in mm). A is a constant which depends upon the viscosity of the water (a function of the temperature), the force of gravity, and the density of the particle.

the sample that is withdrawn. The dry weight of these samples is used to calculate the grain-size distribution of the original sample (Fig. 7.4). This method is useful mainly in the range 0.2–62 μm.

Another sedimentation method utilizes the hydrometer which measures density changes in the suspension as settling occurs. These changes are used to calculate the grain-size distribution. Various electronic devices are also used. They include the Coulter Counter (Tickell 1965: 23), which measures particle volume, and others which measure the density of the suspension.

7.2.3 Gravel

Size analysis of gravel requires a much larger sample than that for sand or finer-grained sediment. Generally, 0.5 to several kilograms is necessary to obtain enough material to *fully evaluate the size distribution*. First remove any sand by hand sieving with a 2 mm screen, and weigh both fractions. Hand sieve the entire gravel fraction with the coarsest sieves available. For larger pebbles (generally > 4 mm) you will have to construct your own "sieves" using wire to make squares of appropriate size. Alternatively, you may use holes cut in metal or plastic plates (Briggs 1977: 64, Billi 1984). Pass the pebbles through edgewise and weigh all those that will not fit through a particular size opening. The particle size is expressed as the midpoint value between the hole through which the particle will not pass and the next larger one.

For regional studies involving particle-size variation of gravel, you may want to report the **mean of the ten largest pebbles**. This can be done by picking through a sample of uniform size (e.g. 1 kg, one full bucket, etc.) and selecting by inspection the 20 or 30 largest pebbles. Then measure the long axis of each and use the ten largest values to calculate the mean. Unless rushed for time you may want to do this in the field. Some workers report only the single largest clast from each sample locality.

7.3 Grain-size analysis of sedimentary rock

7.3.1 Sandstone

In the field the average grain size of sandstone is estimated by using a hand lens (or binocular microscope in the laboratory) and a comparator chart which contains grain images of specified sizes (Fig. 7.5). In cases where grain boundaries are obscure, because of ferruginous cement or a dark clay-rich matrix, grain size can be determined petrographically. This method is time consuming, if one measures 200 to 500 grains as advocated by most devotees, and is fraught with serious problems. In thin section one is rarely able to measure the short and intermediate grain axes (the average of these is more or less what is measured by sieving) because of the random two-dimensional nature of the rock slice under study; instead one generally measures the apparent long axes of the grains. For this reason sieve data and petrographic data *cannot be directly compared*. A number of workers have tried to establish conversion factors to facilitate such comparison (e.g. Friedman 1958, Harrell & Eriksson 1979), but these factors have generally been based on quartz-rich, matrix-free sandstones. It seems clear that statistical parameters, based on the higher

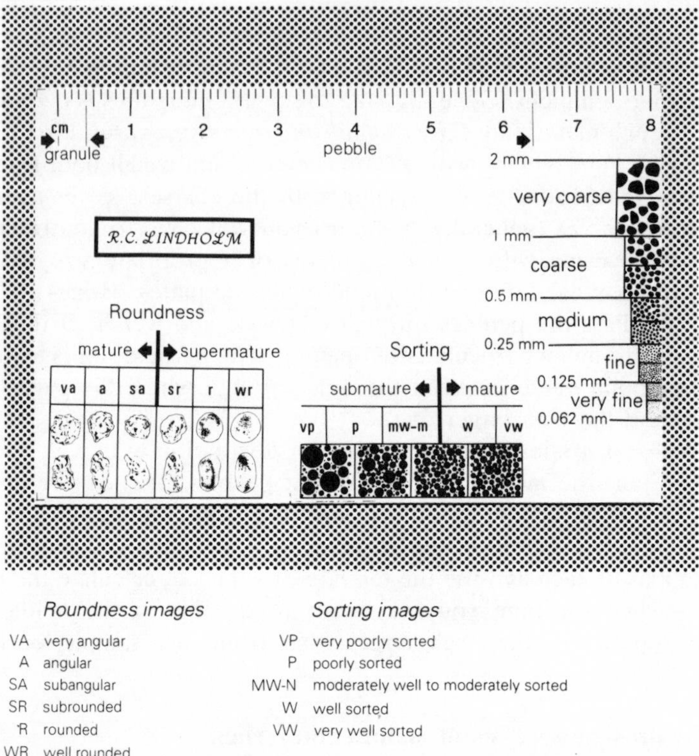

Figure 7.5 Grain images for estimating grain size, roundness and sorting. Roundness images modified from Powers (1953). Boundary between mature and supermature is 3ρ. Sorting images from Harrell (1985). Boundary between submature and mature is standard deviation of 0.5ϕ. Another copy of this chart is given at the back of the book. It is meant to be cut out and used in the field. To preserve the chart I recommend that you cover both sides with clear plastic laminate.

moment measures, i.e. skewness and kurtosis (see Section 7.6.3f) derived from petrographic study of grain size in sandstone, are of little value.

7.3.2 Shale and other silt and clay-rich rocks

The study of shale and related rocks is made difficult by the fine grain size. Where silt is the dominant component ($>\frac{2}{3}$ silt), it is visible with a hand lens. The various silt grades can be estimated with some degree of accuracy by using a binocular microscope (Fig. 7.6). If silt and clay are present in subequal proportions ($>\frac{1}{3}$, $<\frac{2}{3}$ silt) the rock feels gritty when chewed, even though the silt is not obvious to the eye. In mudrocks

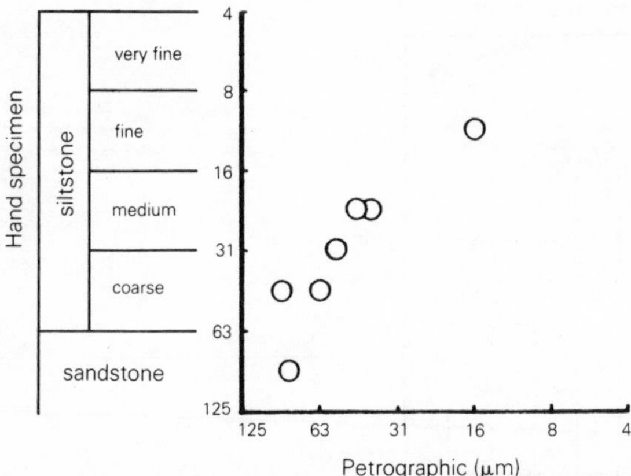

Figure 7.6 A scattergram of mean grain size of siltstone determined by two methods. Mean grain size estimated in hand specimen using a binocular microscope. Petrographic analysis based on point count of 200 grains per sample. Seven samples of fine-grained Triassic red beds from the Culpeper Basin, Virginia.

where clay is dominant (>$\frac{2}{3}$ clay) the rock feels smooth when chewed (Blatt *et al.* 1980: Table 11.1, 382).

7.3.3 Conglomerate

When studying conglomerates several strategies may be used. For regional analysis the ten largest clasts are determined by inspection of the outcrop: the long axis of each clast is measured and the mean size is calculated. Some workers prefer to measure only the largest clast. In cases where grain-size variation in a thick conglomeratic unit (e.g. a debris flow deposit) or a sequence of units is being studied, a different method may be used. It involves measuring all clasts larger than some operational number (e.g. 16 mm), which cross a transect (e.g. a chalk line drawn on the outcrop or a tape laid on the outcrop) of unit length. The length (0.5–5 m) depends on the clast size, and the desired spacing of the transects.

7.4 Graphic presentation of data

7.4.1 Histogram

The histogram is widely used to present grain-size data. It is simply a bar graph in which the weight percent of sediment in each size class is plotted

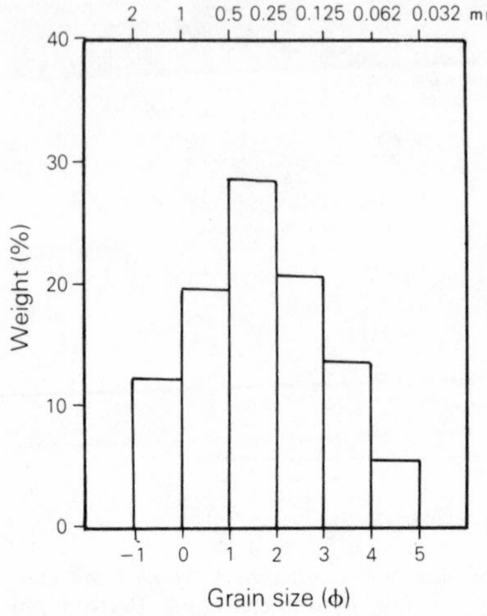

Class (mm)	Class (ϕ)	Weight (g)	Weight (%)
1–2	−1–0	5.31	12.1
0.5–1	0–1	8.70	19.6
0.25–0.5	1–2	12.59	28.5
0.125–0.25	2–3	9.13	20.6
0.0625–0.125	3–4	6.03	13.6
0.0312–0.0625	4–5	2.49	5.6

Figure 7.7 A histogram based on data from Fig. 7.3.

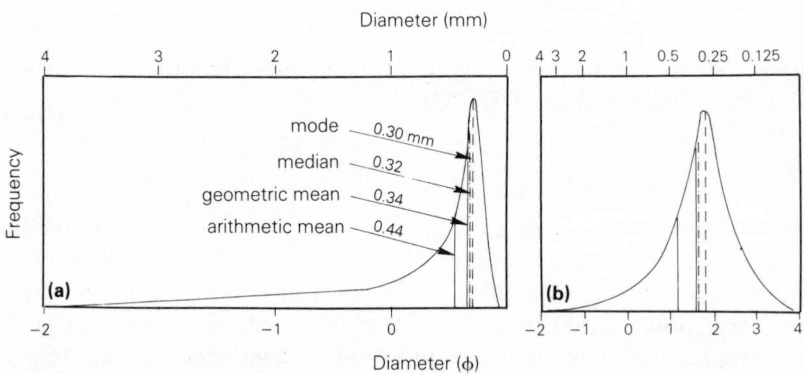

Figure 7.8 Frequency curves showing various statistical measures of average size. (a) and (b) are for the same frequency distribution. (a) Equally spaced subdivisions on abscissa are in metric units; (b) equally spaced subdivisions on abscissa are in ϕ units. Note that statistical parameters for average grain size are not equal to one another, with the arithmetic mean shifted farthest to the left (toward the coarse end of the size scale). (Modified from Krumbein & Pettijohn 1938: Figs 113 & 114.)

as a rectangle. By convention, grain size is plotted on the horizontal axis (abscissa) and the frequency (wt.%) on the vertical axis (ordinate) (Fig. 7.7). Another convention is to plot the grain size so that the *diameter value increases to the left*. Histograms are commonly constructed so that rectangles are of equal width and the class limits are given in ϕ (logarithmic) units. On such a histogram, metric units can be used even though the size classes represented are not equal in absolute terms.

Histograms of most sediment (unimodal) show a prominent size class, called the **modal class**. Less commonly there is a secondary mode (bimodal sediment), or in some cases several secondary modes (polymodal sediment).

7.4.2 Frequency curve

Frequency curves are smooth curves which show the variation of weight percentage as a continuous function of grain size (Fig. 7.8). They represent the limit of a histogram as the class interval decreases to zero, which is in essence a smoothed histogram. Although they give a truer picture of the size distribution, being independent of the class interval, they are difficult to construct (see Krumbein & Pettijohn, 1938: 190–5). Note that simply superimposing a smooth curve over an ordinary histogram will not produce a true frequency curve because of the relatively large size classes involved.

7.4.3 Cumulative curve

Grain size is plotted on the horizontal axis (abscissa) as described above (Section 7.4.1). Cumulative weight percent is plotted on the vertical axis (ordinate) with a scale running from 0 to 100%. The curve may be drawn using an arithmetic ordinate scale or a probability ordinate scale in which the middle portion is condensed. When plotting data, begin with the coarsest material. In the example shown in Figure 7.9, 12.1% (by weight) of the sample was caught on the 1 mm ($\phi = 0$) screen. Thus 12.1% is "coarser than" 1 mm ($\phi = 0$) and 12.1 (%) is plotted on the ordinate against 1 (mm) on the abscissa. After all the values have been plotted a curve is drawn *through all of the points.*

An S-shaped curve is produced when an arithmetic ordinate scale is used (Fig. 7.9a). Sediment with a "normal distribution" plots as a straight line when a probability ordinate scale is used to construct the cumulative curve. Cumulative curves (plotted on probability paper) commonly do not plot as straight lines. Such curves are thought by some to represent sediment composed of several distinct subpopulations, each of which has a lognormal distribution and is related to differing modes of transport (Visher 1969).

Note. Always use graph paper with a probability ordinate when measuring percentile values to be used in calculating graphical statistical parameters.

Class (ϕ)	*Weight (g)*	*Weight (%)*	*Cumulative weight (%)*
−1–0	5.31	12.1	12.1
0–1	8.70	19.6	31.6
1–2	12.59	28.5	60.1
2–3	9.13	20.6	80.7
3–4	6.03	13.6	94.3
4–5	2.49	5.6	99.9

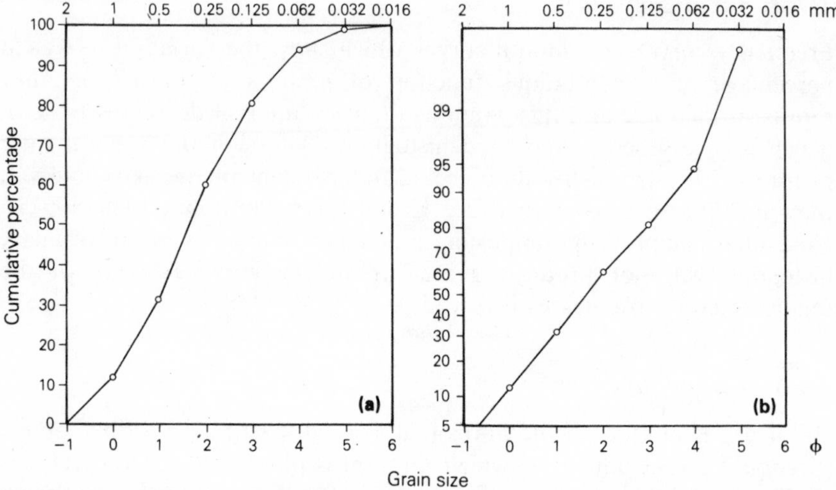

Figure 7.9 Cumulative curves: (a) arithmetic ordinate scale; (b) probability ordinate scale. (Based on data from Fig. 7.3.)

7.5 Statistical parameters of grain size

The **average particle size**, a fundamental property of sedimentary materials, is defined by a variety of statistical parameters. The **mode** is the most frequently occurring particle diameter. The **median** is that size for which half of the particles (by weight) are coarser and half finer. The **arithmetic mean** is calculated using the method of moments, where the midpoint of each grade is the arithmetic midpoint between the grade-size limits in millimeters. For example, the midpoint is 0.75 mm if the grade-size limits are 0.5 and 1.0 mm. The **logarithmic mean** is calculated by the method of moments, where the midpoint and the grade-size limits are in ϕ units. For example, the midpoint is 0.5ϕ if the grade-size limits are ϕ = 1 and ϕ = 0. Note that this differs (0.5ϕ = 0.71 mm) from the arithmetic midpoint in millimeters (0.75 mm) for the same size grade. When the logarithmic mean (calculated in ϕ units) is converted to metric units, the resultant parameter is referred to as the **geometric mean** (Krumbein & Pettijohn 1938: footnote to Table 25, 245). For most samples the median, mode, and geometric mean are clustered near the high point of the frequency curve, whereas the arithmetic mean is offset toward the coarse end of the distribution (Fig. 7.8).

Standard deviation measures the sorting or uniformity of the particle-size distribution. In a normal distribution, 68% of the samples lies within "one standard deviation," plus or minus, of the mean (Fig. 7.10,A). The **arithmetic standard deviation** is calculated using the method of moments, where the midpoint of each grade is the arithmetic midpoint between the grade-size limits in millimeters. This statistic is of little direct value because it can not be used to compare samples with a different mean diameter. For example, a standard deviation of 1 mm does not have the same significance in reference to gravel that it has in reference to sand. Gravel with a mean size of 52 mm and a standard deviation of 1 mm is well sorted, but sand with a mean size of 1.5 mm and a standard deviation of 1 mm is poorly sorted. To avoid this problem the **coefficient of variation** can be used. It is defined as the standard deviation divided by the mean (Simpson *et al.* 1960, Snedecore & Cochran 1967).

The **logarithmic standard deviation** is calculated using the method of moments, where the midpoint and the grade-size limits are in ϕ. Given in ϕ units, it allows comparison of sorting between materials of any size. If converted from ϕ to metric units, the standard deviation will consist of two numbers. For example, a mean of 2ϕ and a standard deviation of 0.5ϕ is equivalent, in metric units, to a mean of 0.25 mm and a standard deviation of plus 0.1 mm or minus 0.073 mm. This results because "it is impossible to convert a deviation in log units to one-number deviation on a linear scale because of the inequality of class intervals" (Pierce & Graus 1981: 1349).

Skewness measures the asymmetry of the distribution. If there is more material in the coarse tail (coarse skewed), the skewness is referred to as being negative (Fig. 7.10,B). If there is more material in the fine tail (fine skewed), it is positive (Fig. 7.10,C). **Kurtosis** measures the ratio between the sorting in the "tails" of the distribution and the sorting in the central portion of the distribution. If the central portion is better sorted than the tails, the frequency curve is said to be excessively peaked or leptokurtic (Fig. 7.10,E). If the tails are better sorted than the central portion, the

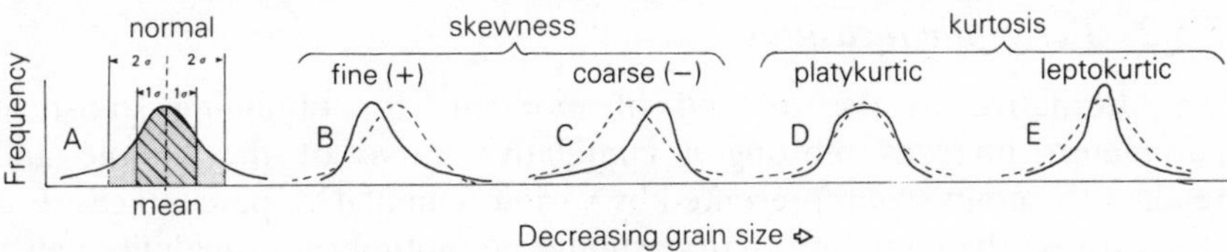

Figure 7.10 Frequency curves showing distributions differing in skewness (B & C) and kurtosis (D & E). Normally distributed sediment shown in A and as dashed line in B–E.

curve is said to be flat peaked or platykurtic (Fig. 7.10,D). "Strongly platykurtic curves are often bimodal with subequal amounts of the two modes; these plot out as a two-peaked frequency curve, with a sag in the middle of the two peaks accounting for its platykurtic character" (Folk 1980: 44). As is the case for mean and standard deviation, skewness and kurtosis are affected by the grain-size units that are used. The values obtained using metric units are different from those obtained using ϕ units.

7.5.1 *Method of moments*

To calculate the statistical parameters discussed above, enter the sample weight in each size class (column 3 in Table 7.2). Then multiply the weight in each size class (W in column 3) by the midpoint size (D in column 2) for that class interval and enter the **product** ($D \times W$) in column 4. Sum all of the values in columns 3 and 4. Divide $\sum (D \times W)$ (sum of values in column 4) by $\sum W$ (sum of values in column 3, which is equal to the total weight). This is the 1st moment and is equal to the mean. Subtract the mean (M) from the midpoint size (D in column 2) and enter this value in column 5. This is the **midpoint deviation** ($D - M$). Take the midpoint deviation to the 2nd, 3rd, and 4th power and enter these values in columns, 6, 7, and 8 respectively. Make sure that any negative values from column 5 are carried to column 7 when ($D - M$) is cubed. All values in columns 6 and 8 will be positive no matter what the sign (+ or −) in column 5. Next multiply the weight (W in column 3) by the values in columns 6, 7, and 8 and enter these values in columns 9, 10, and 11 respectively. Then sum columns 9, 10, and 11.

Divide the summed value from column 9 by the total weight ($\sum W$ from column 3) (Eqn 2). This is the 2nd moment (m_2) which is also called the **variance**. The square root of the variance is the standard deviation (Eqn 3). To get the 3rd moment (m_3 in Eqn 4) divide the summed value from column 10 by the total weight ($\sum W$ from column 3). Skewness is calculated by dividing m_3 by $m_2^{3/2}$ (Eqn 5). Divide the summed value from column 11 by the total weight to get the 4th moment (m_4 in Eqn 6). Divide m_4 by m_2^2 to get the kurtosis (Eqn 7).

7.5.2 *Percentile measures*

An alternative to the method of moments for obtaining statistical parameters involves plotting a cumulative curve of the sample and reading the grain-size represented by various cumulative percentages. For this purpose the cumulative curve should be plotted on **probability paper** because the percentiles can be read with greater accuracy than is possible with arithmetic paper. The *n*th percentile is defined as the value that

Table 7.2 Calculation of moment measures. Based on data from Fig. 7.3.

1 Class interval (mm)	2 D Midpoint (mm)	3 W Weight (g)	4 $D \times W$ Product	5 $D - M$ Midpoint deviation	6 $(D - M)^2$	7 $(D - M)^3$	8 $(D - M)^4$	9 $W(D - M)^2$	10 $W(D - M)^3$	11 $W(D - M)^4$
1–2	1.5	5.31	7.965	1.013	1.025	1.040	1.053	5.443	5.520	5.592
0.5–1	0.75	8.70	6.525	0.263	0.069	0.018	0.005	0.600	0.158	0.042
0.25–0.5	0.375	12.59	4.721	-0.112	0.013	-0.001	0.0002	0.164	-0.018	0.002
0.125–0.25	0.1875	9.13	1.712	-0.300	0.090	-0.027	0.008	0.822	-0.247	0.074
0.0625–0.125	0.0938	6.03	0.566	-0.394	0.155	-0.061	0.024	0.934	-0.369	0.145
pan	0.031*	2.49	0.077	-0.456	0.208	-0.095	0.043	0.518	-0.236	0.108
		44.25	21.57					8.481	4.808	5.963

	Moment	Standard notation	Notation used in grain-size calculation		Calculation	Answer	Statistic
Eqn 1	m_1	$\sum x/n$	$\sum(D \times W)/\sum W$	=	21.57/44.25	= 0.487mm	mean (M)
Eqn 2	m_2	$\sum(x - \bar{x})^2/(n - 1)$	$\sum W(D - M)^2/\sum W$	=	8.481/44.25	= 0.192mm	variance
Eqn 3			$\sqrt{m_2}$	=	$\sqrt{0.192}$	= 0.438mm	standard deviation
Eqn 4	m_3	$\sum(x - \bar{x})^3/(n - 1)$	$\sum W(D - M)^3/\sum W$	=	4.808/44.25	= 0.109mm	
Eqn 5			$m_3/m_2^{3/2}$	=	0.109/0.084	= 1.298mm	skewness
Eqn 6	m_4	$\sum(x - \bar{x})^4/(n - 1)$	$\sum W(D - m)^4/\sum W$	=	5.963/44.25	= 0.135mm	
Eqn 7			m_4/m_2^2	=	0.135/0.037	= 3.649mm	kurtosis

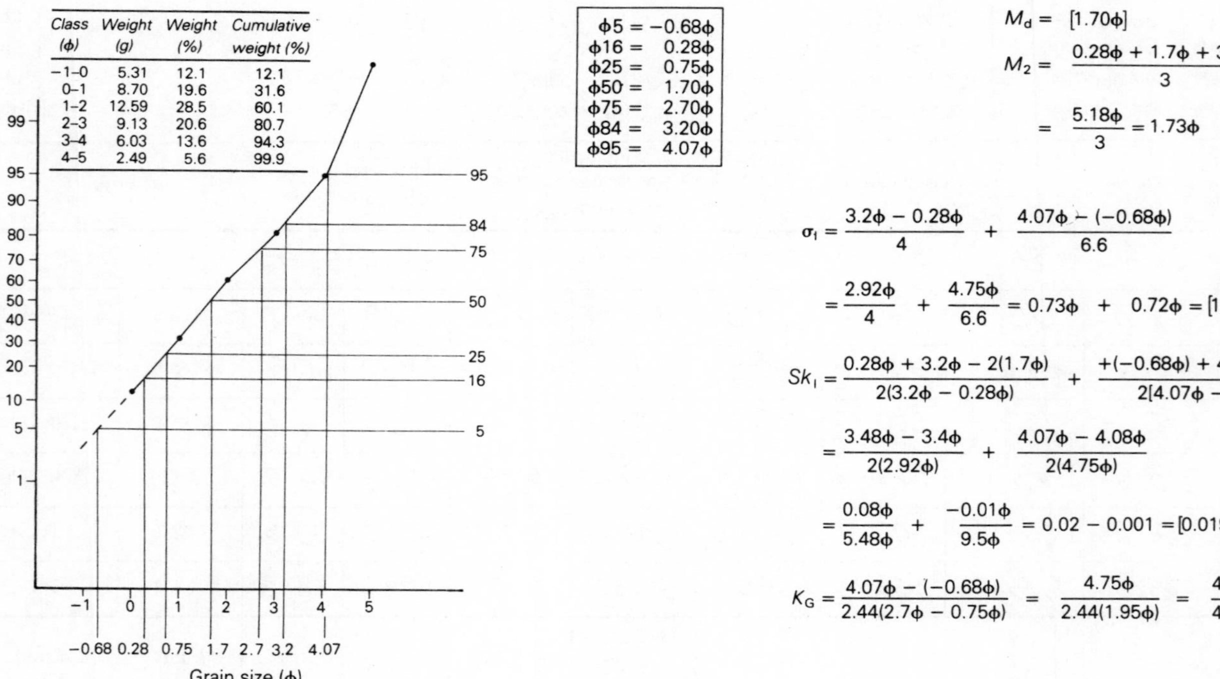

Class (ϕ)	Weight (g)	Weight (%)	Cumulative weight (%)
−1–0	5.31	12.1	12.1
0–1	8.70	19.6	31.6
1–2	12.59	28.5	60.1
2–3	9.13	20.6	80.7
3–4	6.03	13.6	94.3
4–5	2.49	5.6	99.9

$$\phi 5 = -0.68\phi$$
$$\phi 16 = 0.28\phi$$
$$\phi 25 = 0.75\phi$$
$$\phi 50 = 1.70\phi$$
$$\phi 75 = 2.70\phi$$
$$\phi 84 = 3.20\phi$$
$$\phi 95 = 4.07\phi$$

$$M_d = [1.70\phi]$$

$$M_2 = \frac{0.28\phi + 1.7\phi + 3.2\phi}{3} = \frac{5.18\phi}{3} = 1.73\phi$$

$$\sigma_I = \frac{3.2\phi - 0.28\phi}{4} + \frac{4.07\phi - (-0.68\phi)}{6.6} = \frac{2.92\phi}{4} + \frac{4.75\phi}{6.6} = 0.73\phi + 0.72\phi = [1.45\phi]$$

$$Sk_I = \frac{0.28\phi + 3.2\phi - 2(1.7\phi)}{2(3.2\phi - 0.28\phi)} + \frac{+(-0.68\phi) + 4.07\phi - 2(1.7\phi)}{2[4.07\phi - (-0.68\phi)]} = \frac{3.48\phi - 3.4\phi}{2(2.92\phi)} + \frac{4.07\phi - 4.08\phi}{2(4.75\phi)} = \frac{0.08\phi}{5.48\phi} + \frac{-0.01\phi}{9.5\phi} = 0.02 - 0.001 = [0.019]$$

$$K_G = \frac{4.07\phi - (-0.68\phi)}{2.44(2.7\phi - 0.75\phi)} = \frac{4.75\phi}{2.44(1.95\phi)} = \frac{4.75\phi}{4.76\phi} = [1.0]$$

Figure 7.11 A cumulative curve showing percentiles used in calculating graphic statistical measures. Based on data from Fig. 7.3. See Table 7.3 for formulas used in calculations.

Table 7.3 Formulas and verbal scales for graphic size parameters (after Folk & Ward 1957).

Median The diameter corresponding to the 50% mark on the cumulative curve

Graphic mean

$$M_Z = \frac{\phi 16 + \phi 50 + \phi 84}{3}$$

Inclusive graphic standard deviation

$$\sigma_I = \frac{\phi 84 - \phi 16}{4} + \frac{\phi 95 - \phi 5}{6.6}$$

<0.35	very well sorted
0.35 to 0.50ϕ	well sorted
0.50 to 0.71ϕ	moderately well sorted
0.71 to 1.0ϕ	moderately sorted
1.0 to 2.0ϕ	poorly sorted
2.0 to 4.0ϕ	very poorly sorted
>4.0ϕ	extremely poorly sorted

Inclusive graphic skewness

$$Sk_I = \frac{\phi 16 + \phi 84 - 2\phi 50}{2(\phi 84 - \phi 16)} + \frac{\phi 5 + \phi 95 - 2\phi 50}{2(\phi 95 - \phi 5)}$$

1.0 to 0.3	very fine-skewed
0.3 to 0.1	fine-skewed
+0.1 to −0.1	near-symmetrical
−0.1 to −0.3	coarse-skewed
−0.3 to −1.0	very coarse-skewed

Graphic kurtosis

$$K_G = \frac{\phi 95 - \phi 5}{2.44(\phi 75 - \phi 25)}$$

<0.67	very platykurtic
0.67 to 0.90	platykurtic
0.90 to 1.11	mesokurtic
1.11 to 1.50	leptokurtic
1.50 to 3.00	very leptokurtic
>3.00	extremely leptokurtic

divides the sample so the *n*% of the sample is *coarser* than that value. In Figure 7.11 the 50th percentile, written ϕ50, is approximately 1.7ϕ. This is the diameter corresponding to the 50% mark on the cumulative curve. The most commonly used measures are shown in Table 7.3.

7.5.3 Discussion

(a) Comparison of moment and graphic measures

Based on a study of 100 digitally generated samples, moment parameters for grouped and ungrouped data show that "errors due to grouping grain-size data into size classes are small and can be ignored for most sediment types. Errors for standard deviation, skewness and kurtosis are progressively larger because higher moments are used" (Swan *et al.* 1979: 499). Comparison of graphic measures and ungrouped measures shows that values for mean and standard deviation are strongly related in contrast to skewness and kurtosis which are weakly related (Swan *et al.* 1979). Swan *et al.* (1979: 498) conclude that "grouped moment measures yield far more reliable results than the graphic approximations, particularly for skewness and kurtosis."

(b) Sieve interval

The mesh size of the sieves in a stack of sieves decreases from top to bottom. The interval between sieves may reflect whole Udden–Wentworth grades (see Section 7.1.1), e.g. 4, 2, 1, 0.5, 1.25, and 0.0625 mm, referred to as a **whole-grade interval** or a whole ϕ interval. Alternatively a half-grade (e.g. 4, 2.83, 2.00 mm, etc.) or a quarter-grade interval (e.g. 4, 3.36, 2.83, 2.38, 2 mm, etc.) may be used (see Table 7.1). The smaller the grade interval, the more sieves in the stack, assuming the same mesh size for the top and bottom sieves.

When utilizing the **method of moments**, use of a quarter-grade interval generally "results in an improvement in the accuracy of derived statistical parameters. Changes in the values of these measures due to such a decrease in the analysis interval in most cases is small, but, for skewness and kurtosis, becomes larger for better sorted sediments" (Swan *et al.* 1979: 499). If **graphic measures** are used, samples should be sieved at whole-grade intervals. "Obtaining data at finer intervals does not improve the accuracy of graphic statistical measures and, in fact, tends to make them slightly less accurate" (Swan *et al.* 1978, 876).

(c) Assumption for grain size on the pan

Commonly the sediment that accumulates on the pan (less than 0.0625 mm) during sieving is not analyzed any further. When calculating statistical parameters this material is assigned an arbitrary grain size. Folk (1980) suggests using 0.031 mm (5ϕ). When using ϕ units with the method of moments, the calculated values for skewness and kurtosis are strongly affected by the grain size of sediment on the pan (Table 7.4). To the extent that this size is inaccurate, the derived statistics will be inaccurate. This suggests that unless the material on the pan is further analyzed (e.g.

Table 7.4 Grain-size parameters calculated by method of moments using different estimates of the grain-size present on the pan. Samples A and B differ in the amount of sediment on the pan. For sample A the amount on the pan equals 5.6% of the total sample; for sample B the amount on the pan equals 1% of the total sample. Values for the mean and standard deviation are in ϕ units.

Size class (ϕ)	Midpoint Φ	Sample A Weight (g)	Sample B Weight (g)
0 to −1	−0.5	5.31	5.31
1–0	0.5	8.70	8.70
2–1	1.5	12.59	12.59
3–2	2.5	9.13	9.13
4–3	3.5	6.03	6.03
pan	*X*	2.49	0.44
		44.25	42.20

	X (size on pan)	=	5ϕ	6ϕ	7ϕ
Sample A	mean		1.74	1.80	1.85
	standard deviation		1.44	1.57	1.73
	skewness		0.36	0.78	1.21
	kurtosis		2.64	3.69	4.97
Sample B	mean		1.58	1.59	1.60
	standard deviation		1.27	1.30	1.34
	skewness		0.10	0.28	0.55
	kurtosis		2.35	3.00	4.19

by pipette) skewness and kurtosis are unreliable parameters for use in evaluating geologic problems.

(d) Size data as weight percent versus number frequency

Grain-size data based on sieving are given in terms of weight frequency rather than number frequency. The mean size "calculated using weight frequency is not the actual mean size of all the particles in the sample. Rather, it is the size around which the weight of material in a sample is distributed" (Swan *et al.* 1978: 864). To illustrate this point, consider four quartz spheres whose diameters are 0.707, 0.354, 0.177, and 0.088 mm. The mean size, based on number frequency, is 0.332 mm and the mean size, based on weight percent, is 0.165 mm (data from Swan *et al.* 1978: Table 1).

Because the theory of statistical tests is based on number frequencies, not on weight frequencies, common statistical tests cannot be used for most grain-size data. For this and other reasons, some argue that the weight–frequency data should be utilized directly in analyzing geologic problems rather than relying on derived statistical parameters (Blatt *et al.* 1980: 53–4). Although this approach has merit, it is not a panacea (Tucker & Vacher 1980).

(e) Geologic significance of size parameters for mud samples

Although statistical parameters obtained for mud samples may be both accurate and precise, they may have little geologic significance. This is because the physical character of samples which are disaggregated prior to size analysis may be quite different from that in the environment of deposition. Clays are commonly deposited as floccules or fecal pellets. In such aggregates, clay flakes respond to hydrologic conditions differently than if they existed as separate particles. Thus size analysis of individual clay particles may reveal little about the hydrologic régime during deposition.

(f) Assumption of a normal or log-normal distribution

An important fact regarding summary statistics is that the method of moments is designed for normal or Gaussian distributions. Although grain-size distributions are not normal, it is commonly thought that they can be transformed into normal or near-normal distributions by taking the logarithms of the measurements (Blatt *et al.* 1980: Table 3.2, 50). Some studies indicate that the log-hyperbolic distribution provides a better description of sediment than the log-normal distribution (Bagnold & Barndorff-Nielson 1980). Other research suggests that there is no apparent advantage in using the log-hyperbolic distribution (Wyrwoll & Smith 1985). To the degree that grain-size distribution deviates from log-normal, a view strongly held by some, utilization of moment measures may be unwarranted.

(g) Value of grain-size parameters as a guide to interpreting paleoenvironment

Even if we were able accurately to characterize and distinguish modern sedimentary environments using grain-size parameters (something that we cannot do), application of this knowledge to the rock record would be difficult. One problem involves the methods used to collect grain-size data from rock samples. Disaggregation of sedimentary rock generally produces a collection of particles with a different size distribution than that of the original sediment. Petrographic methods utilize a thin slice of rock; thus by these methods grains are rarely cut in the plane of their short and intermediate axes, which are generally the dimensions that determine the size obtained by sieving. Therefore direct comparison of size data obtained by petrographic methods with data obtained by sieving is not possible. Furthermore, the sample size is relatively small (several hundred grains per thin section). Another problem involves diagenetic changes which may strongly alter the original grain-size distribution. They include dissolution of grains, growth of grains (cementation), and addition of new grains (e.g. authigenic clay minerals).

Given these problems, plus those associated with the size analysis of modern sediments and the calculation of size parameters, it is small wonder that the results have been "disappointing and disproportionately small relative to the effort expended" (Pettijohn 1975: 52). As another observer, paraphrasing Winston Churchill, has noted, "Never have so many done so much for so little."

(h) A final comment

Most of the previous discussion reflects widespread despair regarding statistical parameters of grain-size (e.g. Ehrlich 1983). Nevertheless, you should keep in mind that estimates of mean grain size and sorting are essential in rock description and provide a basis for comparing relative differences between samples. Use of a hand lens or binocular microscope with comparator charts (e.g. Harrell 1985) will provide data adequate for most purposes.

7.6 Variation in grain size with distance of transport

Numerous studies have shown that sediment size decreases with transport, especially in a fluvial environment (Pettijohn 1975: 512–15). This aspect of fluvial sediment is an important element in paleogeographic reconstruction (Fig. 7.12). In some fine-grain red-bed sequences lateral decrease in grain size is apparently related to the location of major rivers which fed sediment to alluvial fans (Fig. 7.13).

Part of the decrease is caused by fracturing and abrasion and is directly related to (1) the velocity of the flow, (2) the mineralogy of the sediment, and (3) the size of the sediment, in addition to the distance traveled. Soft clasts (e.g. limestone) are abraded more rapidly than hard clasts (e.g. granite). Size loss due to abrasion of gravel is several orders of magnitude faster than for sand. This accounts for the fact that most observations are based on conglomeratic sequences.

Although mechanical destruction (e.g. fracturing and abrasion) is important in size reduction, it accounts for less than half of the observed variation. Other factors include downstream decrease in competency and fluctuations in flow, which allow finer material entrained at lower

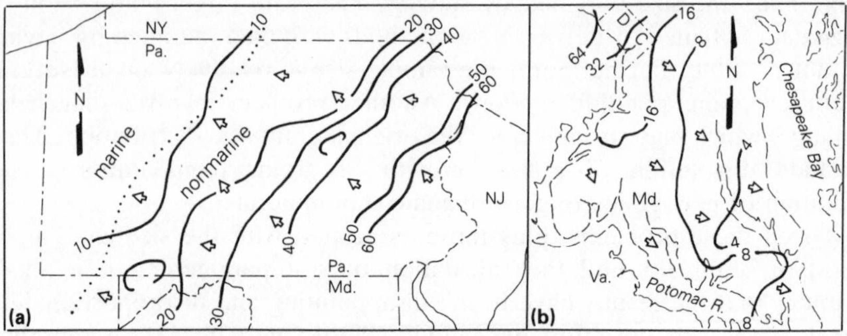

Figure 7.12 Maps showing lateral variation in pebble size: (a) Pocono Formation (Mississippian) in Pennsylvania and adjacent states (modified from Pelletier 1958); (b) Brandywine Gravel (Pleistocene) in Maryland (modified from Schlee 1957). Isopleths (in mm) indicate (a) maximum pebble size and (b) modal pebble size. Arrows show generalized paleocurrents based on cross-bed azimuths. Dotted line in (a) indicates approximate position of the shoreline during Pocono time.

velocities to be moved more frequently (and therefore farther) than coarser material.

Generally the downstream decline in gravel size is exponential, as expressed by **Sternberg's law** in the form:

$$D = D_o \, e^{-as}$$

where D_o = the initial size (mm) of the largest clasts, D = the size (mm) at distance s from the source, s = the distance (miles), a = the coefficient of size reduction, and e = exponential function. The coefficient of side reduction, a, is equal to

$$1/s \; 1n \; D_o/D$$

Values for this coefficient are much greater for alluvial fan deposits than for fluvial deposits (Fig. 7.14).

7.7 Exercises: grain size

1 Use the nomogram in Table 7.1 to convert the following values from millimeters to ϕ and from ϕ to millimeters.

15 mm = ______ ϕ   −8.1ϕ = ______ mm

1.3 mm = ______ ϕ   −5.2ϕ = ______ mm

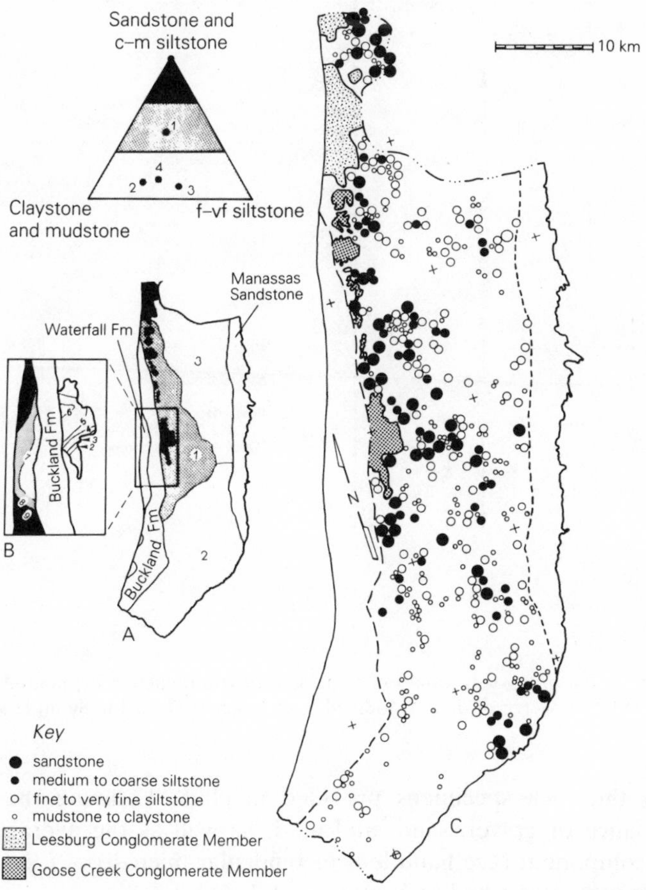

Figure 7.13 The grain size of red beds in the Triassic–Jurassic Bull Run Formation in the northern part of the Culpeper Basin, Virginia. Note that the coarsest-grained rocks (area 1 on map A) are associated with conglomerates on the west side of the basin. These conglomerates indicate the source of sediment that spread eastward into the basin. Paleocurrent data, showing an eastward flow direction (Lindholm 1979b), support this interpretation.

0.6 mm = ______ ϕ   1.3ϕ = ______ mm

0.12 mm = ______ ϕ   6.7ϕ = ______ mm

0.036 mm = ______ ϕ   9.75ϕ = ______ mm

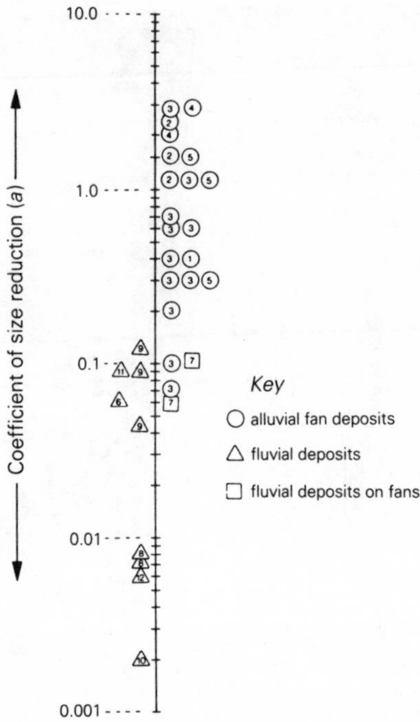

Figure 7.14 A bar graph with values of coefficient of size reduction (a) plotted. Numbers in symbols indicate source of data. (Modified from Fagin 1977, in Lindholm *et al.* 1979b.)

2 Study the rock specimens provided in class. Estimate the relative abundance of gravel, sand, and mud, as well as the average size of each component (use hand lens or binocular microscope). Name each specimen as described in Sections 7.1.3 and 7.3.1.

3 Construct a histogram for *one* of the samples given in Table 7.5 (see Section 7.4.1). Your instructor will indicate which sample to use.

Table 7.5 Problem sets for grain-size analysis. Use only the one set assigned by your instructor.

Class interval (mm)	Class interval (φ)	Sample A Weight (g)	Sample B Weight (g)
1–2	0 to −1	1.06	4.33
0.5–1	1–0	4.11	6.73
0.25–0.5	2–1	9.87	20.87
0.125–0.25	3–2	18.37	12.32
0.062–0.125	4–3	4.31	1.63
pan	pan	6.10	2.49

4 Construct cumulative curves, using arithmetic and probability paper, for the sample used in (3) above. See Section 7.4.3.
5 Use the cumulative curve drawn on probability paper, in (4) above, to calculate graphic statistical measures (see Section 7.5.2). *Put your results in Table 7.6.*
6 Use the method of moments to calculate grain-size statistics (same sample as used before) using *both millimeter and ϕ midpoints* (use Tables 7.7 & 7.8) (see Section 7.5.1). *Put your results in Table 7.6.*
7 *Results*

Percentiles ϕ5 ______ ϕ75 ______

ϕ16 ______ ϕ84 ______

ϕ25 ______ ϕ95 ______

ϕ50 ______

Table 7.6 Results of grain-size analysis.

	Median	Mean	Standard deviation	Skewness	Kurtosis
(a) graphic method	______ ϕ	______ ϕ ______ mm*	______ ϕ	______	______
(b) Method of moments using ϕ midpoint		______ ϕ ______ mm*	______ ϕ	______	______
(c) Method of moments using millimeter midpoint		______ mm	______ mm	______	______

* Use nomogram to convert mean from ϕ to millimeter equivalent.

Table 7.7 Table to use in calculating moment measures (millimeter midpoint).

1	2	3	4	5	6	7	8	9	10	11
	D	W	$D \times W$	$D - M$	$(D - M)^2$	$(D - M)^3$	$(D - M)^4$	$W(D - M)^2$	$W(D - M)^3$	$W(D - M)^4$
Class interval (mm)	Midpoint (mm)	Weight (g)	Product	Midpoint deviation						
1–2	1.5									
0.5–1	0.75									
0.25–0.5	0.375									
0.125–0.25	0.1875									
0.0625–0.125	0.938									
pan	0.031*									
		____	____					____	____	____

	Moment	Standard notation	Notation used in grain-size calculation		Calculation		Answer	Statistic
Eqn 1	m_1	$\sum x/n$	$\sum(D \times W)/\sum W$	=	______ / ______	=	______	mean (M)
Eqn 2	m_2	$\sum(x - \bar{x})^2/(n - 1)$	$\sum W(D - M)^2/\sum W$	=	______ / ______	=	______	variance
Eqn 3			$\sqrt{m_2}$	=	$\sqrt{}$	=	______	standard deviation
Eqn 4	m_3	$\sum(x - \bar{x})^3/(n - 1)$	$\sum W(D - M)^3/\sum W$	=	______ / ______	=	______	
Eqn 5			$m_3/m_2^{3/2}$	=	______ / ______	=	______	skewness
Eqn 6	m_4	$\sum(x - \bar{x})^4/(n - 1)$	$\sum W(D - m)^4/\sum W$	=	______ / ______	=	______	
Eqn 7			m_4/m_2^2	=	______ / ______	=	______	kurtosis

Table 7.8 Table to use in calculating moment measures (ϕ midpoint).

1 Class interval (ϕ)	2 D Midpoint (ϕ)	3 W Weight (g)	4 $D \times W$ Product	5 $D - M$ Midpoint deviation	6 $(D - M)^2$	7 $(D - M)^3$	8 $(D - M)^4$	9 $W(D - M)^2$	10 $W(D - M)^3$	11 $W(D - M)^4$
0.0 to −1.0	−0.5									
1.0–0.0	0.5									
2.0–1.0	1.5									
3.0–2.0	2.5									
4.0–3.0	3.5									
pan	5.0*									
		____	____					____	____	____

	Moment	Standard notation	Notation used in grain-size calculation		Calculation		Answer	Statistic
Eqn 1	m_1	$\sum x/n$	$\sum(D \times W)/\sum W$	=	______ / ______	=	______	mean (M)
Eqn 2	m_2	$\sum(x - \bar{x})^2/(n - 1)$	$\sum W(D - M)^2/\sum W$	=	______ / ______	=	______	variance
Eqn 3			$\sqrt{m_2}$	=	$\sqrt{}$	=	______	standard deviation
Eqn 4	m_3	$\sum(x - \bar{x})^3/(n - 1)$	$\sum W(D - M)^3/\sum W$	=	______ / ______	=	______	
Eqn 5			$m_3/m_2^{3/2}$	=	______ / ______	=	______	skewness
Eqn 6	m_4	$\sum(x - \bar{x})^4/(n - 1)$	$\sum W(D - m)^4/\sum W$	=	______ / ______	=	______	
Eqn 7			m_4/m_2^2	=	______ / ______	=	______	kurtosis

8 Sedimentary rock classification

Sedimentary rock is composed of framework grains, matrix, chemically precipitated cement, and pores (Fig. 8.1). Framework grains and matrix are generally deposited from a fluid medium after transport. Transport distances may be thousands of kilometers or only a few meters. The grains, as the name indicates, form the framework of the rock. Matrix material occurs between the framework constituents. There is no clearly defined boundary between the absolute size of framework grains and the matrix. In very coarse-grained rock, such as conglomerate, gravel comprises the framework and sand (and/or mud) the matrix. This contrasts with sandstone, in which sand makes up the framework and mud the matrix. Cement is post-depositional, and when present may partially or completely fill the original pore space. Primary porosity, formed at the time of deposition, is reduced not only by cementation but also by compaction. Secondary porosity, which develops after deposition, forms in a variety of ways, including selective leaching of unstable components or cement and fracturing of brittle grains and cemented rock.

8.1 Sandstone

8.1.1 Introduction

Various sandstone types, commonly called **clans**, are distinguished by the modal composition of **framework grains** and in some cases the amount of **matrix**. Other textural parameters and the composition of chemical cements are used to further modify the clan name. Grain-size names (see Section 7.1.3) are generally used in combination with the clan names.

Framework components are (1) quartz, (2) feldspar, and (3) rock fragments (also referred to as lithic fragments, they are sand-sized fragments of fine-grained rock, especially shale, chert, phyllite, and aphanitic igneous rock), and (4) accessory minerals (e.g. mica and glauconite). Petrographic analysis is necessary for the accurate identification of these constituents, as well as to determine the composition of feldspar and rock fragments. Nonetheless, composition can and should be

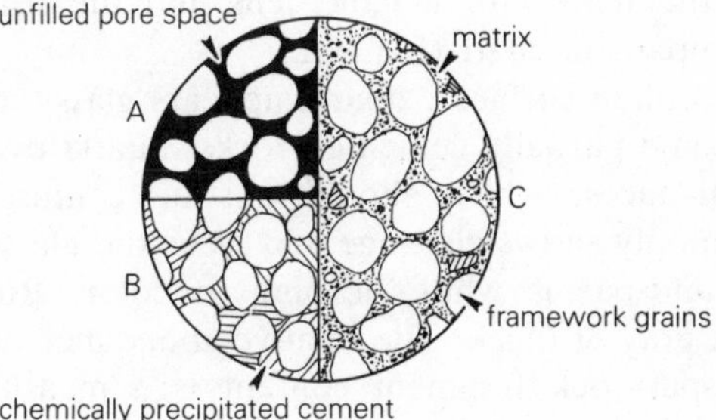

Figure 8.1 The major constituents of sedimentary rock. Texturally mature rock (A) before and (B) after cementation. C, Texturally immature rock.

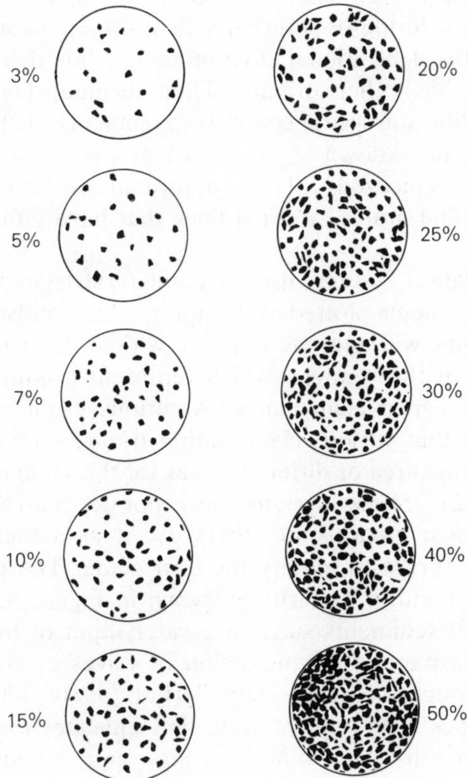

Figure 8.2 A comparison chart for estimating percentage composition (modified from Terry & Chilingar 1955).

evaluated in the field with a hand lens and the use of a percentage estimation comparison chart (Fig. 8.2).

On freshly broken surfaces, quartz appears glassy and grey and lacks cleavage. In some partially cemented rocks, quartz overgrowths develop minute crystal faces, which should not be confused with cleavage. **Feldspar** commonly shows cleavage and lacks the glassy luster of quartz. In addition, feldspar is white or pink in color. **Rock fragments** are generally dark gray or black. The relative abundance of quartz compared with the feldspar–rock fragment content is a measure of **mineralogic maturity**, which is the extent to which sand "approaches the ultimate end-product to which it is driven by the formative processes that operate upon it" (Pettijohn 1975: 491). These processes include weathering in the source area, as well as the effects of transportation and deposition, which tend to destroy the less durable and less stable (labile) components (i.e. feldspar and rock fragments).

Matrix, composed of silt and clay, is commonly assumed to represent fine-grained detrital sediment deposited in the space between the sand framework grains during or soon after deposition. As such it reflects the energy level in the depositional environment. While this is generally true, some "matrix" has other origins. They include: (1) authigenic clay crystallized within the pore space (i.e. cement), (2) authigenic clay produced by the breakdown of framework grains, (3) soft rock fragments that have been squeezed (plastic deformation) into the pore space between more rigid grains, and (4) fines that have infiltrated into pores after deposition.

Most classification systems use an equilateral triangle with the three framework components plotted at the apices. Any sandstone composed of these constituents will plot as a point within the triangle (Fig. 8.3). Different areas of the triangle, which represent a limited compositional variation, are assigned clan names. A serious problem with sandstone nomenclature is that various classification triangles utilize different clan names for the same area or different areas for the same name (see Blatt *et al.* 1980: 370–2). Some systems incorporate matrix as a defining parameter for clan names and others use it as a measure of **textural maturity**, which serves to modify the clan name. The most widely used terminology for textural maturity is shown in Figure 8.4. "This concept proposes that, as sediments suffer a greater input of mechanical energy through the abrasive and sorting action of waves or currents, they pass sequentially through . . . four stages" (Folk 1980: 100). Thus textural maturity "provides a descriptive scale that indicates the effectiveness of the environment in winnowing, sorting, and abrading the detritus furnished to it." You should bear in mind that textural maturity and mineralogic maturity are quite different concepts and must not be confused.

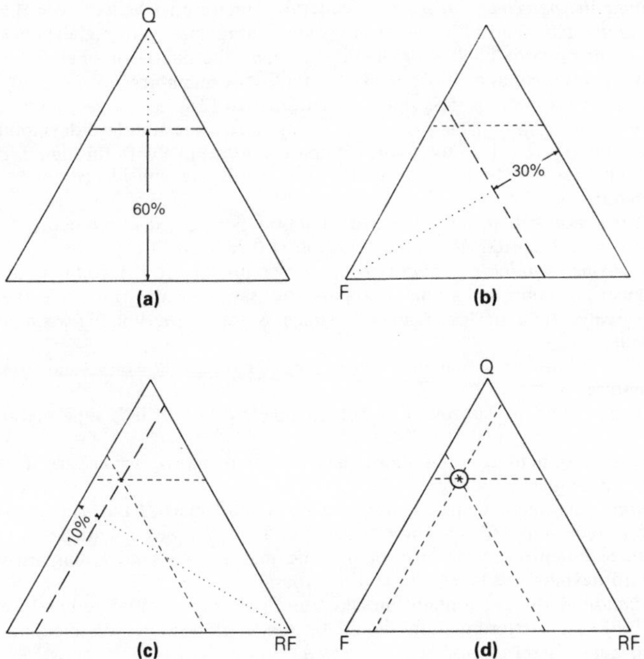

Figure 8.3 A method for plotting sandstone composition on a classification triangle. The sandstone illustrated contains 60% quartz, 30% feldspar, and 10% rock fragments. (a) To plot the quartz content draw a dashed line that is parallel to the base of the triangle and six-tenths of the way up from the base to the apex (which is the Q pole). Do the same for feldspar (b) and rock fragments (c). If done correctly, the dashed lines intersect at a point that represents the composition of the sandstone (d).

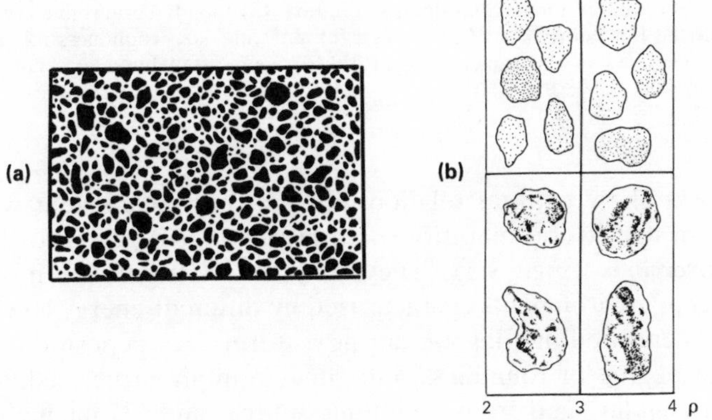

Figure 8.4 A key for determining textural maturity (modified from Folk 1980: 100–1).

Figure 8.4 continued

(1) *Determine the percentage of mud.* In general, immature rocks have very little original visible pore space and little chemical cement; submature (and higher) rocks have the pores either open or filled with chemical cement like quartz or calcite.
   (a) If the rock contains more than 5% mud, it is **immature**.
   (b) If the rock contains less than 5% mud, go to (2).

(2) *Determine the sorting of the rock.* The sorting borderline standard deviation = 0.5ϕ is illustrated in figure (a), to the right. Compare your sample with this figure to see if it is well enough sorted to be mature. Bimodal sands are considered to be mature or supermature.
   (a) If it is not well sorted (standard deviation > 0.5ϕ), it is **submature**.
   (b) If it is well sorted (standard deviation < 0.5ϕ), go to (3).

(3) *Determine the roundness of sand-sized quartz grains.* Figure (b), to the right, illustrates subangular and subround grains. Compare your sample with (b) to see if the roundness (ϱ) is greater than or less than 3.0, which is the borderline between mature and supermature.
   (a) If the grains are subangular to very angular on the Power's scale (ϱ < 3.0), it is **mature**.
   (b) If the grains are subround to well rounded (ϱ > 3.0) it is **supermature**.

Immature. Sediment contains more than 5% mud matrix; grains are usually poorly sorted and angular.
Submature. Sediment contains more than 5% mud matrix, but sand grains are still poorly sorted (standard deviation > 0.5ϕ) and are not well rounded.
Mature. Sediment contains little or no mud matrix, and sand grains are well sorted (standard deviation < 0.5ϕ) but still not rounded.
Supermature. Sediment contains no clay; sand grains are well sorted and well rounded (ϱ > 3.0). This determination should be made, if possible, on medium- and fine-grained quartz sand grains.

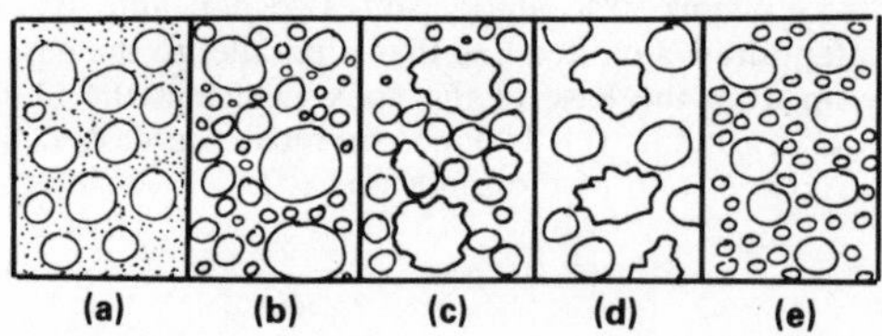

Figure 8.5 Examples of textural inversions. Numbers in parentheses refer to possible reasons for types of textural inversions discussed in text. (a) rounded grains in clayey matrix (1,3); (b) rounded but poorly sorted grains (1); (c) abnormal size–roundness relations (2); (d) bimodal roundness in the same grade (1,2); (e) well sorted bimodal sediments (2). (Modified from Folk 1980: 104.).

Some rocks show textural relationships that are inconsistent with the usual pattern of textural maturity. Folk (1980: 103–4) refers to these as **textural inversions** (Fig. 8.5). They may result from: (1) mixing of sediment from environments characterized by different energy levels (e.g. dune sands deposited in a lagoon during a storm); (2) deposition of sand with a high degree of roundness, inherited from an earlier sedimentary cycle, with angular sand from a plutonic source; and (3) mixing of well sorted sand beds with clay interbeds through bioturbation.

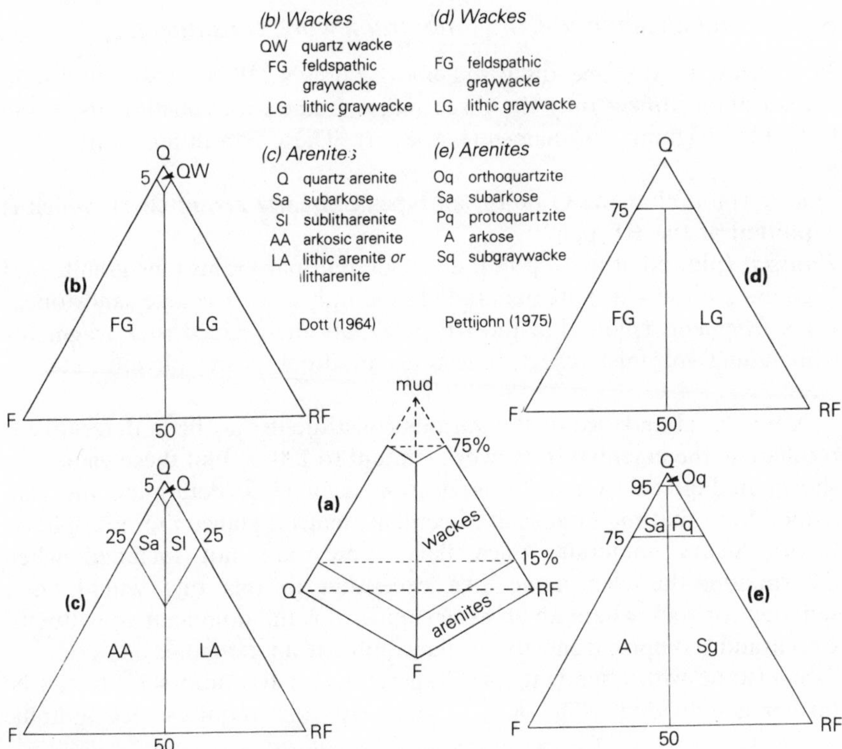

Figure 8.6 A sandstone classification utilizing framework grains and matrix content. Main components are quartz (Q), feldspar (F), and rock fragments (RF). (a) Compositional tetrahedron showing general classes of sandstone with 15–75% mud matrix for wackes and less than 15% mud matrix for arenites (modified from F.W. Clark in Pettijohn 1957). Terminology for (b) wackes and (c) arenites in current use (Dott 1964). This is the classification used in Pettijohn (1975). Terminology for (d) wackes and (e) arenites commonly used prior to 1975 (Pettijohn 1957).

8.1.2 Classification utilizing framework constituents and matrix content

This scheme separates sandstones into two major families on the basis of the matrix content – long the hallmark of F.J. Pettijohn's sandstone classification. **Arenites** contain less than 15% detrital matrix and **wackes** contain between 15 and 75% matrix. The subdivision of arenites and wackes is based on the relative abundance of quartz, feldspar, and rock fragments. In addition to the clan names in current use (shown in Fig. 8.6 a & b), I have included terminology (Fig. 8.6 d & e) from the earlier editions of Pettijohn's book *Sedimentary Rocks* because of its common usage in the literature prior to 1975.

8.1.3 Classification utilizing only framework constituents

In contrast to the one discussed above, Folk's (1954, 1980) sandstone classification utilizes only the three major framework constituents as the basis for assigning clan names (Fig. 8.7a). These constituents are:

Quartz (plotted at the Q pole): all types of quartz *except* chert, which is plotted at the RF pole.
Feldspar (plotted at the F pole): all single feldspar grains plus granite and gneiss grains, which are generally found only in very coarse sandstones.
Rock fragments (plotted at the RF pole): all fine-grained rock fragments including volcanics, chert, limestone, mudrock, slate, phyllite, etc.

After the abundance of the various constituents has been determined, recalculate the essential framework content to 100%. Plot these values (as shown in Fig. 8.3) on the classification triangle to determine the clan name. Note that material such as cement, matrix, glauconite, phosphate, fossils, heavy minerals, mica flakes, etc. are not included when determining the clan name. An exception to this rule would be a sediment or rock where an **accessory** mineral is the dominant constituent. **Greensand**, composed mostly of glauconite, is an example.

Sandstone with abundant rock fragments (F : RF ratio <1 : 1) can be further subdivided (Fig. 8.8). Obviously this requires petrographic

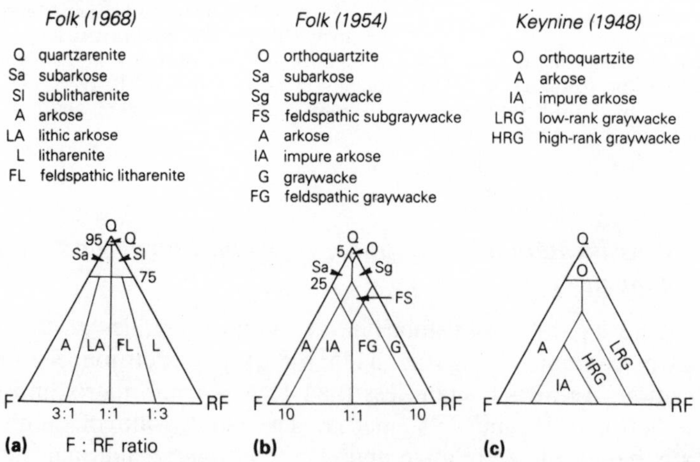

Figure 8.7 A sandstone classification utilizing only framework grains. Main components are quartz (Q), feldspar (F), and rock fragments (RF). (a) Folk's (1980) classification in current use. For varieties of lithic sandstones see Fig. 8.8. (b) Folk's (1954) classification used prior to 1968 and Krynine's (1948) classification are included because of their use in the literature in the 1950s and 1960s.

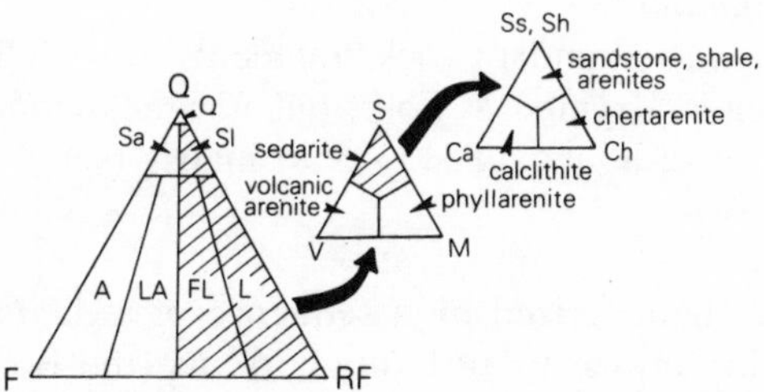

Figure 8.8 Folk's (1980) subdivisions of lithic sandstones. If feldspathic litharenite, prefix variety name with "feldspathic"; if sublitharenite, prefix variety name with "sub-." When used, recalculate rock fragments to 100% and plot on VMS (volcanic rock fragments, metamorphic rock fragments, and sedimentary rock fragments) triangle. If the rock falls in the "sedarenite" field, recalculate sedimentary rock fragments to 100% and plot on CaChSS, Sh (carbonate, chert, sandstone, and shale) triangle. Remember that carbonate rock fragments are extrabasinal.

analysis. With the exception of **calclithite** (composed of extrabasinal carbonate grains) and **phyllarenite**, these terms have not gained widespread popularity.

Folk (1980) recommends that a complete rock name should include a grain-size name and a clan name as well as terms to indicate the textural maturity, the type of cement, and miscellaneous transported constituents. The later two may be absent and therefore omitted. The suggested sequence is:

(Grain size): (cements) (textural maturity) (miscellaneous transported constituents) (clan name)

(a) *Grain size*: see Section 7.1.3.
(b) *Cement*: terms include siliceous, chert-cemented, opaline, calcitic, dolomitic, sideritic, hematitic, feldspar-cemented, etc.
(c) *Textural maturity*: see Section 8.1.1
(d) *Miscellaneous transported constituents*: terms include micaceous, glauconitic, collophane-bearing (if > 1 or 2% of rock), chert-bearing (if > 5% of rock), volcanite-bearing (if 2–5% of rock).

Examples of complete "fivefold" names are:

Fine sandstone: siliceous submature glauconitic quartzarenite.
Silty very fine sandstone: calcitic submature arkose.

8.1.4 Comments on the term "graywacke"

"Graywacke" has fallen in disrepute mainly because of a lack of uniform usage (Folk 1980: 128, Blatt *et al.* 1980: 373–5). Various definitions include:

Petrographic definitions

(a) a sandstone with abundant rock fragments, especially metamorphic rock fragments (Krynine & Folk, but now abandoned by Folk);

(b) a sandstone with abundant (15–75%) matrix (see Section 8.1.2).

Field definitions

(c) a sandstone characterized by a sequence of sedimentary structures thought to be formed by turbidity currents (the Bouma cycle);

(d) a sandstone that is "dark, dirty, and highly indurated."

8.1.5 Special applications

(a) Plotting varieties of feldspar

Plotting sandstone composition on a conventional ternary diagram may fail to show important relationships as exemplified by the Mesozoic deposits in northern Virginia (Fig. 8.9a). The Triassic–Jurassic sandstones were deposited in a basin (the Culpeper Basin) bounded on the west by an east-dipping normal fault. The Cretaceous sandstones were deposited on a surface that sloped gently to the east. Paleocurrent data show that the transport direction for both sequences was from west to east. Plotting the sandstone composition of these rocks shows that, although both sequences are arkosic, the Triassic–Jurassic ones contain a greater abundance of rock fragments (Fig. 8.9a). Although important, this fails to show a more significant difference, which is clearly illustrated when the data are recalculated so that quartz + feldspar = 100% and then plotted on a ternary diagram with quartz, plagioclase (albite), and microcline as end members (Fig. 8.9b). The feldspar in the Cretaceous sandstone is dominantly microcline, whereas the feldspar in the Triassic–Jurassic sandstone is dominantly plagioclase (albite). The source of Triassic–Jurassic sediment rich in plagioclase (albite) (field 1 in Fig. 8.9b) is interpreted to have been the metamorphic rock of the Blue Ridge which lies to the west of the Culpeper Basin. In contrast, the Cretaceous sands (field 2 in Fig. 8.9b) were derived mainly from crystalline rocks in the Piedmont which provided mainly microcline. The paucity of plagioclase (albite) suggests that little of the sediment deposited during Cretaceous time came from the area west of the Piedmont.

(b) Plotting normative mineral composition

When studying metamorphic terrain, a major goal is to evaluate the character of the rock prior to metamorphism. One approach to this problem involves comparison of the normative composition of the metamorphic rock with that of possible parent rocks. Hopson (1964), in his excellent study of the Maryland Piedmont, utilized this method in an effort to determine whether the gneisses and schists were derived from

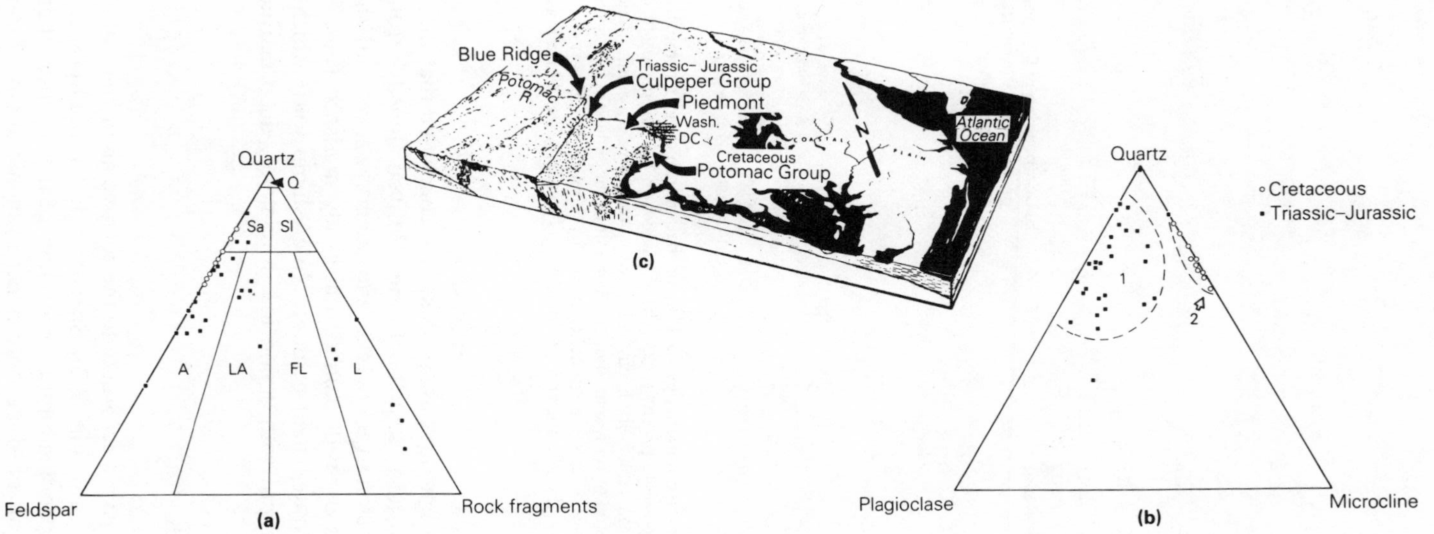

Figure 8.9 The composition of a sandstone from the Triassic–Jurassic sequence in the Culpeper Basin and the Cretaceous Potomac Group in northern Virginia. (a) Composition of framework grains plotted on Folk's (1968) classification triangle. (b) Feldspar plus quartz recalculated to 100%. Field 2 includes all of the Cretaceous rocks (Lindholm 1978) and field 1 includes most of the Triassic–Jurassic rocks (Lindholm, unpublished data). (c) Block diagram of northern Virginia and Maryland showing important geologic features (modified from *The river and the rocks*, 1970, USGS and the National Park Service).

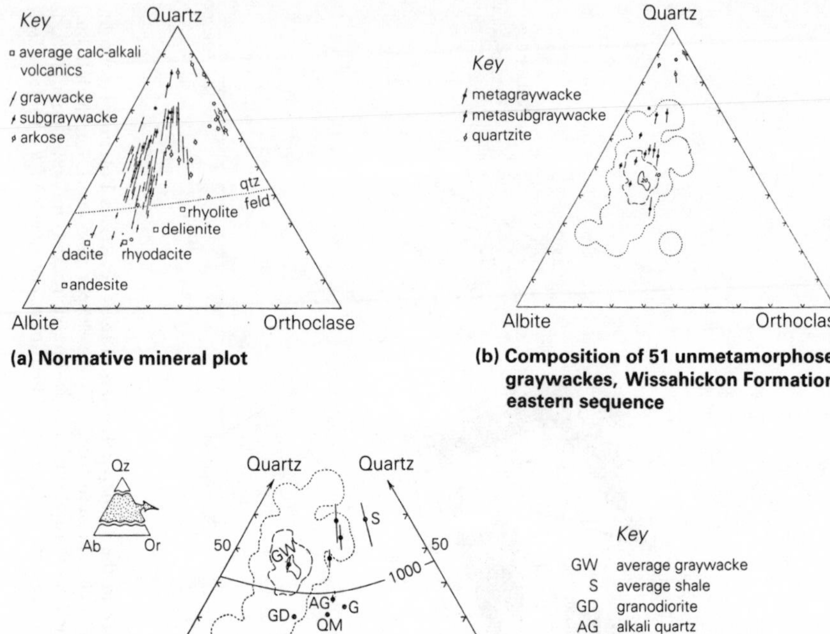

Figure 8.10 Normative mineralogy (CIPW) of metamorphic rocks compared with possible parent rocks: (a) possible parent rocks; (b) Wissahickon Formation, eastern sequence; (c) Sykesville Formation (solid black circles). Steep lines through points indicate normative corundum interpreted to represent high clay content in the sedimentary parent rock. Curved dashed lines denote a graywacke field, made by contouring 51 graywackes from (a). Contours drawn for the 20, 10, and 1% maxima. (From Hopson 1964: Figs 23 & 28.)

sedimentary or igneous parent rocks. He concluded that the Wissahickon Formation (eastern sequence) was derived mostly from texturally immature sandstone (graywacke and subgraywacke) and the Sykesville Formation was derived mainly from sandy mudrock (Fig. 8.10). These results corroborated field evidence (e.g. slump fold) which indicated a sedimentary origin, with deposition in relatively deep marine water.

8.2 Mudrock

Mudrock is classified according to the relative abundance of clay, silt, and sand (Section 7.1.3, Fig. 7.2). Specific types of mudrock can be further subdivided, depending on the mineralogy of the constituent grains. This is optional and can be done only if petrographic and/or X-ray diffraction analysis has been made. Rocks with abundant silt (siltstone and mudstone etc.) are designated as:

arkosic if the feldspar content is greater than 25% and the quartz content is less than 75% (when quartz + feldspar are recalculated to 100%);
subarkosic if the feldspar content is 5–25% and the quartz is 75–95%;
quartzose if is the feldspar content is less than 5% and the quartz content is greater than 95%.

Feldspathic varieties (arkosic and subarkosic) may be further described according to the dominant feldspar present (e.g. albite arkosic siltshale). Mudrock with abundant clay (claystone, mudshale, etc.) is designated according to the dominant clay mineral present (e.g. illitic clayshale or kaolinitic quartzose mudstone).

8.3 Conglomerate

Conglomerate is classified according to the relative abundance of sand and mud (Section 7.1.3, Fig. 7.1). The composition of the dominant pebble lithologies can be indicated by simply using the appropriate rock name, e.g. quartz pebble conglomerate or granite–gneiss pebble sandy conglomerate. Those with a large variety of lithologies represented are referred to as **polymictic** (Pettijohn 1975: 164). The terms **orthoconglomerate** (with < 15% matrix) and **paraconglomerate** (with > 15% matrix) may be used in order to stress grain-supported versus matrix-supported fabrics, an important aspect in the interpretation of transport history and depositional environment.

8.4 Limestone

Limestone is composed of more than 50% intrabasinal carbonate (calcite and/or aragonite produced within the basin of deposition). If noncarbonate grains comprise 10–50% of the rock, it is called a sandy limestone, muddy limestone, etc. (Fig. 8.11). Marl is an ill defined term for rock composed of subequal mixtures of carbonate and silicate mud. Rock composed of extrabasinal carbonate is a variety of sandstone, known as a **calclithite** (Fig. 8.8).

Limestone, like terrigenous rock, is composed of framework grains, matrix, cement, and pore space. Carbonate sand is generally deposited in a high-energy setting, as is terrigenous sand, and carbonate mud is deposited in quiet water, as is terrigenous mud. The fundamental difference between terrigenous rock and limestone involves the minera-

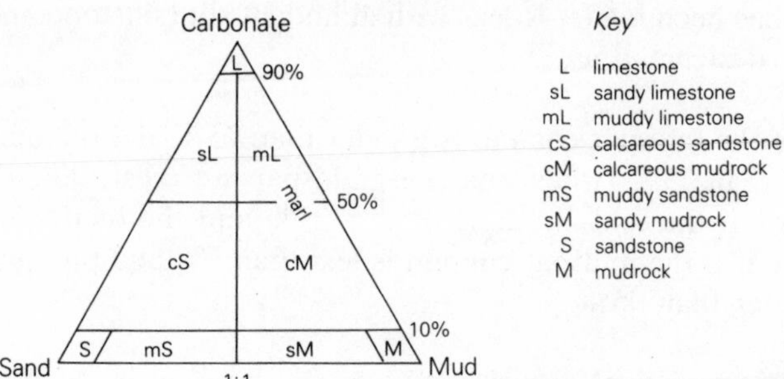

Figure 8.11 Terminology for pure limestone. Carbonate pole includes calcite and aragonite; sand and mud poles include silicate minerals. For bottom tier of rocks see Figure 7.2.

logy and the source of the sediment. In terrigenous rock it is extrabasinal and in limestone it is intrabasinal. Textural maturity (Section 8.1.1) has the same significance for limestone that it has for sandstone and is an integral feature of modern classification.

Calcarenite is a useful field term to differentiate a limestone composed of sand-size carbonate grains from a sandstone composed of silicate grains. **Calcilutite** is a companion term of calcarenite and is the limestone equivalent of mudrock. Although **micrite** has been narrowly defined by Folk (1959), many workers use it loosely to describe any fine-grained limestone (i.e. synonymous with calcilutite). **Calcirudite** is the limestone equivalent of conglomerate, but it has not gained the popularity enjoyed by calcarenite.

8.4.1 Folk's limestone classification

Folk's (1959, 1962) terminology, used to describe the major constituents of limestone, is considerably different than that used for terrigenous rock. Framework grains, called **allochems**, include (1) intraclasts, (2) oolites, (3) fossils, and (4) pellets (see Fig. 8.12 for description of allochems). Fine-grained carbonate is called **micrite** (short for microcrystalline calcite) and chemically precipitated cement is called **sparry calcite**, or **spar** for short.

Rock names used in Folk's classification are composite words. The first part, which refers to the allochem content, includes the prefixes "intra-," "oo-," "bio-," and "pel-." Determining the appropriate prefix, *after the allochem content has been recalculated to 100%*, is done as follows. If intraclasts are more than 25% of the total, use "intra-." If intraclasts are less than 25% and oolites are more than 25%, use "oo-." If intraclasts are less than 25%, and oolites less than 25%, and the fossil content

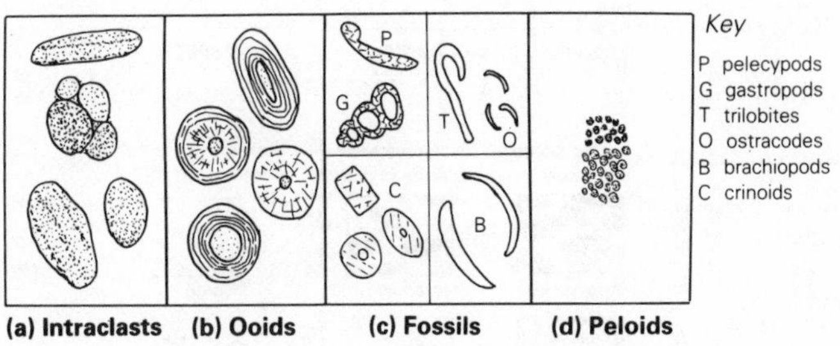

Figure 8.12 The description of allochems.

(a) *Intraclasts*. Fragments of penecontemporaneous, generally weakly lithified carbonate sediment. Commonly composed of micritic or pelletiferous sediment. Clasts are well rounded and range in size from a few millimeters to several tens of centimeters. Indicative of high-energy environment.

(b) *Oolites*, also called ooids or ooliths. Spherical or subspherical round grains with concentric or radial internal structure and a nucleus generally composed of micritic sediment. Commonly range up to 2 mm in diameter; larger than 2 mm rare and called pisoliths by some. Indicative of high-energy environment.

(c) *Fossils*. Common varieties include mollusks, recognized by characteristic shapes and generally preserved as sparry calcite; "crinoid" fragments (echinoderms in general) composed of "single calcite crystals" which display well defined cleavage (columnals are the most abundant fragments) and are recognized by circular cross sections; triobites, ostracodes, and brachiopods, which are recognized by their characteristic shapes and are composed of fibrous calcite which commonly appears as dark, rather opaque material in hand specimen.

(d) *Pellets*. Generally silt-size grains composed of micritic material. In hand specimen they are rarely recognizable and pellet-rich rocks are commonly mistaken for micrite. Some authors use "peloid" as the general term and restrict "pellets" for fecal pellets (something that is hard to prove in ancient limestone).

(volumetric abundance) is greater than the pellet content, use "bio-;" but if there are more pellets than fossils, use "pel-."

The second part of the name indicates the abundance of micrite versus spar. If there is more micrite than spar, use "-micrite." If there is more spar than micrite, use "-sparite."

Combining the four prefixes and the two suffixes produces eight rock names (Fig. 8.13). In addition, there are the two other terms, micrite (a fine-grained limestone with less than 10% allochems) and dismicrite (a fine-grained limestone with irregular areas of spar produced by burrowing, gas bubbles, algae, etc. – *dis-* for disrupted). When studying limestone with a hand lens or binocular microscope, you should probably restrict your efforts to these ten terms. For additional comments on hand specimen study, see Section 8.4.3. Further subdivision of limestone rock types (Fig. 8.14) involves petrographic analysis.

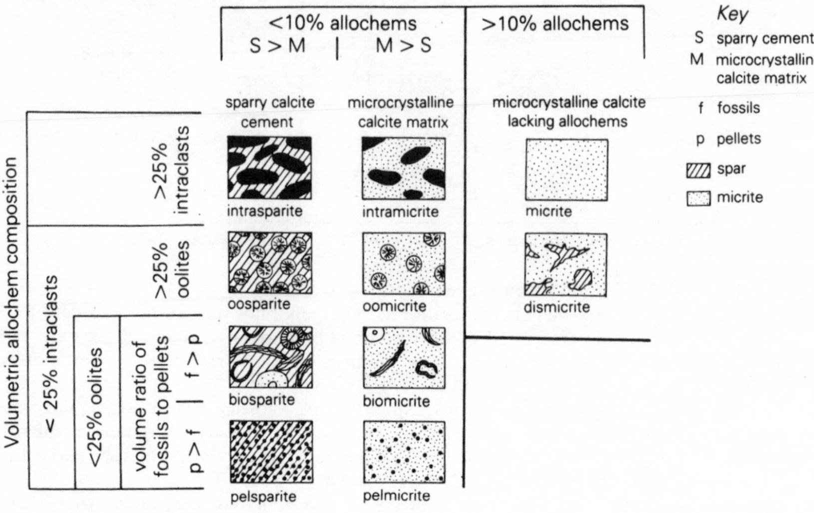

Figure 8.13 Folk's (1959) limestone classification.

	Over 2/3 lime mud matrix				Subequal spar and lime mud	Over 2/3 spar cement		
Allochems	0–1%	1–10%	10–50%	over 50%		sorting poor	sorting good	rounded and abraded
Representative rock terms	micrite and dismicrite	fossiliferous micrite	sparse biomicrite	packed biomicrite	poorly washed biosparite	unsorted biosparite	sorted biosparite	rounded biosparite
1959 terminology	micrite and dismicrite	fossiliferous micrite	biomicrite			biosparite		
Terrigenous analogues	claystone		sandy claystone	clayey or immature sandstone		submature sandstone	mature sandstone	supermature sandstone

Key

lime mud matrix

sparry calcite matrix

Figure 8.14 Folk's (1962) limestone classification showing subdivision of "-micrites" and "-sparites."

8.4.2 Dunham's limestone classification

Dunham (1962) emphasizes the textural relationships between framework grains, matrix, and cement in his limestone classification (Fig. 8.15). **Grainstone** is composed mainly of allochems and sparry cement.

Contains mud (fine silt and clay-size particles)			Lacks mud
Mud-supported		Grain-supported	
<10% grains	>10% grains		
mudstone	wackestone	packstone	grainstone

Figure 8.15 Dunham's (1962) limestone classification. The names may be modified by the word "lime" and the dominant allochems present, e.g. crinoid lime packstone.

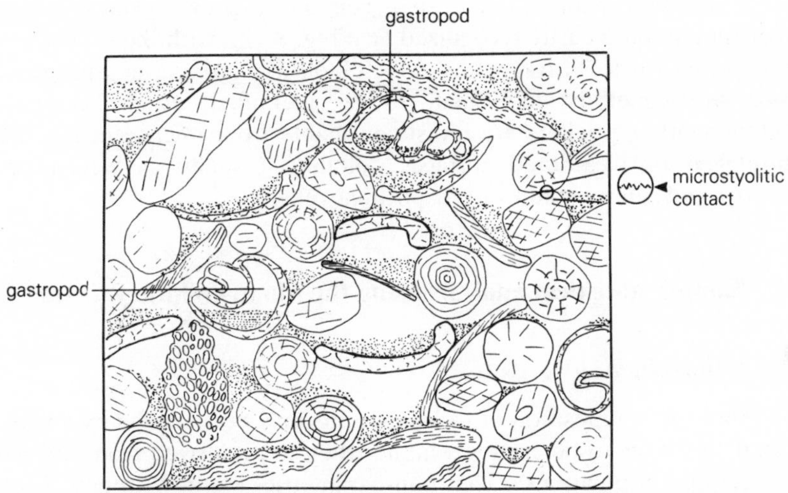

Figure 8.16 Evidence of grain-support fabric in limestone. This rock is composed of allochems (mostly oolites and fossils) and micrite (stipple pattern). Notice that micrite fills the lower part of the cavities between the allochems and that the upper part is empty space, which is ultimately filled with spar in most limestone. This fabric forms as carbonate mud settles to the floor of cavities in a grain-supported sediment and is a type of **geopetal structure** (variously referred to as an umbrella void, floored interstice or shelter effect). Microstylolitic contact is additional evidence of grain support but cannot be identified except by petrographic study. Partial filling of a shell (e.g. by a gastropod) is a type of geopetal structure that does not require grain support. Field of view approximately 1 cm.

Wackestone and **packstone** are mixtures of allochems, micrite, and spar. The main distinction between these rock types is that packstone is **grain supported** and wackestone is **matrix supported**. Whether or not a limestone is grain supported is difficult to determine from a hand specimen (for criteria see Fig. 8.16), which makes the identification of packstone and wackestone in the field very problematic. **Mudstone** is composed of micrite with less than 10% allochems. Because of the confusion with nonfissile mudrock composed of silt and clay, some workers use micrite rather than mudstone as a limestone type.

8.4.3 Study of limestone in hand specimen

Although both Folk's and Dunham's systems require petrographic analysis for a full description and accurate classification, they can and should be used in the field. Most of the constituents can be identified by studying, with the aid of a 10× or 20× hand lens, a freshly broken surface etched with a few drops of 10% HCl. Mineral oil or glycerin applied to this surface greatly enhances the visibility of the various components. Micrite appears dull and opaque, in contrast to spar which is clear and has a vitreous luster. Coarse spar commonly shows cleavage. Most allochem types are easily recognized (see Fig. 8.12), with the exception of heavily abraded fossil fragments, which look like intraclasts, and pellets, which are generally too small to be identified. Rocks composed predominantly of pellets are indistinguishable from micrite in the field. On etched or weathered surfaces dolomite (usually as well formed rhombs) and quartz stand out in positive relief.

8.5 Sample statistical analysis using the Mann–Whitney *U*-test

8.5.1 Introduction

The lithologic composition of two rock units may be analyzed by a variety of statistical tests to determine whether they were derived from the same or different populations. The non-parametric Mann–Whitney *U*-test, which can be used on ordinal or interval data, is well suited for data based on the abundance of a key component. Two features of this test statistic are: (1) the two sample sets do not have to be the same size, and (2) the number of samples does not have to be large (five or more).

8.5.2 The problem

Having collected data on the framework mineralogy from sandstone beds in two formations, we note that the average feldspar content in Formation A is 21% and that in Formation B it is 16% (Table 8.1 & Fig. 8.17). To evaluate whether this difference is significant we shall use the Mann–Whitney *U*-test.

8.5.3 The Mann–Whitney U-test

(1) Set up the **null hypothesis** (H_0) which states that there is *no difference* between the two formations in terms of the abundance of feldspar. The "no difference" aspect is a structural feature of the null hypothesis and must be stated this way.

Table 8.1 Composition of 23 sandstone beds from Formation A and Formation B.

	Quartz	Feldspar	Rock fragments
Formation A			
	87	10	3
	63	25	12
	72	21	7
	73	17	10
	71	24	5
	55	30	15
	54	28	18
	72	16	12
	66	28	6
	86	14	0
mean	70%	21%	9%
Formation B			
	80	16	4
	68	22	10
	79	18	3
	75	19	6
	87	11	2
	86	13	1
	84	15	1
	88	12	0
	77	15	8
	55	31	14
	83	12	5
	85	11	4
	85	13	2
mean	79%	16%	5%

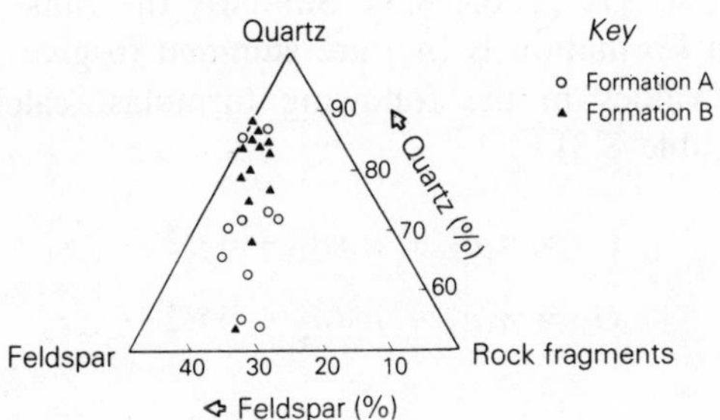

Figure 8.17 A plot of the data from Table 8.1.

(2) Rank the feldspar abundance on a continuous scale from the lowest to the highest (Table 8.2). If more than one sample has the same value, the mean rank for those samples is used (rank values in parentheses in Table 8.2).

Table 8.2 Samples ranked in terms of feldspar abundance. Rank values in parentheses indicate samples with the same feldspar content and are used to calculate *U*.

Feldspar (%)	Rank
10	1
11	2 (2.5)
11	3 (2.5)
12	4 (4.5)
12	5 (4.5)
13	6 (6.5)
13	7 (6.5)
14	8
15	9 (9.5)
15	10 (9.5)
16	11 (11.5)
16	12 (11.5)
17	13
18	14
19	15
21	16
22	17
24	18
25	19
28	20 (20.5)
28	21 (20.5)
30	22
31	23

(3) The rank values for all of the samples from Formation A (n_1) are summed to give $\sum r_1$ (Table 8.3). Similarly the rank values for the samples from Formation B (n_2) are summed to give $\sum r_2$.

(4) Using these values in the following formulas, calculate the test statistic *U* (Table 8.3).

$$U_1 = n_1 n_2 + n_1(n_1 + 1)/2 - \sum r_1$$

$$U_2 = n_1 n_2 + n_2(n_2 + 1)/2 - \sum r_2$$

or

$$U_2 = n_1 n_2 - U_1$$

Table 8.3 Method for calculating Mann–Whitney *U*-test statistic. See Section 8.4.3 (4) for formulas used.

Feldspar (%)		Rank	
Formation A (n_1)	Formation B (n_2)	n_1	n_2
10	16	1	11.5
25	22	19	17
21	18	16	14
17	19	13	15
24	11	18	2.5
30	13	22	6.5
28	15	20.5	9.5
16	12	11.5	4.5
28	15	20.5	9.5
14	31	8	23
	12		4.5
	11		2.5
	13		6.5
	$\sum r_1 = 149.5$		
		$\sum r_2 =$	126.5

$U_1 = 10{\cdot}13 + 10(10{+}1)/2 - 149.5$
$130 + 110/2 - 149.5$
$185 - 149.5 = \mathbf{35.5}$

$U_2 = 130 - 35.5 = \mathbf{94.5}$

(5) Next determine the **critical value of *U*** that will allow rejection or acceptance of the null hypothesis. This value depends on the sample number in the two sample sets and significance level used. With a significance level of 0.05 and sample sizes of $n_1 = 10$ and $n_2 = 13$, the critical value of $U = 33$ (Table 8.4). Note that this is a two-tailed test because we are not interested in the direction of difference between the sample sets.

(6) Use the **lower computed value of *U*** to assess whether there is a significant difference between the two sample sets. In our example the lower value of $U = 35.5$, which is greater than the critical value of 33. We therefore accept the null hypothesis at the 0.05 level of significance, and can say with confidence that there is no difference in the feldspar content between the two formations.

The general rule for the Mann–Whitney *U*-test is:

reject if the computed value is less than the critical value;
accept if the computed value is greater than the critical value.

Table 8.4 Partial list of critical values of U for the Mann–Whitney U-test.

n_2	n_1 5	6	7	8	9	10
5	2	3	5	6	7	8
6	3	5	6	8	10	11
7	5	6	8	10	12	14
8	6	8	10	13	15	17
9	7	10	12	15	17	20
10	8	11	14	17	20	23
11	9	13	16	19	23	26
12	10	14	18	22	26	29
13	12	16	20	24	28	33
14	13	17	22	26	31	36
15	14	19	24	29	34	39

8.6 Exercises: rock classification

1 Using the data in Table 8.5, plot the composition of the sandstone on Folk's classification triangle (Fig. 8.18). Give the rocks as complete a name (see Section 8.1.3) as possible.

Table 8.5 Problem set: sandstone composition for five samples.

	Sample A	Sample B	Sample C	Sample D
quartz grains	55	43	31	70
plagioclase grains	15	5	11	0
microcline grains	2	0	29	2
chert	0	0	5	5
phyllitic RX frags	0	10	0	0
basaltic RX frags	0	12	0	0
quartz cement	0	30	0	20
calcite cement	0	0	24	3
matrix	28	0	0	0
roundness (ϱ)	2.2	3.5	2.6	2.1
standard deviation (ϕ)	1.2	0.3	0.7	2.0

Sample A ________________________

Sample B ________________________

Sample C ________________________

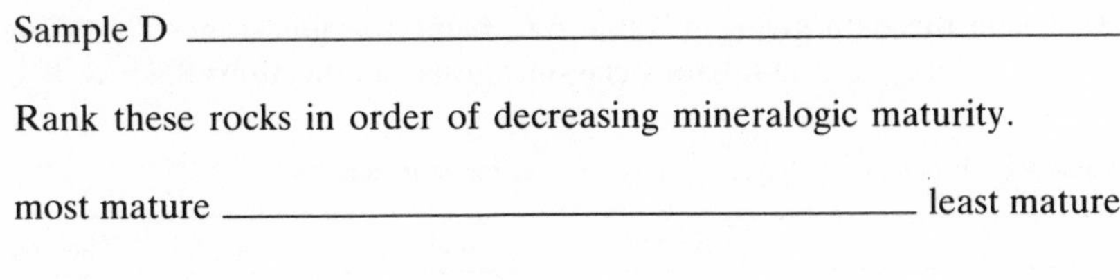

Sample D ____

Rank these rocks in order of decreasing mineralogic maturity.

most mature ________________________________ least mature

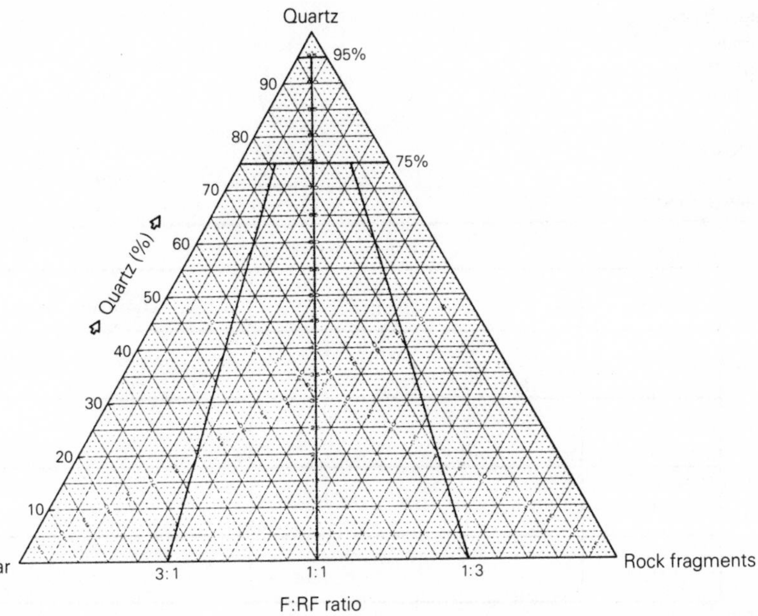

Figure 8.18 A classification triangle showing fields used in Folk's sandstone classification.

2 Study the hand specimens of sandstone provided in class. Estimate the abundance of quartz, feldspar, and rock fragments (see Section 8.1.1) and plot the results on Folk's classification triangle (given above) to determine the clan name.

Sample no.	Quartz	Feldspar	Rock fragments	Clan name (Folk)

3 Using the data given in Table 8.6, name the limestones according to both Folk's and Dunham's classifications (see Sections 8.4.1 & 8.4.2).

Table 8.6 Problem set: limestone composition for four samples.

	Sample A	Sample B	Sample C	Sample D
intraclasts	10	5	0	0
ooids	5	8	12	3
fossils	2	17	43	5
peloids	0	0	10	0
micrite	64	31	0	92
spar	0	29	29	0
quartz sand	0	0	6	0

Sample	Folk's name	Dunham's name
A		
B		
C		
D		

4 Study the hand specimens of limestone provided in class. Estimate the abundance of the various allochems, spar, and micrite (see Section 8.4.3). Use water or glycerin but *not* HCl. Name each according to Folk's classification.

Sample no.	Intraclasts	Ooids	Fossils	Micrite	Spar	Name

5 Table 8.7 contains data on the relative abundance of oolites with a radial structure compared to those with a concentric structure. The values listed under "percent radial oolites" were determined by dividing the number of oolites with radial structure by the total number of oolites in a sample. Each data set contains at least five samples from two limestone beds.

First determine the mean percentage of radial oolites in each bed. Then use the Mann–Whitney U-test to evaluate whether there is a significant difference (at the 0.05 level) between the two beds as regards the abundance of radial oolites. Your instructor will indicate which data set to use.

Table 8.7 Problem sets. Values indicate the percentage of radial ooids in a limestone sample.

Data set 1		Data set 2		Data set 3	
Bed A	Bed B	Bed C	Bed D	Bed E	Bed G
21	30	42	30	60	28
11	5	12	0	52	30
60	14	38	42	55	45
40	8	100	21	75	28
9	11	85	3	30	29
21	2	30	26	51	47
	13	51	0	52	50
			43	29	37
			32		39
					42

Statement of H_0 ____

____

____

Mean percentage of radial oolites in bed _____ = __________

Mean percentage of radial oolites in bed _____ = __________

Calculated values of U _____ _____

Critical value of U (from Table 8.4) _____

Reject or accept H_0 ______________

9 Heavy minerals

9.1 Introduction

Heavy minerals are volumetrically minor constituents in terrigenous rocks. They are characterized as having a specific gravity greater than 2.85. Until the 1950s, heavies were studied as a tool for stratigraphic correlation. This application has long since been replaced by microfossils and geophysical methods. Heavy minerals are now studied as a guide to source rock lithologies and dispersal patterns. They are also useful in evaluating diagenetic history as well as the pre-erosional weathering and tectonic history of the source area. Age dating of some heavy mineral species (e.g. tourmaline – ^{40}Ar : ^{39}Ar and zircon U : Pb) can provide important information regarding paleogeographic reconstruction (P. Allen 1972).

Heavies are difficult to extract from lithified material and they require a somewhat different approach regarding identification than that used in petrographic analysis of thin sections. For these reasons they are frequently not included as a standard part of sedimentologic investigation. Nonetheless their potential value should not be underestimated.

9.2 Heavy mineral assemblage

The various heavy mineral species present in sediment or rock comprise the heavy mineral assemblage. An important aspect of interpretation involves comparison of these assemblages. Rock units in a vertical succession containing different assemblages are called **heavy mineral zones**. In the case of lateral variation within a lithologic unit, the various assemblages are known as **heavy mineral associations**. Several related associations characterize a sedimentary petrologic province (Blatt *et al.* 1980).

9.3 Factors that control heavy mineral assemblages

Heavy minerals make up the most varied and complex component of terrigenous rocks. They are influenced by a variety of factors which must be carefully evaluated if a correct interpretation is to be reached. Although the principal factor is source-rock composition, other important ones are mineral shape, specific gravity, and size, as well as stability during weathering and diagenesis. The heavy mineral assemblage is generally less varied than the suite of minerals originally derived from the source rock, because of selective sorting and destruction of unstable species.

9.3.1 Source-rock composition and dispersal

Although most heavy mineral assemblages contain a variety of mineral species, they rarely constitute more than 1% of the total volume of sediment particles. For some species (e.g. zircon and rutile) this is due to the fact that they are minor constituents in the source rock. Other more abundant species (e.g. amphibole and pyroxene) are relatively unstable and most are destroyed during weathering in the source area.

The origin of many heavy mineral species is limited to rather specific rock types. Thus heavies provide valuable information concerning **provenance**, which describes the character of the source terrain, especially the lithologies present. Sedimentary source rock yields rounded grains of the most stable and durable species, which are able to survive several cycles through the sedimentary mill. They are zircon, rutile, and tourmaline. Other suites are listed in Table 9.1.

Heavy mineral assemblages in marine deposits are strongly influenced by major rivers, on adjacent land masses, with drainage basins of different lithologic makeup. Quaternary sediments in the northern Gulf of Mexico fall into several associations which are related to rivers flowing into the Gulf (Fig. 9.1a). Mineral dispersal patterns indicate that marked changes in longshore transport have occurred during the past 20 000 years (Fig. 9.1 b–d). In fluvial sequences heavy mineral associations which are controlled by the distribution of different rock types in the source area can provide significant clues to paleogeography.

Table 9.1 Detrital heavy mineral suites characteristic of source rock types (modified from Pettijohn 1975: 487).

Reworked sediments	rutile, rounded tourmaline, and rounded zircon
Low-rank metamorphic	biotite, chlorite, epidote, glaucophane, and tourmaline (small pale brown euhedra)
High-rank metamorphic	andalusite, chloritoid, diopside, epidote, garnet, hornblende (blue-green variety), kyanite, sillimanite, and staurolite
Silicic igneous	apatite, hornblende (brownish green variety), monazite, sphene, tourmaline (small pink euhedra), and zircon (euhedra)
Mafic igneous	anatase, augite, enstatite, hypersthene, hornblende (reddish brown variety), and olivine

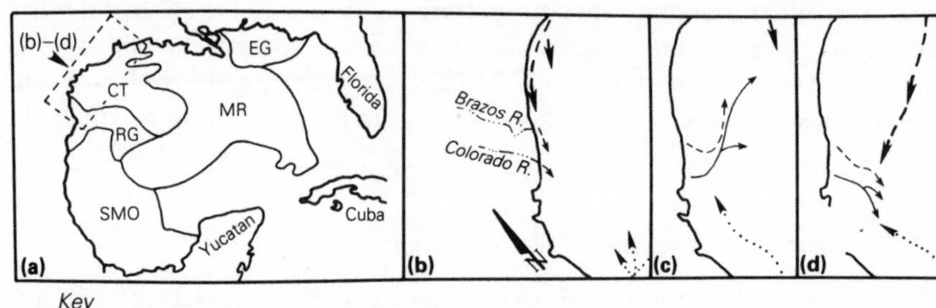

Figure 9.1 Heavy mineral associations in Holocene sediments in the Gulf of Mexico. Sediment transport directions in the western portion of the Gulf are shown during (b) the present time, (c) the main transgressive phase and (d) Early Holocene. Heavy dashed line, Mississippi River sediment; solid line, Colorado River sediment; dotted line, Rio Grande sediment. ((a) modified from Davies and Moore 1970; (b)–(d) modified from van Andel and Poole 1960.)

9.3.2 Temporal variation in the source area

During the time when a sedimentary sequence is being deposited the character of the source area will very likely change. Such changes may be reflected in the succession of heavy mineral zones. The trend most often cited is an upward increase in the complexity of the assemblages. Minerals present in the younger beds but absent in the older ones are commonly less stable species. This situation generally involves deposition through several geologic epochs (Fig. 9.2). A number of hypotheses have been proposed to explain this phenomenon. One involves progressive erosion and unroofing of new source rocks (Fig. 9.3a). A second one involves uplift and increased stream gradients (Fig. 9.3b). During the initial stages only the most stable minerals survive weathering. During the final stages accelerated downcutting causes erosion of less weathered regolith, allowing less stable minerals to enter the sediment pool. A third hypothesis involves climatic change, where intense weathering caused by a humid climate results in the destruction of all but the most stable species during the initial stages (Fig. 9.3c). During the final stages arid conditions prevail and less stable species survive weathering and are carried to the site of deposition.

In some cases heavy mineral zones in younger beds are less complex than older ones (Hester 1974, Lindholm 1978). Where this trend has been described, the sequence is restricted to a single formation. Hypotheses that might explain this phenomenon include: (1) progressive burial of source rock by onlap of a sediment wedge (Fig. 9.3e), (2) lowering of the

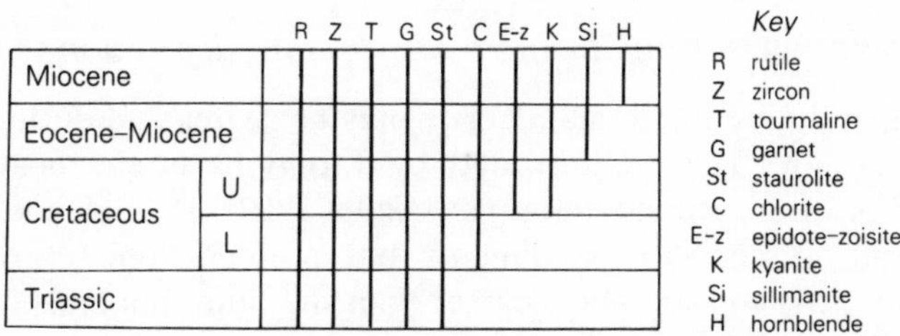

Figure 9.2 Heavy mineral zones in the Maryland coastal plain (modified from Pettijohn 1975, based on data from Anderson 1948).

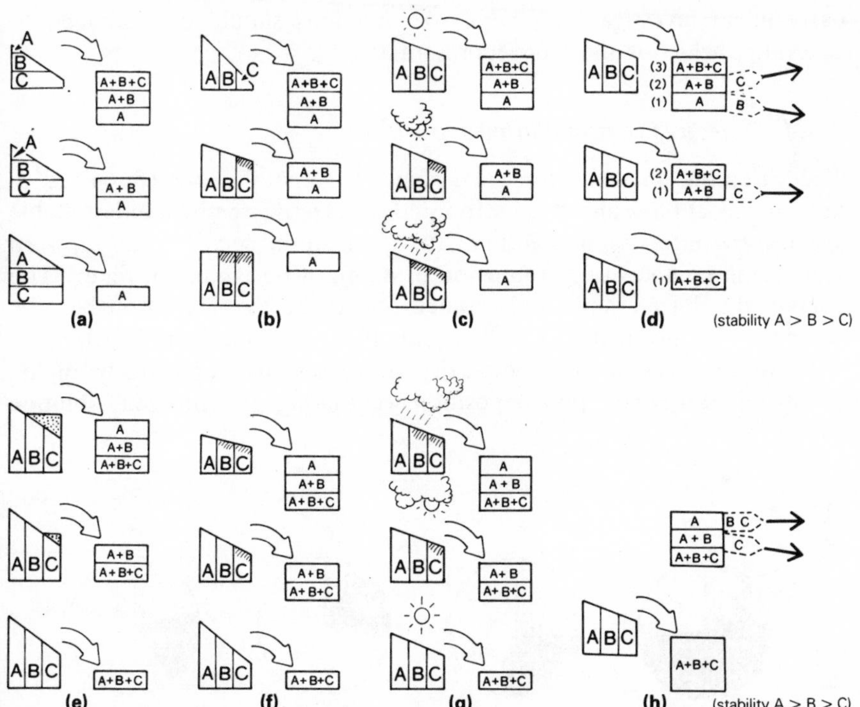

Figure 9.3 Models used to explain heavy mineral zonation. Increasingly complex zones upward shown in (a)–(d). Increasingly complex zones downward shown in (e)–(h). (In part modified from Pettijohn 1975.) See text for explanation.

stream gradient by erosion (Fig. 9.3f), and (3) climatic change in the source area from arid to humid (Fig. 9.3g).

An alternative to the hypotheses discussed above invokes post-depositional weathering and intrastratal solution as a means of selectively destroying less stable species (see Section 9.3.4).

9.3.3 *Selective sorting during transport and deposition*

Minerals of different size and density may be segregated during transport and deposition. This is illustrated by variations in the heavy mineral assemblage of the Rhone delta (van Andel 1959). Hornblende is a major component in nearshore sediments but a minor one in outer delta sediments. It is considerably coarser than the other minerals in this suite (i.e. epidote and pyroxene) and is interpreted as representing a nearshore lag deposit caused by selective sorting.

Although all heavies are concentrated in the finer size fractions, differences in density and size may cause the various mineral species to be unevenly distributed within a given sediment (Fig. 9.4). This means that early in an investigation several size fractions should be examined to determine which is the most representative.

9.3.4 *Selective removal after deposition*

The variations in the complexity of heavy mineral zones (discussed in Section 9.3.2) have also been attributed to selective removal of less stable species by intrastratal solution. Pettijohn proposed that an upward increase in complexity is a function of depth of burial and of time: "The deeper the burial and/or the older the rock, the less probable the presence of a given species" (Pettijohn 1975: 497) (see Fig. 9.3d).

In those cases where complexity decreases in progressively higher heavy mineral zones, post-deposition weathering or intrastratal solution

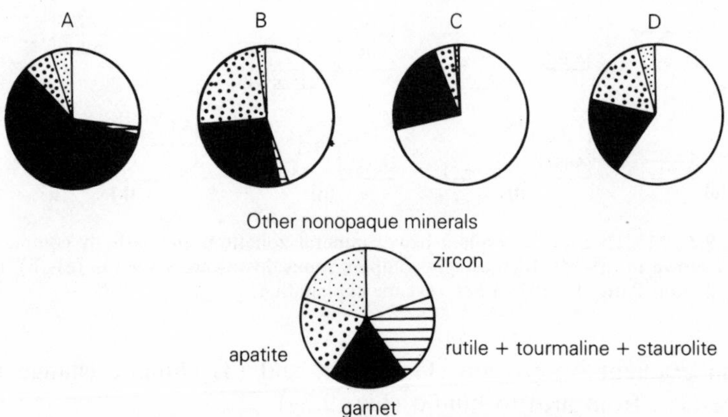

Figure 9.4 Heavy mineral composition in several size fractions: A, coarser than 0.25 mm; B, 0.125–0.25 mm; C, 0.0625–0.125 mm; D, bulk sample. Cretaceous sand from core sample, Fairfax County, Virginia. (Modified from Lindholm 1978.)

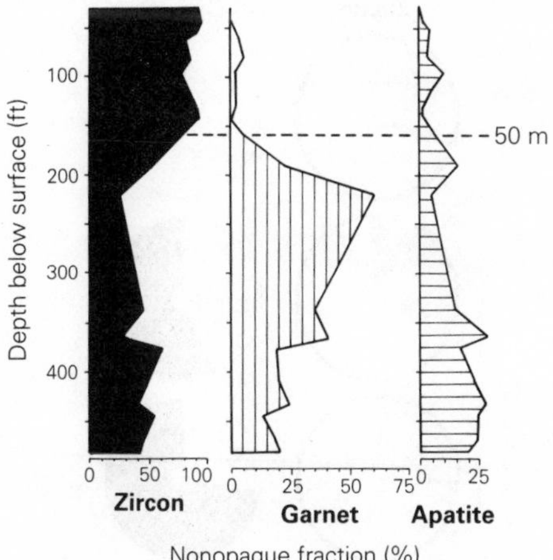

Figure 9.5 The distribution of dominant nonopaque heavy minerals in a well in Fairfax County, Virginia (modified from Lindholm 1978).

may also be the cause. This seems to be the case in the Potomac Group sands (Lower Cretaceous) in northern Virginia (Lindholm 1978). Outcrop samples and shallow (< 150 ft) borehole samples (Fig. 9.5) have a very limited suite dominated by zircon (92% of the nonopaque fraction). In the subsurface, at depths greater than 150 ft the suite is more diverse, containing zircon, garnet, apatite, and staurolite. Garnet in the shallower beds shows more evidence of solution (etched and embayed grains) than garnet from deeper beds (Fig. 9.6). This indicates that the paucity of garnet in near-surface beds was caused by dissolution. The fragile character of some deeply embayed grains further suggests that the garnet was destroyed after deposition (Fig. 9.3h) rather than by weathering in the source area (Fig. 9.3g). Progressive burial of garnet-bearing source rock by the advancing Cretaceous sediment wedge seems unlikely because of the uniformity of zircon varieties throughout the sequence (Fig. 9.6). This example clearly demonstrates the importance of **varietal studies** in interpreting heavy mineral assemblages.

When evaluating the possible importance of intrastratal solution one might examine concretions where the effects of destructive processes would be minimal. Blatt and Sutherland (1969) suggest that shale interbeds contain a more diverse and less altered heavy mineral assemblage than associated sandstone. Analysis of heavies in shale has not gained widespread popularity, because of the added difficulty in grain extraction, which requires the use of a centrifuge.

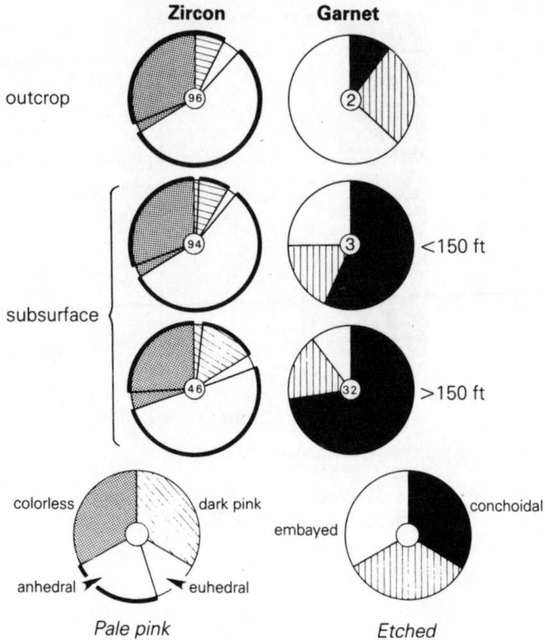

Figure 9.6 The variability in garnet and zircon in a Cretaceous outcrop and core samples from Fairfax County, Virginia. The number in the center of the circle is the percentage of the total nonopaque fraction. The heavy border of zircon circles indicates abundance of anhedral grains.

9.4 Methods of separation and analysis

Heavy minerals are removed from the more abundant light minerals by gravity separation in a high-density liquid. Three of the most commonly used heavy liquids are:

Name	*Formula*	*Sp. gr. at 20°C*
bromoform (tribrom-methane)	$CHBr_3$	2.87
acetylene tetrabromide (tetrabrom-ethane)	$C_2H_2Br_4$	2.96
methylene iodide	CH_2I_2	3.32

The light mineral fraction (i.e. quartz, feldspar, calcite, and most lithic grains) can be easily separated from the heavy fraction by using bromoform or acetylene tetrabromide. After the initial separation, methylene iodide may be used to segregate the heavy minerals whose specific gravity is less than 3.3 from those whose specific gravity is greater than 3.3.

Warning. The organic heavy liquids and their fumes are *all highly toxic and suspected carcinogens*. They should be used in a fume hood in a well ventilated room. Care should also be taken not to let these nasty liquids come in contact with your skin. Hydrocarbons such as bromoform may be absorbed through the skin and are potentially cumulative in the body, especially in fatty tissue. For more on this see Hauf and Airey (1980).

Several organic liquids can be used as solvents to wash the heavy liquid from mineral grains and from the apparatus used in the separation procedure. They include acetone and benzene. As with the heavy liquids, these solvents should be used with *caution*. Avoid breathing the fumes and avoid contact with your skin. They are also *highly flammable* and should not be used near an open flame.

An alternative to the organic heavy liquids previously discussed is the inorganic compound sodium polytungstate. This water-soluble material can be used to produce liquids with a maximum specific gravity of 3.1 and is said to be nontoxic. It can be ordered from Metawo (Falkenried 4, D-100, Berlin 33, West Germany).

Unlithified sand samples should be sieved prior to heavy liquid separation. Lithified material must be first disaggregated by pounding small fragments using a porcelain mortar and pestle. Heavy minerals which comprise less than 1% of most terrigenous grains are concentrated in the fine size fractions. The size fraction used depends in part on the overall size distribution of the grains. I would suggest analyzing the fine sand (0.125–0.250 mm) and very fine sand (0.062–0.125 mm) separately.

The equipment for heavy mineral separation can be found in any well stocked laboratory. A typical apparatus is shown in Figure 9.7a. The upper funnel (A) may be replaced by a special separatory funnel (Fig. 9.7 b or c). The general procedure is:

(1) Put filter paper in funnel C. It should be the type that allows rapid flow. The sample number should be written (in pencil) on the filter paper.
(2) Pour the heavy liquid into funnel A. Be the sure that the pinchcock (B) is secured and the storage bottle (D) is in place.
(3) Put the sand sample into funnel A and stir with a glass rod.
(4) Allow the apparatus to sit for at least 20 minutes (one hour in some cases) and stir again.
(5) After another 20 minutes, open the pinchcock and allow the heavy minerals to collect in the lower funnel (C). Be sure that the liquid

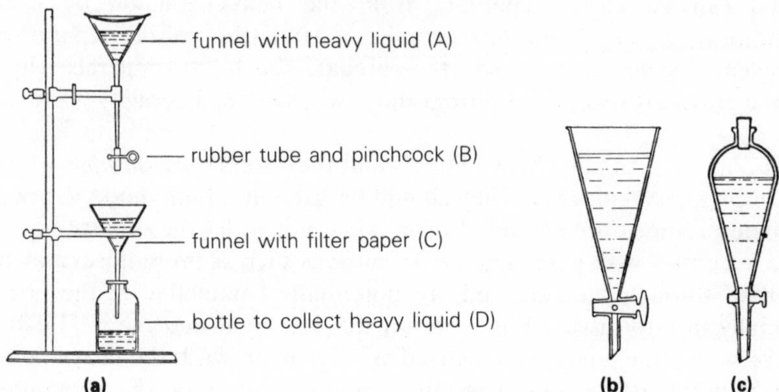

Figure 9.7 Apparatus for heavy-liquid separation shown in (a). Separatory funnels with valves in stem shown in (b) and (c). (Modified from Krumbein & Pettijohn 1938.)

containing the light mineral fraction (floating on the top in funnel A) does not pass into funnel C.

(6) After the liquid has drained from the lower funnel (C), replace it with a clean funnel and filter paper.

(7) Again open the pinchcock and allow the light sand fraction to collect in the lower funnel (C).

(8) After all the liquid has drained into the storage bottle (D), remove and cap it.

(9) Put a second bottle (labeled "Bromoform washings") under the lower funnel (D in Fig. 9.7a) and wash all funnels (together with the sand) with acetone. When all the heavy liquid has been washed from the glassware, sand, and filter paper, remove and cap the bottle. Place the filter paper and sand in a beaker. The bromoform may be reclaimed by placing a beaker containing the "washings" in cold brine. The bromoform will freeze at 9°C and separate from the admixed solvent. An alternative method involves mixing the "washings" with water, which absorbs the solvent. Reclamation, unless done very carefully with proper apparatus, will not normally yield a pure heavy liquid, and my opinion is that the effort does not justify the additional exposure to these toxic liquids. If the unreclaimed "washings" are discarded, they should be *properly disposed of*, not poured down the drain.

(10) Air-dry the filter paper and the contained sample or use a drying oven at temperatures less than 50°C.

(11) Weigh both the light and heavy fractions, and calculate the "weight percent heavy minerals" in the size fraction analyzed.

(12) Remove the magnetic fraction with a hand magnet and calculate the

"weight percent magnetic" of the total heavy-mineral sample. Save the magnetic fraction for possible petrographic (reflected polarized light) and/or X-ray diffraction analysis.

(13) Use a microsplitter to obtain enough grains to make one slide. Experience will determine "how much is enough."

(14) Heat a glass microscope slide on a hot plate and melt enough Lakeside 70 to cover the slide. Pour the sample split on the slide and spread the grains using a wire probe. A flame (match or Bunsen burner) applied briefly to the surface of the Lakeside 70 will destroy any bubbles. Put a cover glass on the slide. Use the eraser end of a wooden pencil to position the cover glass and remove any bubbles that were trapped when the cover glass was laid down.

(15) Remove the slide and clean it. Most of any Lakeside 70 which may have accidently reached the upper surface of the cover glass can be removed by scraping with the edge of another microscopic slide. The remainder can be removed with xylene.

(16) Study the slide with a petrographic microscope and determine the abundance of opaque grains as well as that of nonopaque grains. Using a mechanical stage, count 100 grains to determine the "percent opaque," while at the same time counting the various nonopaque species. Continue the count until a total of 200 nonopaque grains has been recorded. During this phase of the count, ignore the opaque grains. Calculate the abundance (as a percentage of the nonopaque fraction) of each mineral species present.

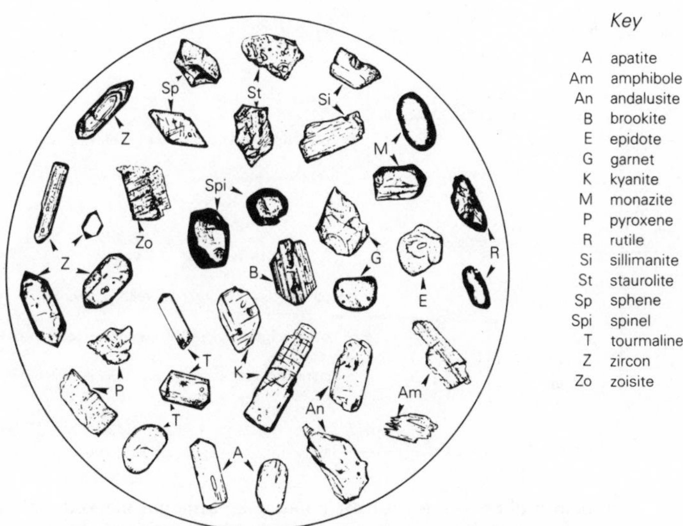

Figure 9.8 Typical heavy mineral grains (modified from Krumbein & Pettijohn 1938).

9.5 Mineral descriptions

The optical characteristics of some common minerals are outlined below. The most diagnostic properties for each mineral are in *italics*. Some typical grains are illustrated in Figure 9.8.

The identification keys (Figs 9.9–9.12) are intended as an aid to those just beginning the study of heavy minerals. The first step is to determine whether an unknown grain is isotropic or anisotropic. If the former, go to Figure 9.9. If the grain is anisotropic, determine whether it is colorless or colored and whether it is pleochroic or nonpleochroic and go to the appropriate key. Once you have gone through the key, you may find that there are several possible answers. At this point compare the optical characteristics of the unknown grains with those listed under the detailed descriptions.

(a) **Opaque grains**

Magnetite–ilmenite grains are blue-black in reflected light. Ilmenite is brownish or purplish and commonly weathers to *leucoxene* (a mixture of titanium oxides), which is white in reflected light.

Hematite is usually red in reflected light. Some grains may show nonopaque blood-red areas.

Pyrite is brass yellow in reflected light. *Marcusite* is similar but commonly fibrous.

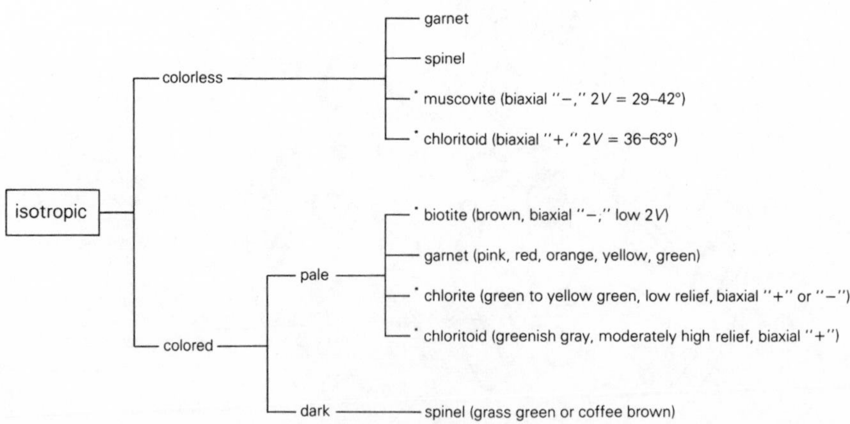

Figure 9.9 An identification key for isotropic minerals. Minerals marked with an asterisk are really anisotropic, but they occur as thin flakes which lie on basal cleavage and *appear* to be isotropic in heavy mineral mounts.

(b) **Rock fragments** are polycrystalline and commonly coated with iron oxide.

(c) **Alterites** are nonopaque grains that are too altered to be identified. Do not use this category as an excuse for the inability to identify difficult grains.

(d) **Nonopaque heavy minerals**

ACTINOLITE (see AMPHIBOLES)

Shape	Anhedral (elongate cleavage fragments; more elongate than pyroxenes; may show dentate ends)
Extinction	*Inclined*, *<25°* (see below for details)
Birefringence:	Moderate (0.018–0.027)
Pleochroism:	*Strong* (see below for details)
Color	N.A.
Relief	Moderately high (n = 1.599–1.722)
Sign of elongation	Depends on species (see below for details)
Optic sign	Depends on species (see below for details)

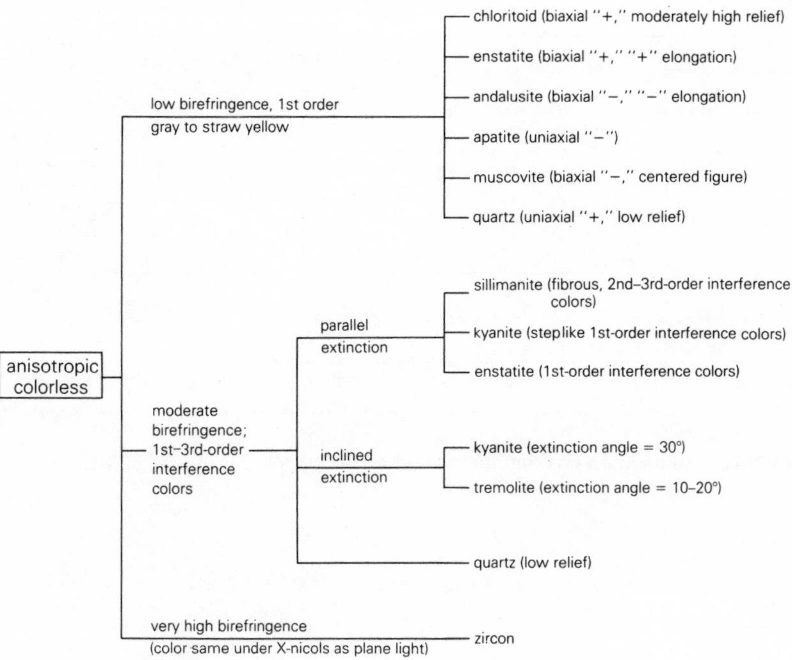

Figure 9.10 An identification key for colorless anisotropic minerals.

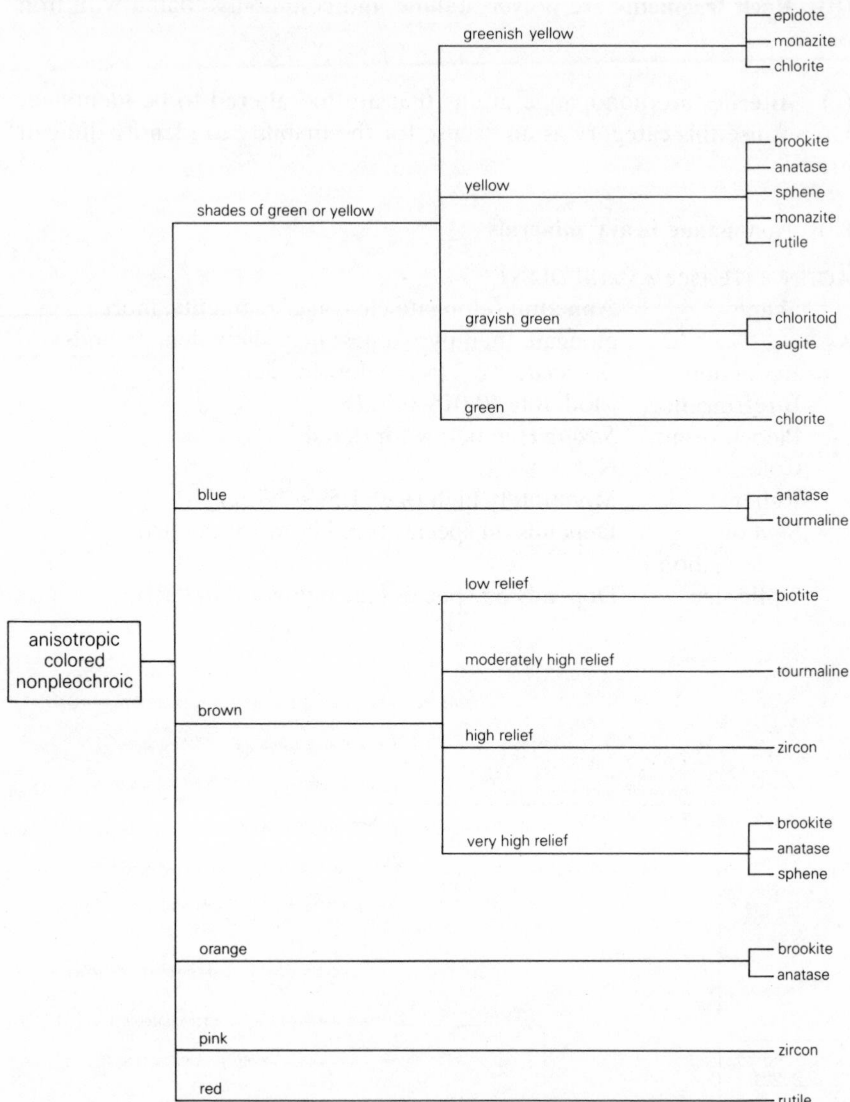

Figure 9.11 An identification key for colored nonpleochroic anisotropic minerals.

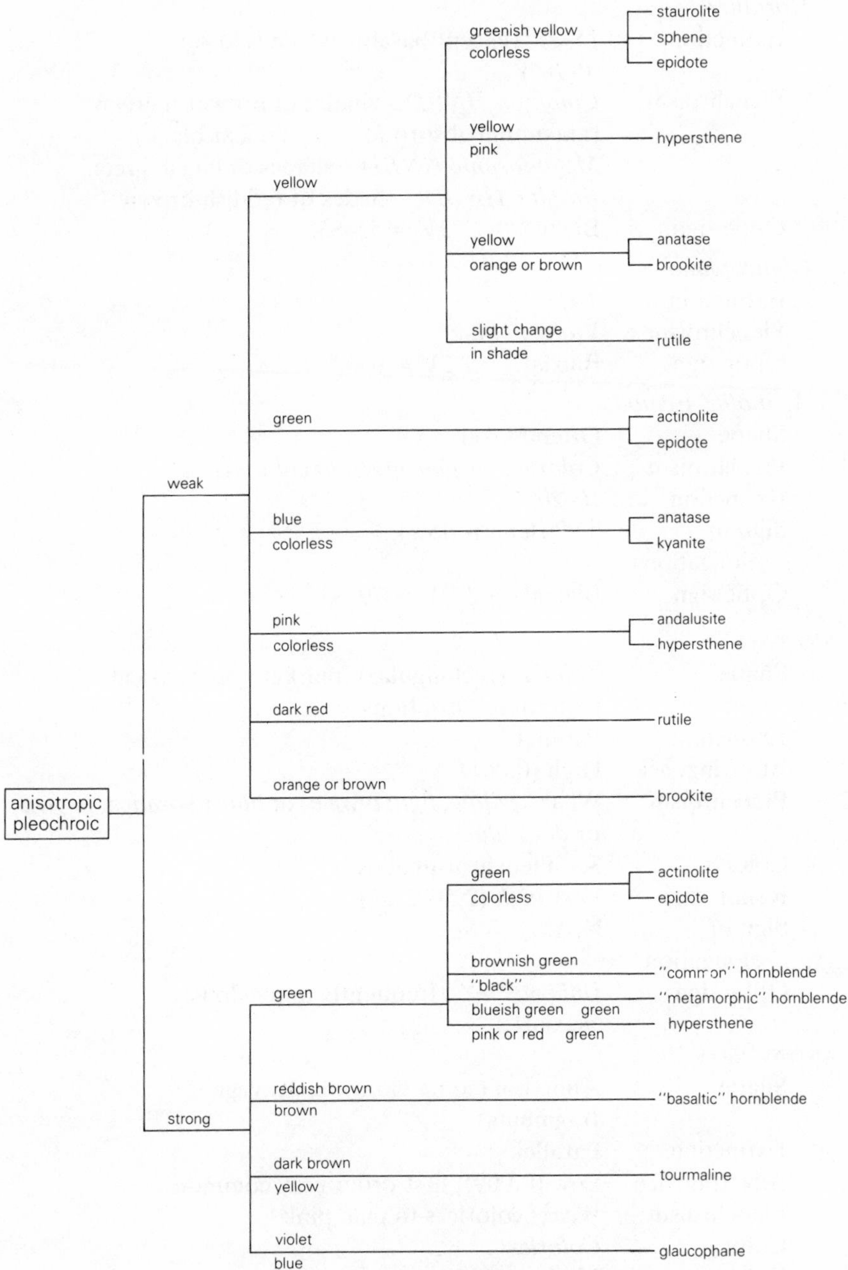

Figure 9.12 An identification key for pleochroic minerals.

Hornblende

Extinction	*15–25°* (except basaltic which is lower, *0–10°*)
Pleochroism	*Common HNBD* – shades of brownish green (maximum absorption may appear black) *Metamorphic HNBD* – shades of bluish green *Basaltic HNBD* – shades of reddish brown
Optic sign	Biaxial "−," $2V = 52–85°$

Glaucophane

Extinction	*4–6°*
Pleochroism	*Violet to blue*
Optic sign	Biaxial "−," $2V = 0–68°$

Actinolite–tremolite

Shape	Often fibrous
Pleochroism	*Colorless or pale green to colorless*
Extinction	*10–20°*
Sign of elongation	"+" (length slow)
Optic sign	Biaxial "−," $2V = 79–85°$

ANATASE

Shape	*Tabular* (rectangular); market "geometrical patterning" striations
Extinction	Parallel
Birefringence	High (0.061)
Pleochroism	Weak; *yellow*, *light brown*, or *blue* to *orange*, *brown*, or *deep blue*
Color	See Pleochroism above
Relief	*Very high* (2.50–2.55)
Sign of elongation	N.A.
Optic sign	*Uniaxial "−"* (frequently anomalously biaxial)

ANDALUSITE

Shape	Anhedral (some elongate cleavage fragments)
Extinction	Parallel
Birefringence	Low (0.009), first-order gray common
Pleochroism	*Weak*; colorless to pale pink
Color	*Colorless*
Relief	Moderately high ($n = 1.63–1.64$)
Sign of elongation	"−" (length fast) (sillimanite "+")
Optic sign	Biaxial "−," $2V = 85$

APATITE

Shape	Euhedral (rounded) common; prismatic grains occur but are less common
Extinction	Parallel (if prismatic)
Birefringence	*Low* (0.003–0.005); first-order gray
Pleochroism	N.A.
Color	*Colorless*
Relief	Moderately high (n = 1.63–1.65)
Sign of elongation	"–" (length fast)
Optic sign	*Uniaxial* "–" (in some cases anomalously biaxial with small $2V$)

AUGITE (see PYROXENES)

BIOTITE

Shape	Equant; perfect (001) basal cleavage.
Extinction	N.A.
Birefringence	*Very low interference colors* (lies on basil cleavage)
Pleochroism	None when lying on basal cleavage
Color	*Brown*
Relief	Low to moderate (n = 1.57–1.65)
Sign of elongation	N.A.
Optic sign	*Biaxial "–," 2V very small* (pseudouniaxial interference figure)

BROOKITE

Shape	Squarish grains, with truncated corners, flattened parallel to (100) common; striae parallel to long axis
Extinction	Parallel
Birefringence	Very high (0.158); *incomplete extinction* due to high dispersion
Pleochroism	Weak; shades of yellow, orange, and brown
Color	See Pleochroism above
Relief	Very high (n = 2.58–2.74)
Sign of elongation	N.A.
Optic sign	Biaxial "+," $2V$ = 0–30°

CHLORITE

Shape	Equant to irregular; perfect (001) basal cleavage
Extinction	N.A.
Birefringence	*Very low interference colors*, may appear isotropic, may show abnormal interference colors
Pleochroism	N.A.

Color	Green to yellow-green
Relief	*Low to moderate* (n = 1.56–1.65)
Sign of elongation	N.A.
Optic sign	Biaxial "+" or "−," *2V = 0–30°*

CHLORITOID

Shape	Equant or irregular; perfect (001) basal cleavage
Extinction	N.A.
Birefringence	*Very low interference colors* (may appear isotropic)
Pleochroism	N.A.
Color	Colorless to greenish gray
Relief	*Moderately high* (n = 1.72–1.74)
Sign of elongation	N.A.
Optic sign	Biaxial "+," *2V = 45–68°*

CLINOZOISITE

Shape	Anhedral
Extinction	*Inclined* 14–20°
Birefringence	Low (0.01)
Pleochroism	Faint green to red or pink or yellow
Color	*Colorless* or *yellow*
Relief	Moderately high (n = 1.72–1.73)
Sign of elongation	N.A.
Optic sign	Biaxial "+," 2V = 66° (some are "−")

ENSTATITE (see PYROXENES)

EPIDOTE

Shape	Anhedral, equidimensional (angular to subrounded)
Extinction	N.A.
Birefringence	*High* (0.028–0.051); high-order interference colors which make grain appear same under crossed nicols and ordinary light; anomalous blue or brownish interference colors common
Pleochroism	*Colorless* to *pale greenish yellow*; some grains may be nonpleochroic
Color	Pale greenish yellow; these will show centered optic axis figure
Relief	Moderately high (1.72–1.78)
Sign of elongation	"+" or "−"
Optic sign	Biaxial "−," 2V = 69–80°; grains which rest on (001) basal cleavage show straight-centered optic axis

figure ("*compass-needle figure*"); these grains will be nonpleochroic

GARNET

Shape	Angular to rounded (conchoidal)
Extinction	N.A.
Birefringence	*Isotropic*; anisoptropic inclusions or strain may mislead one to think that it is anisotropic
Pleochroism	N.A.
Color	*Colorless*; shades of *pale* pink, red, orange, or yellow
Relief	*High* (n = 1.76–1.94, depending on variety)

GLAUCOPHANE (see AMPHIBOLES)

HORNBLENDE (see AMPHIBOLES)

HYPERSTHENE (see PYROXENES)

KYANITE

Shape	Anhedral, but cleavage excellent producing generally rectangular grains
Extinction	*Commonly 30*°; this is the case when the grain rests on the (100) cleavage (see Fig. 9.13a); there are exceptions; grains resting on the (010) or (001) will show parallel extinction or a very low extinction angle (< 7) (see Fig. 9.13 b & c)
Birefringence	Moderate (0.016); excellent cleavage in three directions results in *steplike areas of bright* first- and second-order interference colors
Pleochroism	Rarely colorless to pale blue
Color	*Colorless*
Relief	Moderately high (1.71–1.73)
Sign of elongation	"+" or "−"

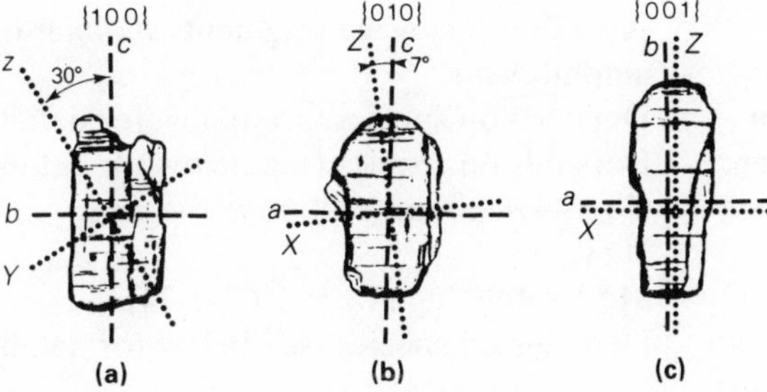

Figure 9.13 Kyanite grains lying on cleavage parallel to (a) (100), (b) (010), (c) (001).

Optic sign	Biaxial "−," 2V = 82°; excellent centered biaxial bar figure when grain is resting on (100); grains resting on (001) or (010) are so far off perpendicular to *Z* or *Y* as to give no centered figure at all

MONAZITE

Shape	Anhedral, equidimensional, and rounded (*egg shaped*)
Extinction	N.A.
Birefringence	*High* (0.049–0.051)
Pleochroism	Faint at best
Color	*Pale yellow* or *pale greenish yellow*
Relief	Moderately high (n = 1.79–1.85)
Sign of elongation	N.A.
Optic sign	Biaxial "+," 2*V* = 11–14°; grains resting on (001) basal cleavage will show acute bisectrix figure with small 2*V* and numerous isochromatic curves; such grains would show low interference colors

MUSCOVITE

Shape	Equant; perfect (001) basal cleavage
Extinction	N.A.
Birefringence	*Very low interference colors*; first-order gray to nearly "black" (isotropic); lies on basal cleavage
Pleochroism	N.A.
Color	Colorless
Relief	*Low* (n = 1.55–1.62)
Sign of elongation	N.A.
Optic sign	*Biaxial "−,"* 2*V* = 29–42°

PYROXENES

Shape	Anhedral (cleavage fragments *stubbier* than amphiboles)
Extinction	Depends on species (see below for details)
Birefringence	Depends on species (see below for details)
Pleochroism	Clino – *none*; ortho – *none* to *strong*
Color	N.A.
Relief	Moderately high (n = 1.67–1.74)
Sign of elongation	Depends on species (see below for details)
Optic sign	Depends on species (see below for details)

Orthopyroxene

Hypersthene

Extinction	Parallel
Pleochroism	Pale *pink or red* to *yellow or green* (very faint to strong)
Birefringence	*Low to moderate* (0.009–0.016); bright first-order colors to first-order gray
Sign of elongation	"+" (length slow)
Optic sign	biaxial "−"; $2V = 63–90°$

Enstatite

Extinction	Parallel
Color	*Colorless*
Birefringence	*Low to moderate* (0.009–0.016); bright first-order colors to first-order gray
Sign of elongation	"+" (length slow)
Optic sign	Biaxial "+"; $2V = 58–80°$

Clinopyroxene (*Augite*)

Extinction	$> 40°$
Color	Pale brownish gray or pale grayish green; nonpleochroic
Birefringence	*High* (0.018–0.043)
Optic sign	biaxial "+"; $2V = 58–62°$

QUARTZ

Shape	Generally equant, angular to round
Extinction	N.A.
Birefringence	*Low* (0.009); commonly shows *first-order colors*
Pleochroism	N.A.
Color	Colorless
Relief	*Very low* ($n = 1.54–1.55$)
Sign of elongation	N.A.
Optic sign	*Uniaxial "+"*

RUTILE

Shape	Generally elongate and well rounded
Extinction	Parallel
Birefringence	*Very high* (0.287) (same color as in plane light)
Pleochroism	None to faint
Color	*Deep red* or yellow
Relief	*Very high* ($n = 2.6–2.9$) which causes grains to appear opaque; increase light intensity to see color

Sign of elongation	"+" (length slow)
Optic sign	Uniaxial "+"

Longitudinal and oblique *striations* common

SILLIMANITE

Shape	Anhedral, irregular to short prismatic: striae parallel to length; commonly fibrous
Extinction	Parallel (note kyanite *commonly* 30°)
Birefringence	Moderate (0.021, second- and third-order colors) but *higher* than kyanite or andalusite
Pleochroism	N.A.
Color	Colorless
Relief	Moderately high (n = 1.66–1.68)
Sign of elongation	"+" (length slow) (versus andalusite which is "−" or length fast)
Optic sign	Biaxial "+" (resting on (010) perpendicular to Y will show a centered flash figure; such grains will not show striae and might be confused with kyanite)

SPHENE (*titanite*)

Shape	Euhedral to anhedral (conchoidal)
Extinction	N.A.
Birefringence	Very high (0.134); *incomplete extinction* due to high dispersion (grain turns *bluish* as maximum extinction is reached)
Pleochroism	Weak, colorless to pale yellow to brownish
Color	*Pale yellow* or *brownish*
Relief	*Very high* (1.9–2.0)
Sign of elongation	N.A.
Optic sign	Biaxial "+," $2V$ = 27°

SPINEL

Shape	Subhedral to well rounded
Extinction	N.A.
Birefringence	*Isotropic*
Pleochroism	N.A.
Color	Colorless, *grass green* or *coffee brown* (*darker* than garnet in colored varieties)
Relief	High (n = 1.72–2.05)
Sign of elongation	N.A.
Optic sign	N.A.

"Common" spinel, which is colorless or pale pink, is very difficult to distinguish from garnet

STAUROLITE

Shape	Anhedral, angular
Extinction	Parallel (although there are rarely crystal faces or cleavage to determine this)
Birefringence	*Moderate* (0.01) with bright first-order interference colors
Pleochroism	*Strong*, *colorless* to *pale* or *golden yellow*; also straw yellow to yellowish brown
Color	N.A.
Relief	Moderately high (n = 1.74–1.75)
Sign of elongation	N.A.
Optic sign	Biaxial "–," $2V = 88°$
	Commonly (especially deeper-colored grains) contains abundant inclusions (i.e. highly poikiloblastic) resulting in a porous appearance ("Swiss cheese")

TOURMALINE

Shape	Enhedral to rounded
Extinction	*Parallel*
Birefringence	High (0.019–0.032)
Pleochroism	*Strong*; maximum parallel to east–west direction = ω *Common tourmaline* – ω = dark brown, ε = yellow *Indicolite* (variety) – ω = indigo blue to black, ε = pale violet to colorless *Note*. Grains cut normal to *c* (optical axis) will *not* show pleochroism; rather they will show a color similar to the darker pleochroic color. Such grains *will show* centered optic axis figure
Color	N.A.
Relief	Moderately high (n = 1.62–1.69)
Sign of elongation	"–" (length fast)
Optic sign	Uniaxial "–"

TREMOLITE (see AMPHIBOLES)

ZIRCON

Shape	*Enhedral* to subhedral; elongate
Extinction	*Parallel*
Birefringence	*High* (0.055–0.059)
Pleochroism	None (faint in some strongly colored grains)
Color	90% colorless; color related to radioactive bombardment, which with time changes structure

faintly brown → pale brownish red → pale red → pale violet (hyacinth)

$\xrightarrow{\hspace{5cm}}$

increasing age

Relief	*High* (h = 1.99–1.93)
Sign of elongation	"+" (length slow)
Optic sign	Uniaxial "+"

ZOISITE

Shape	Euhedral, prismatic or irregular cleavage fragments
Extinction	*Parallel*
Birefringence	Low (0.006), incomplete extinction, abnormal ultra-blue interference colors
Pleochroism	Thulite (var.) strong pink to deep rose or yellow, generally faint shades of rose, green, or brown
Color	Commonly colorless, see Pleochroism above
Relief	Moderately high (n = 1.70–1.71)
Sign of elongation	N.A.
Optic sign	Biaxial "+," $2V$ = 0–60°

10 Rock color

Color is one of the most conspicuous properties of sedimentary rock and in some ways one of the most neglected. Although commonly utilized in stratigraphic correlation, its value in solving other geologic problems has not been fully tested. It is recognized that most thick gray-to-black sequences are marine or lacustrine and red ones are nonmarine (especially alluvial), but the significance of subtle color variations remains unknown.

10.1 Description of colors

Precision in describing color is possible only when rock samples are compared to a standard color guide. Highly recommended is the Rock Color Chart (Goddard *et al.* 1948), which is based on the Munsell three-parameter color system and contains 115 colors. Folk (1969) suggests as an alternative the more extensive Munsell Soil Color Chart and presents a modified terminology to be used with it.

Each color is assigned a code, such as 10R 5/2. The first element in the code designation (10R) refers to the **hue** (e.g. red), which is defined in terms of the wavelength of light. The second term (5/) is the **value** (brightness), which is based on the relative amount of black versus white. The third term (/2) is the chroma (saturation), which is based on the relative amount of pure color versus neutral gray. The color chips on the chart are arranged systematically according to hue, value, and chroma.

When determining rock color compare the sample directly to the chart. By trial and error pick the color that is closest to that of the specimen. In some cases this may require interpolation between color chips on the chart. When fresh and weathered surfaces are different colors, determine both. Record code designation as well as the color name.

10.2 Factors that influence color

Color depends on (1) the color of the rock-forming minerals, (2) grain size (Fig. 10.1), (3) the amount and oxidation state of iron present, and (4) the amount and type of organic material present. Without question iron-rich minerals and organic carbon are the most important coloring agents in sedimentary rock. Organic matter is important not only as a pigment but also as a reducing agent that affects the amount of iron and its oxidation state.

10.2.1 Sandstone

The color of sandstone, with no iron oxide, is determined by the color of the framework grains. Quartz arenites are pale gray to white, as are some arkosic sands. Arkosic sandstones rich in K-feldspar are commonly pink. Litharenites are generally darker shades of gray due to the presence of black or dark gray mineral and rock fragments. Glauconitic sandstones are green.

The pigment in reddish sandstone is ferric oxide (Fe_2O_3), generally present as hematite. Even very small concentrations of hematite, often less than 1%, impart a pronounced color to the rock. Whether the iron is deposited as soil-derived detrital particles (VanHouten 1973) or produced by breakdown of detrital iron-rich minerals after deposition (Walker 1974) is still a matter of controversy.

10.2.2 Mudrock

Red and reddish brown mudrock owes its color to hematite grain coatings and interstitial crystals. Presumably the original sediment was drab. Reddening occurred by "aging" of hydrous ferric iron plus the breakdown of iron-rich detrital grains (McBride 1974). In red-bed sequences decreasing grain size is usually accompanied by increasingly darker colors (Fig. 10.1). This may be related to the greater surface area of the detrital grains in the finer rocks or more total iron.

Black to gray mudrock owes its color to finely disseminated organic matter and possibly iron sulfide. Darkness (value), a function of the amount of included organic carbon, is controlled by (1) the flux of organic matter during deposition, (2) the sedimentation rate, and (3) the rate of oxidation of the organic matter (Potter *et al.* 1980: 56–7). The organic content in black (N1 to N2) mudrocks generally ranges between 1.5 and 5%; in gray (N5) to dark gray (N3-N4) mudrock it ranges between 0.3 and 1.5% (Potter *et al.* 1980: Fig. 1.25). In interbedded light gray and dark gray shale sequences, the lighter-colored ones are bioturbated (oxygenated bottom conditions), in contrast to the lack of bioturbation in the darker ones (anoxic conditions) (Byers 1977).

Hematite and organic material ($< 0.3\%$) are absent in greenish and olive gray mudrock. The greenish hue is due to the color of illite and chlorite, which contain ferrous iron (Fe^{2+}). In some cases the progression from red to gray shows a decrease in the Fe^{3+}/Fe^{2+} ratio, but little change in the total iron content (McBride 1974). Other studies show that greenish gray rock contains less iron than the associated red beds.

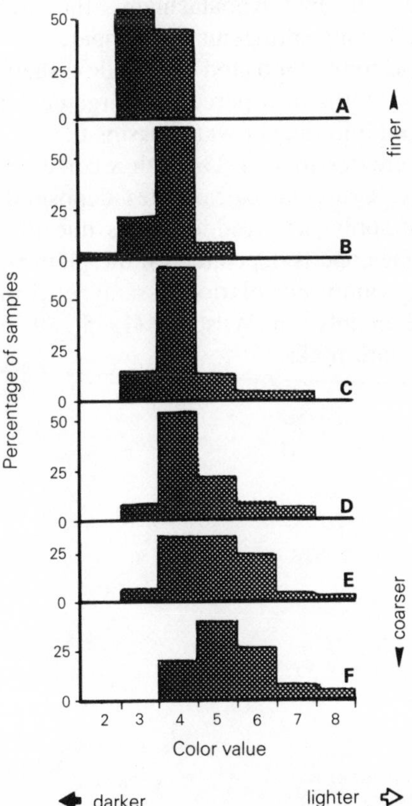

Figure 10.1 Histograms showing the color value of red beds of differing grain size: A, claystone; B, mudstone; C, fine siltstone; D, medium-to-coarse siltstone; E, very fine to fine sandstone; F, medium-to-coarse sandstone. Based on 556 samples from the Triassic–Jurassic Culpeper Basin in northern Virginia.

Presumably this is because some iron was removed after being reduced to the more soluble Fe^{2+} (Potter *et al.* 1980: 55). The extent to which ferrous iron (Fe^{2+}) is added to the silicate lattice of clay minerals (illite and chlorite) in the presence of iron-rich reducing waters is unknown.

10.2.3 Carbonate rock

Although pure calcite and dolomite are colorless to white, a great many carbonates are gray. As with shale this is a function of the amount of organic carbon present.

Weathered dolomite is inclined to have pale brownish hues resulting from oxidation of ferrous iron in the dolomite crystals. In many dolomitic limestone sequences in the Appalachians, the "dolomite" beds and laminae contain abundant authigenic K-feldspar.

Fine-grained limestone deposited in shallow-shelf lagoons generally contains only a few tenths of a percent of organic carbon and is usually medium gray. Traced into deeper water basins the organic carbon content in the limestone increases to 1 or 2% with a corresponding darkening to black or dark gray. Crinoidal calcarenites deposited in relatively deep starved basins commonly have reddish hues due to slow sedimentation rates. Light gray limestone is deposited on the platform margin in organic reefs and in the winnowed platform sand environment. This brief summary is based mainly on Wilson's (1975: 89, 350–60) exhaustive discussion of carbonate rocks.

11 Environmental Analysis

11.1 Introduction

Most of the previous chapters have dealt with the practical aspects of studying sedimentary rocks, particularly those that are observed in the field. Once collected and organized, they provide the basis for understanding the origin of the rock, especially the environment and processes of deposition. Neglect during the initial planning and subsequent data collection will doom the final phase of interpretation to failure. Time must be spent formulating the goal of the study and plan of attack. Once in the field, your observations and measurements should be made with the greatest care. This takes time, but not as much as a return trip to redo a poorly done job.

11.2 Field data

Sedimentary rocks are generally studied by measuring the exposed succession in stream beds, on ridge crests, in the open field and any other place where there is a reasonably continuous outcrop. Bore-hole cores, when available, furnish a valuable supplement to natural exposures. Although cores only provide a thin cylinder of rock to study, they are generally more continuous than rock at the surface, and they are always unweathered. Cliff faces and quarry walls provide a two-dimensional view not available in measured sections, which are essentially one dimensional.

11.2.1 Two-dimensional exposures

The main value of two-dimensional exposures is that they show how the various lithologies are related laterally and something of the shape of the lithogic units (Fig. 11.1). One approach to studying them simply involves making a detailed field sketch keyed to your observations, measurements, and sample locations. A better choice is to use photographs or photomosaics of the rock face. Each photograph should include an adequate scale, such as a stadia rod or a 2–3 m long board with photogenic, clearly marked subdivisions (e.g. 10 cm units as well as 1 m

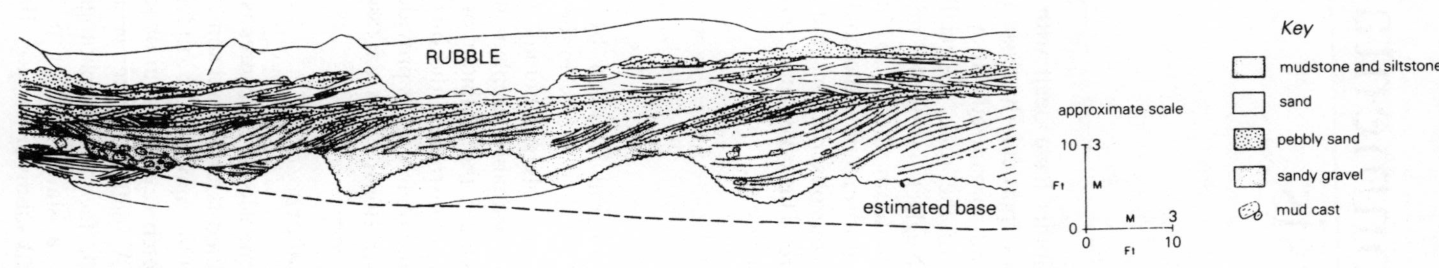

Figure 11.1 A line tracing of a photomosaic showing the internal structure and composition of a conglomeratic braided channel fill (modified from Galloway *et al*. 1979).

units). Using photographs may require a second trip to the field unless a Polaroid (or similar type) camera is used. Alternatively, field data may be keyed to the photos after you return, provided a relatively simply, annotated sketch has been made in the field. A final detailed tracing of the exposure showing the various lithologic units, contacts, and sedimentary structures will be invaluable in your environmental analysis of the sequence.

11.2.2 Measured sections

Although I shall not go into the details of section measuring because they are discussed in any book on field methods, a few comments on recording field data seem worth while. Each lithologic unit should be described in the detail required for a particular study. For very detailed investigations the description should include the following information:

(a) *Thickness and geometry*. If variable, give the maximum, minimum, and average values; the latter should be used in tabulating the total thickness of the section.
(b) *Contacts*. Describe the nature of the upper and lower contact as sharp or gradational.
(c) *Grain size*. Note if graded (see Section 7.3).
(d) *Rock type*, e.g. arkose (see Sections 8.1.1 & 8.4.3).
(e) *Color* (see Chapter 10).
(f) *Sedimentary structures*. Indicate if variable in distribution (e.g. trough cross bedding at base, burrowed at top) (see Chapter 1).
(g) *Paleocurrent measurements*.
(h) *Trace fossils* (see Chapter 4).
(i) *Body fossils*.
(j) *Miscellaneous*, e.g. abundant stylolites, calcite-filled fractures, etc.

The information may be coded (e.g. coarse-grained sandstone = SSc) to save time, but do not be so cryptic that the notation has no meaning a few months after it is recorded. A complete set of code symbols should be included in your field book, preferably on the first or last page.

If the rock is composed of thinly interbedded lithologies of different type, you obviously cannot record each centimeter scale unit. Such heterogeneous rocks should be described and then given an informal designation such as "lithology A." As it re-occurs in the section, simply record "lithology A." Indeed, the same can be done for more homogeneous units. When using such names, one thing to avoid is establishing a new one for each unit in the succession. In the long run this will cost more time and lead to confusion. We will return to this topic in Section 11.3.1.

11.2.3 Graphic logs

A flexible-scale log (Fig. 11.2) can be drawn into your field book to complement detailed notes. Although each bed is drawn at a scale which allows presentation of internal structures, the scale may change by orders of magnitude from unit to unit (Anderton 1985: 36). From this log a true scale can be made when you return from the field.

There are many ways to present graphic logs of measured vertical sequences (Collinson & Thompson 1982: Fig. 10.6, Miall 1984: 55–7). The method illustrated in Figure 11.3 utilizes two columns. One column is used to show lithology and is of constant width. The other shows sedimentary structures by various symbols and grain size by column width. This column mimics a weathering profile, where fine-grained beds are recessive, and allows rapid visual comparison of units. Stylized symbols, such as those in Figure 11.3, allow standardization, although some workers prefer realistic symbols which convey more information (Anderton 1985: 37). Other information, such as fossil content, may be indicated by narrow secondary columns to the right of the main columns. Similarly paleocurrent measurements may be put opposite the units from which they were recorded. Azimuths are plotted, as on a map, with north toward the top of the page.

A sample measured section with five distinctive lithologic units is

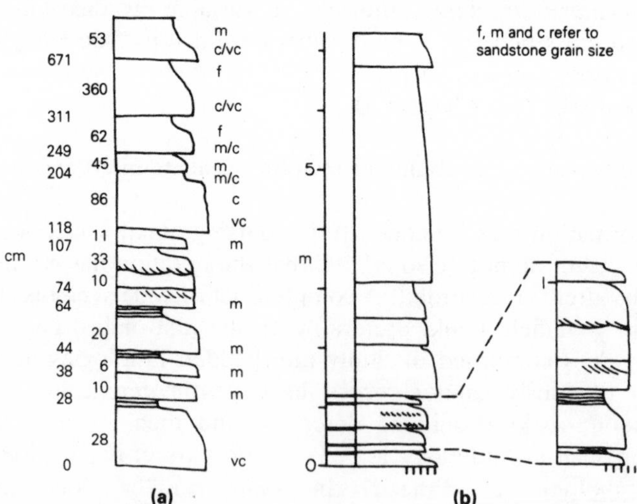

Figure 11.2 A flexible-scale field log and a corresponding true-scale log: (a) flexible-scale field log with each bed drawn on a scale sufficient to show relevant detail; (b) true-scale log derived from (a) with more detailed log of lower portion of log. (Modified from Anderton 1985: Fig. 2.)

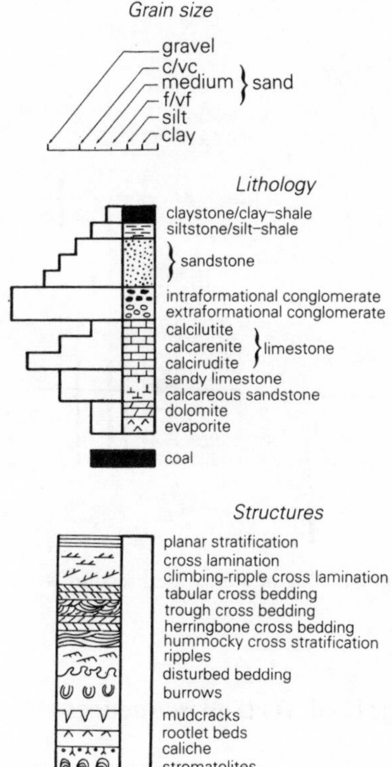

Figure 11.3 Symbols used in making a two-column graphic log of a measured section. One column shows grain size and sedimentary structures; the other shows dominant lithology.

described below. Unit 1 is the oldest and unit 5 is the youngest. The graphic log for this sequence is illustrated in Figure 11.4.

Unit 5 Coarse sandstone with intraformational conglomerate at base; trough cross bedding with foreset dip azimuth equal to 120°; erosional contact at the base; plant fragments; 25 m thick.

Unit 4 Siltshale; planar stratification and burrows; foraminifers; sharp lower contact; 10 m thick.

Unit 3 Very fine sandstone; cross lamination with foreset dip azimuth equal to 250°; brachiopods; gradational lower contact; 5 m thick.

Unit 2 Medium sandstone; tabular cross bedding with foreset dip azimuth equal to 230°; brachiopods; erosional contact at base; fines upward; 15 m thick.

Unit 1 Calcarenite; tabular cross bedding with foreset dip azimuth equal to 10°; brachiopods, crinoids and ooids; thin (less than 1 m) clay interbeds; 30 m thick; erosional upper contact.

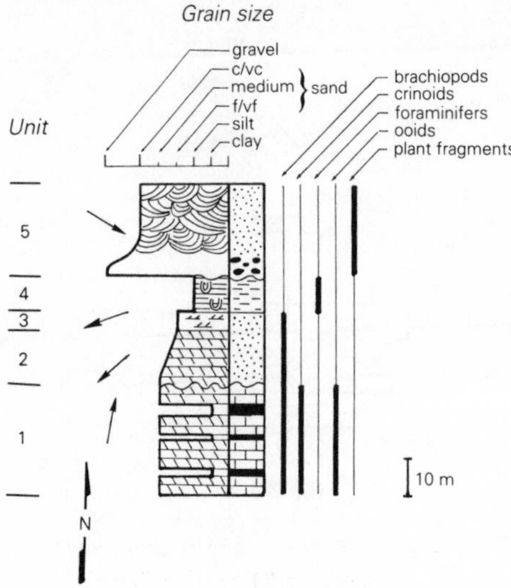

Figure 11.4 A sample graphic log of a measured section: see text for description of units.

11.3 Facies analysis of vertical sequences

Gressly's definition of facies (discussed by Middleton 1973) as the sum total of the lithologic and paleontologic aspects of a depositional unit generally reflects modern usage. Facies are defined on the basis of distinctive combinations of lithology, rock color, sedimentary structures, trace fossils, and body fossils. Facies analysis involves the description and classification of a sedimentary rock unit followed by an interpretation of depositional processes and environmental setting. Interpretation is based on the way in which various facies are associated, and on the geometry and orientation of the rock units. Determining the depositional environment is done by comparison with modern and ancient models.

11.3.1 Facies definition and description

Do not start subdividing a sedimentary sequence into facies until you have examined the rocks and are familiar with their variability. The essential step here is to measure and log the succession in detail (Section 11.2.2).

One of the most difficult aspects of facies analysis is establishing objective and usable **facies definitions**. A classification scheme should utilize one or more criteria arranged in a systematic hierarchy and may have to be modified and refined as work progresses. "The object is to

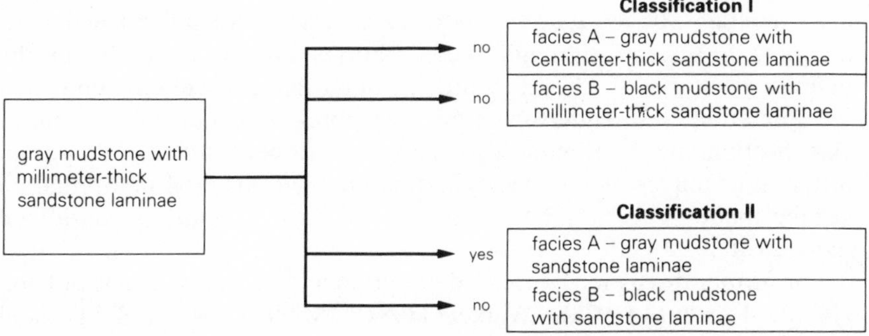

Figure 11.5 Facies classification. Classification I lacks a hierarchical relationship between parameters used. For this reason the rock to be classified cannot be assigned to either facies. In classification II there is a workable hierarchy between the criteria used, and the sample fits the description of facies A. (Based on example in Anderton 1985: 40.)

erect a set of definitions that will subdivide all the rock under study into a series of facies such that every rock unit can be classified and that no unit can be included in more than one facies" (Anderton 1985: 41). Suppose, for example, you wish to assign a bed of gray mudstone with millimeter-thick sandstone laminae into one of the facies shown in Figure 11.5. The problem with classification I is that the mudstone to be classified has characteristics of both facies A and facies B, but it fits neither one perfectly. On the other hand it fits facies A in classification II, making classification II the preferable one to use.

There is no master list of facies available which we can use to pigeonhole the rocks encountered in a new study area. Indeed it is unlikely that such a list will ever exist because of the variability of sedimentary systems. Trying to force the rock present in a new study area into a set of facies, previously encountered or read about, may cause one to overlook significant features. Nevertheless, some environments seem to be characterized by a limited number of re-occurring facies. Although one should never slavishly rely on published facies descriptions as a basis for classification, neither should one attempt to work in a vacuum.

The scale used in establishing facies descriptions is determined mainly by the objectives of the study. Other factors include the time available and the character of the rocks being studied. Although facies are generally defined on the basis of one's experience and knowledge, with a healthy dose of common sense, multivariate statistical methods may be useful in some cases (e.g. Imbrie & Purdy 1963, Friend *et al.* 1976).

Once the facies have been categorized, the various features not used in the definition can be compiled. This is the **facies description** as distinct from the facies definition. For example, facies A (classification II in Fig. 11.5) is defined as a gray mudstone with sandstone laminae. Individual samples may contain trace fossils; they may also contain branchiopods and/or fish scales. Although these features are not essential in the definition of facies A, they may provide important clues to environmental interpretation. As Anderton (1985: 41) notes, one objective of facies classification and description is to enable one to pool sufficient data from different examples of each facies so that an environmental interpretation can be made. This may not be possible if each example is considered individually.

For further discussion of facies description and definition see Middleton (1978), Reading (1978), Walker (1984), Miall (1984: 133–54), and Anderton (1985).

11.3.2 Interpretation

Certain aspects regarding the depositional environments of some facies can be interpreted in isolation. For instance shale with mudcracks and salt casts clearly points to subaerial exposure. The presence of branchiopods further indicates that the environment may have been an exposed lacustrine mud flat. Although important, facies exhibiting such specific environmental information are rare. Commonly the clues are more veiled, indicating an aspect that might be common to a variety of settings. Cross-bedded sandstone, for example, suggests active currents that can occur in a great many environments. Some facies are so enigmatic as to defy interpretation.

Attempting to evaluate individual facies in a succession of many facies is obviously difficult. A better approach is to study the vertical sequence and lateral relationships, which may contribute more information about the environment than the individual facies themselves. Numerous studies have shown that sedimentary sequences contain assemblages of facies with a restricted range of interrelationships between them. These assemblages, called **facies associations**, are commonly cyclic and characteristic of particular depositional environments.

The key to interpretation is that facies occurring in a comformable vertical sequence were formed in laterally adjacent environments. Stated another way, the vertical sequence of facies, laid on its side, reflects lateral juxtapositions of environments. During transgressions and regressions, environments migrate laterally, resulting in a vertical transition from one facies to another. This fundamental relationship, known as Walther's law, is illustrated in Figure 11.6.

Walther's law is not applicable to sequences with major disconformities. If the area, shown in Figure 11.6, were to experience a rapid sea-level rise, the offshore environment would migrate landward (to the right) and be superimposed directly on top of all of the other

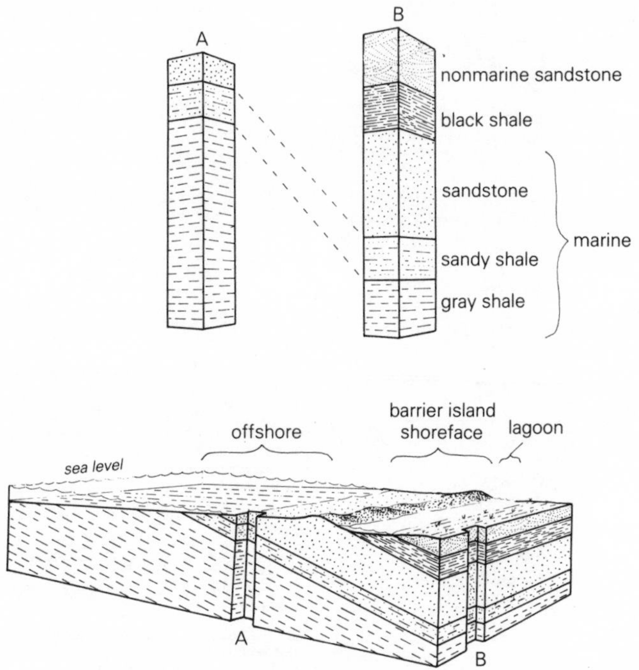

Figure 11.6 Sedimentary environments and their relationship to representative stratigraphic sections developed during progradation (regression) of environments. Note how the vertical sequence corresponds to the lateral distribution of environments.

environments. In this case the upward transition from lagoonal shale to offshore shale would not reflect deposition in environments that were once adjacent.

Determining whether the upward transition of one facies to another is significant in a succession containing numerous facies generally requires more than a subjective approach. Statistical analysis, using the **Markov chain**, or variants of it, has gained popularity in recent years, although this has not been without some controversy. Some complaints are philosophical. Three cited by Reading (1978: 8) are: (1) the type of contact is frequently ignored; (2) the data are oversimplified to facilitate statistical analysis; and (3) minor facies, which may be statistically insignificant but geologically important, are subordinated or eliminated. Other difficulties involve the statistical test as applied to facies analysis. For further discussion of this rather complex problem see Carr (1982), Powers and Easterling (1982), Miall (1984: 147), Walker (1984), and Harper (1984). The method presented below is relatively simple and can be performed using only an electronic calculator. Although Walker (1984: 3)

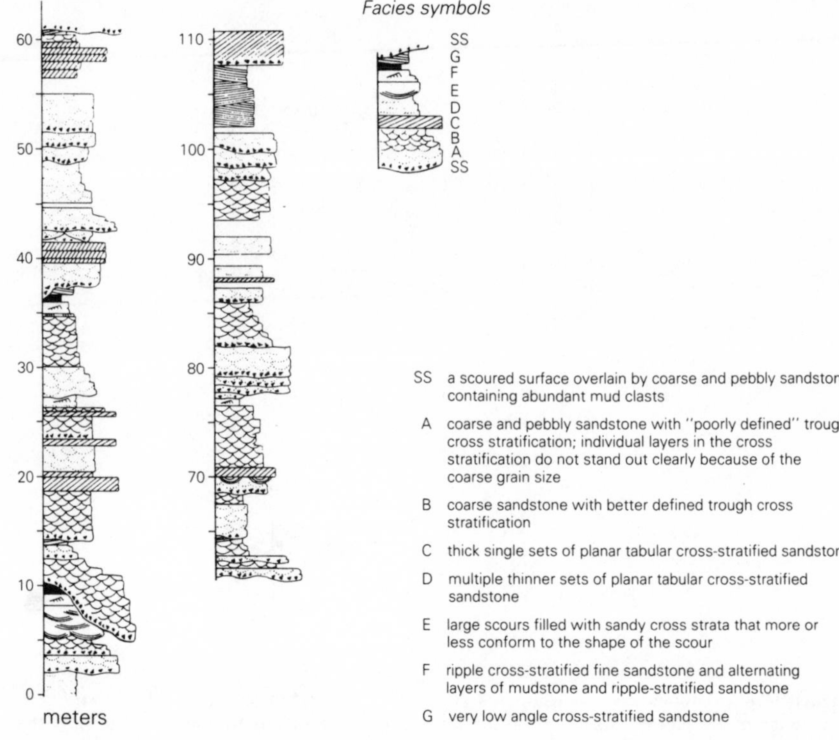

Figure 11.7 A measured section of the Lower Devonian Battery Point Sandstone with facies definitions (from Cant 1974, and Cant & Walker 1976).

claims that it is "statistically incorrect," this view is not universal. Time will tell. Even if it is eventually abandoned, the general approach is valid.

To illustrate the use of statistical methods in analyzing facies sequences we shall examine a typical sequence in the Devonian Battery Point Sandstone exposed at Gaspe, Quebec. The facies defined by Cant (1974) are illustrated and described in Figure 11.7. The method described below is based on Selley's (1970) method as discussed by Walker (1979, 1984) and Harper (1984).

(a) The vertical sequence is coded using letters and symbols to facilitate tabulation of transitions from one facies to another. The coded sequence (Fig. 11.8) is read like words in a paragraph. Starting with D (upper left in Fig. 11.8), the sequence is "facies D overlain by a scoured surface overlain by facies A overlain by facies B, etc."

D.A,B,E,F.B.A,G.B,C,A,C,B,C,B,D,F/
A,B,D,F,G. A,C,A/A.A/C,B,G. A,G.
A,B,G. A,,B. A,E,C,B,F. A,B. A,C,D/
A/B.A.A/G.C

Key
. SS, SCOURED SURFACE
, SHARP CONTACT
,, GRADUAL CONTACT
/ FAULT OR COVERED INTERVAL

Figure 11.8 A facies sequence in the Battery Point Sandstone. The vertical sequence, from bottom to top, begins with the first facies in the first line and reads left to right as with words in a sentence. Letters and symbols represent various facies (see Fig. 11.7 for description) and the types of contacts. (From Walker 1975.)

(b) The observed numbers of transitions are tabulated and put into a **tally matrix** (Fig. 11.9a). From this matrix we see that facies A passes upward into facies SS twice in the sequence and facies SS passes upward into facies A twelve times. The type of boundary between facies (sharp or gradational) is indicated in the coded sequence (Fig. 11.8) but not necessarily in the tally matrix (Fig. 11.9a). To more fully utilize the type of contact, one may erect a **contact matrix** (Miall & Gibling 1978), although this is not done in the present example.

The numbers to the right of the matrix indicate the total number of transitions in each row. For example, there are 13 occurrences of facies A passing upward into another facies. The numbers below the matrix indicate the total number of transitions in each column. For example, there are 15 occurrences of an upward transition into facies A. Row and column totals for a given facies may not be the same. This is because of faults and covered intervals in the section measured.

(c) The transitions can be illustrated in a **facies relationship diagram** (Fig. 11.10a), which at this stage may be too complicated to be of much value. The rest of our analysis will seek to determine which of the transitions are "significant" and which are not.

(d) Construct a second matrix by converting the observed numbers of transitions to **transition probabilities** (Fig. 11.9b). This is done by dividing the number of transitions in each cell by the total number of transitions for the row containing the cell (row total) in the tally matrix (Fig. 11.9a). For example, in row one you will note that facies SS passes upward into facies A twelve times, into facies B twice, and into facies C once. The observed transitions probabilities (p_{ij}) are 0.800 (12/15), 0.133 (2/15), and 0.067 (1/15) respectively (row one in Fig. 11.9b).

(e) Construct an **independent trials probability matrix** (Fig. 11.9c), based on the assumption that all facies transitions are random.

	SS	A	B	C	D	E	F	G	Row total
SS	–	12	2	1	–	–	–	–	15
A	2	–	6	3	–	1	–	1	13
B	4	1	–	2	2	1	1	2	13
C	–	2	4	–	1	–	–	–	7
D	1	–	–	–	–	–	2	–	3
E	–	–	–	1	–	–	1	–	2
F	2	–	–	–	–	–	–	1	3
G	5	–	–	–	–	–	–	–	5
column total	14	15	12	7	3	2	4	4	61

(a)

	SS	A	B	C	D	E	F	G
SS		0.800	0.133	0.067				
A	0.154		0.462	0.231		0.077		0.077
B	0.308	0.077		0.154	0.154	0.077	0.077	0.154
C		0.286	0.571		0.143			
D	0.333						0.667	
E				0.500			0.500	
F	0.667							0.333
G	1.000							

(b)

	SS	A	B	C	D	E	F	G
SS		0.320	0.255	0.149	0.064	0.042	0.085	0.085
A	0.304		0.161	0.152	0.065	0.043	0.087	0.087
B	0.286	0.306		0.143	0.061	0.041	0.082	0.082
C	0.259	0.278	0.222		0.056	0.037	0.074	0.074
D	0.241	0.259	0.207	0.121		0.034	0.069	0.069
E	0.237	0.254	0.203	0.119	0.051		0.068	0.068
F	0.246	0.263	0.210	0.123	0.053	0.350		0.070
G	0.246	0.263	0.210	0.123	0.053	0.035	0.070	

(c)

	SS	A	B	C	D	E	F	G
SS		+0.480	−0.122	−0.082	−0.004	−0.042	−0.085	−0.085
A	−0.150		+0.201	+0.079	−0.065	+0.034	−0.087	−0.010
B	+0.022	−0.229		+0.011	+0.093	+0.036	−0.005	+0.072
C	−0.259	+0.008	+0.349		+0.087	−0.037	−0.074	−0.074
D	+0.092	−0.259	−0.207	−0.121		−0.034	+0.593	−0.069
E	−0.237	−0.254	−0.203	+0.381	−0.051		+0.432	−0.068
F	+0.421	−0.263	−0.210	−0.123	−0.053	−0.035		+0.260
G	+0.754	−0.263	−0.210	−0.123	−0.053	−0.035	−0.070	

(d)

Figure 11.9 Matrices used to analyze transitions in the Battery Point Sandstone: (a) tally matrix (also called transition count matrix) showing the number of times any one facies passes upward into any other facies (based on sequence shown in Figure 11.8); (b) observed transition probabilities matrix; (c) transition probability for random sequence matrix; (d) observed minus random transition probability matrix (also called difference matrix). See Figure 11.7 for explanation of letters. (Modified from Walker 1979.)

Matrix elements (i.e. the values in each cell) are calculated using the equation

$$R_{ij} = SC_j/(T - SC_i)$$

where R_{ij} is the random probability of transition from facies i to j, SC_j is the random number of occurrences of facies j (column total for facies j), T is the total number of transitions for all facies, and SC_i is the number of occurrences of facies i (column total for facies i). The use of column totals follows the suggestion of Hiscott (1981).

To illustrate this, let us evaluate the transition of facies SS upward into facies A (note that the equation given above uses the notation R_{ij} where i = SS and j = A). From Figure 11.9a, we see the column total (SC_i) for facies SS is 14, the column total (SC_j) for facies A is 15, and the total for all transitions (T) is 61. Using these values, the random possibility of transition (R_{ij}) from SS to A is $15/(61 - 14) = 0.320$. This value is the first entry in row one in Figure 11.9c.

In Figure 11.9c you will notice that the main diagonal contains "structurally empty cells" (i.e. all values = 0). This is the characteristic feature of an **embedded** Markov chain. It occurs because of the difficulty (impossibility?) of recognizing the transition of a given facies upward into another bed of the same facies (e.g. a transition of facies A upward into facies A).

(f) Construct a "**difference**" **matrix** (Fig. 11.9d) which shows the observed minus the random probabilities. Values used in constructing the matrix are produced by subtracting the value of each cell in Figure 11.9c from the corresponding cell in Figure 11.9b. The range of values is +1.0 to −1.0. Positive values indicate transitions that occur more frequently than would be the case if the facies were arranged randomly. Negative values indicate transitions that occur less frequently than random.

(g) Draw a simplified **facies relationship diagram** using those transitions with "high" positive values (Fig. 11.10b). Transitions with lower positive values may be added using different symbols (e.g. light solid lines or dashed lines). Examination of the original facies relationship diagram (Fig. 11.10a) may suggest that arrows be drawn which indicate gradational versus sharp contacts.

(h) A positive value obtained by subtracting the random from the observed probability does *not* prove that the difference is statistically significant. Indeed one of the most serious problems with the method described above is the uncertainty of determining which transitions are significant.

To remedy this difficulty, Harper (1984) suggests use of the

binomial probability of at least N_{obs} *successes in* N trials, given by

$$\sum_{n = n_{obs}}^{n = N} C(N,n)\ p^n q^{N-0}$$

where $C(N,n)$ = the number of possible combinations of N objects taken n at a time, and is given by

$$C(N,n) = \frac{N!}{(N - n)!n!}$$

p = the probability of success on a single trial, given in Fig. 11.9c.

$$q = 1 - p$$

To illustrate this method, let us consider the transition of facies C to facies B (probability difference if in Fig. 11.9d row four is +0.351), where p = the probability of success in a single trial = 0.22 and q = the probability of failure in a single trial = 1 − 0.22 = 0.78. From Figure 11.9a we note that four successes (transitions from facies C to facies B) were observed in seven transitions from facies C upward to another facies; hence n_{obs} = 4 and N = 7. The binomial probability of at least n_{obs} successes in N trials, calculated from the formula given above, is 0.45 (Table 11.1a). This means that four

Table 11.1 Binomial probability (BP) for facies transitions in Battery Point Sandstone: (a) BP for at least four successes (occurrence of B over C) in seven trials (occurrences of any other facies other than C over C); (b) BP (probability) of M or more successes in N trials over the null hypothesis of random sequence. Data from transitions with BP greater than 0.2 not listed. (From Harper 1984.)

(a)

n	$C(7,n)$	p^n	q^{7-n}	Probability (n)
4	35	0.0023	0.475	0.038
5	21	0.0005	0.608	0.006
6	7	0.0001	0.780	0.0005
7	1	0.00002	1.00	0.00002
Total				0.045

(b)

Facies transition	P	N	M	Probability
SS → A	0.32	15	12	0.0002
A → B	0.26	13	6	0.094
C → B	0.22	7	4	0.045
D → F	0.06	3	2	0.011
E → F	0.06	2	1	0.120
F → SS	0.22	13	1	0.126
G → SS	0.23	5	5	0.0006

Notes: In **(b)** above, P = transition probability for random sequence; N = number of transitions from lower facies; M = number of transitions from lower to upper facies.

successes in seven trials would occur 4.5% of the time if the transitions occurred randomly. If we choose a significance level of 0.10, then the observed transition of facies C to facies B is significant.

In contrast, the probability difference for the transition of facies E to facies F, which is +0.432 (row six in Fig. 11.9d), is not significant at the 0.1 level because the transition probability is 0.120 (Table 11.1b). Of all the transition possibilities for the eight facies in the Battery Point Sandstone, only five are significantly larger (at the 0.1 level of significance) than predicted for a random sequence (Table 11.1b). This can be illustrated by modifying the simplified facies relationship diagram to show relationships significant at 0.1 with heavy solid lines (Fig. 11.10c).

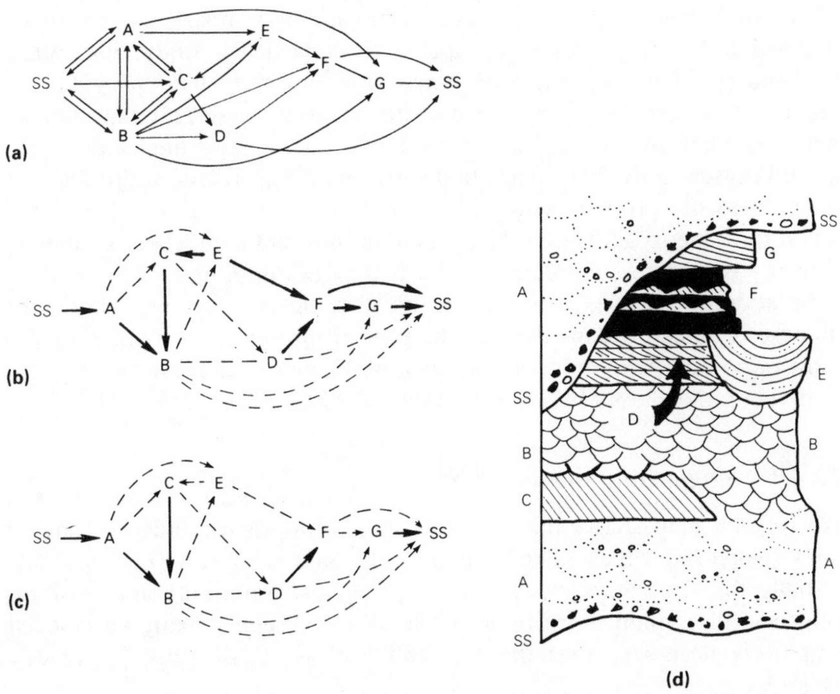

Figure 11.10 Facies relationship diagram (FRD) for the Battery Point Sandstone. (a) FRD showing the observed transitions (data from Figs 11.8 & 11.9a). (b) Simplified FRD showing transitions that occur more commonly than random. Solid lines represent values greater than +0.2; dashed lines represent values between +0.01 and 0.2. (from data in Fig. 11.9d). (c) Simplified FRD showing transitions that occur more commonly than random. Solid lines indicate transitions significant at 0.1 (see Table 11.1b). (d) Summary sequence based on simplified FRD. Approximate thickness is 30 m. See Fig. 11.7 for explanation of letters.

An alternative to the method described above involves testing the whole matrix (Miall 1973, Powers & Easterling 1982) or individual rows and columns in a matrix (Hobday *et al* 1975) for nonrandomness using the chi-square test.

11.4 Facies maps

The aerial distribution of facies can be shown on maps, collectively known as facies maps. Although the emphasis in environmental analysis has shifted to the study of vertical sequences, facies maps may still be used to advantage. Thickness measurements which comprise the original data can be modified into various forms. The first step generally involves determining the net thickness in a stratigraphic unit of particular rock types (Fig. 11.11a).

Even though the most common components of facies maps are sandstone, shale, and limestone, you are not restricted to these lithologies. Use whatever is appropriate for a particular study. You might find that plotting the ratio of green shale to red shale provides an important insight for the problem at hand. Be creative and experiment, but remember that when the time comes to write your final report you should present only those maps that show significant relationships and are relevant to the problem you are trying to solve. Just because you have taken the time to generate a facies map do not feel compelled to share it with the rest of the world, especially if it shows nothing of value.

In addition to the great variety of possible components, there are numerous types of maps that can be used to present them. Some of the most important ones are discussed below. For more detailed reviews see Krumbein and Sloss (1963: 4342–500) and Miall (1984: 213–23).

11.4.1 Single component maps

An **isopach** map shows the thickness of a stratigraphic unit by contour lines (isopachs) which connect points of equal thickness (Fig. 11.12a). Usually the stratigraphic unit (e.g. a group or formation) shown on an isopach will contain more than one lithology. When making an isopach map it is necessary that the top and bottom of the unit be readily identifiable.

A variety of isopach map, sometimes called an isolith map, shows the total thickness of a selected lithology contained within a stratigraphic unit. Such isopach maps, showing lines of equal sandstone thickness, may define the geometry of sand bodies and suggest a specific origin, such as barrier islands (Fig. 11.13) or tidal channels (see Weimer *et al*. 1982: Fig. 54).

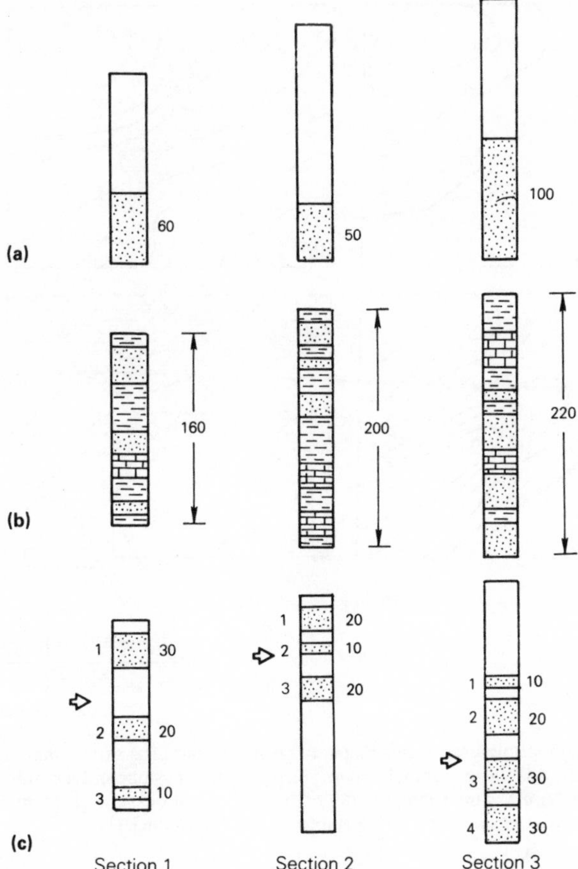

Figure 11.11 Examples of stratigraphic sections, showing methods of compiling data for facies maps: (a) rock type summarized for conventional maps (e.g. sandstone isopach map, sand–shale ratio map, and clastic ratio map); (b) original sections (thickness used in isopach maps); (c) position and thickness of particular rock type recorded for vertical variability maps. Arrows indicate sandstone "center of gravity". See Fig. 11.15 for sample calculation.

11.4.2 Multicomponent maps

If two lithologies occur in a stratigraphic unit, the thickness ratio of one rock type to another may be plotted. A commonly used ratio is the **sand : shale ratio**, which is determined by dividing the net thickness of the sandstone by the net thickness of the shale (Fig. 11.12b). A numerical value of 1.0 means that the thickness of the sandstone is equal to that of the shale.

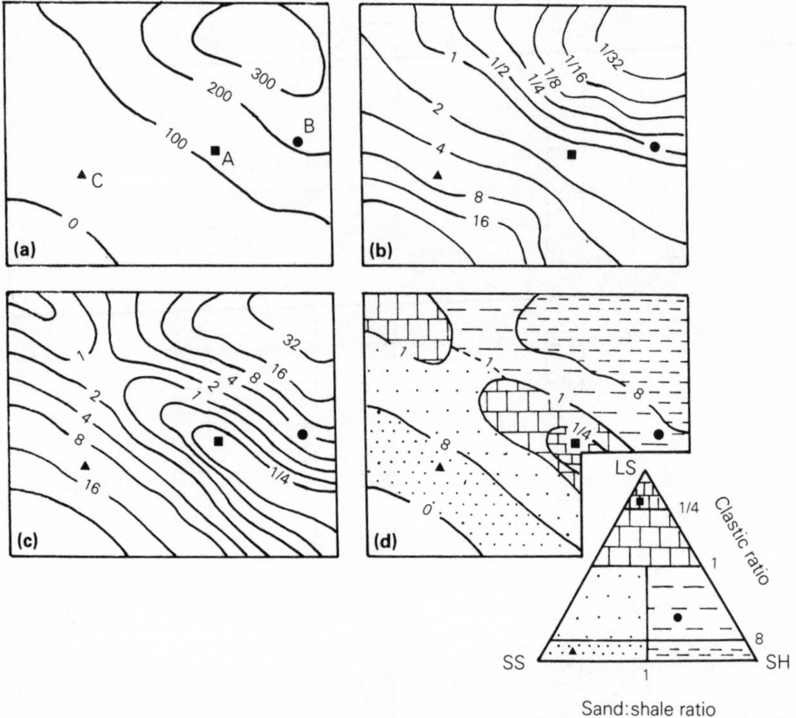

Figure 11.12 Commonly used facies maps: (a) isopach map; (b) sand : shale ratio map; (c) clastic ratio map; (d) facies triangle map. Representative sample localities indicated by symbols (square, circle, and triangle); data for these localities are given in Figure 11.14. (Modified from Sloss *et al.* 1960, and Krumbein and Sloss 1963.)

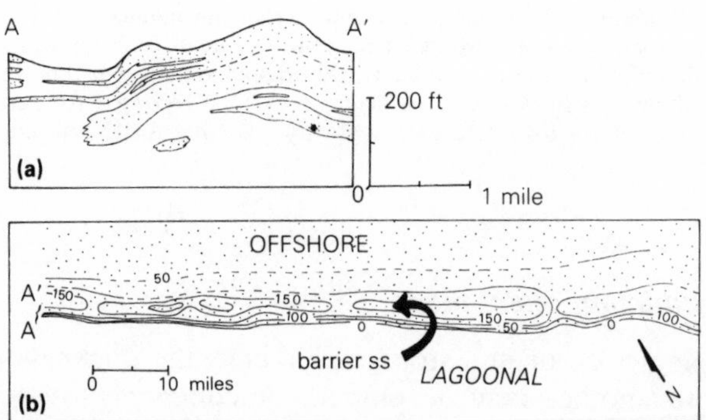

Figure 11.13 A sandstone isopach (isolith) map showing a barrier island complex: (a) map of La Ventana Tongue of the Cliff House Formation, New Mexico (contour interval is 50 ft); (b) cross section through the northwest portion of area shown in (a). (Modified from McCubbin, 1982: Figs 50 & 51.)

If more than two lithologies are present, the **clastic ratio** can be used (Fig. 11.12c). The clastic component includes the net thickness of sandstone, mudrock, and conglomerate; the nonclastic component includes limestone, dolomite, anhydrite, gypsum, and halite. The clastic ratio is determined by dividing the total thickness of the clastic components by that of the nonclastic components.

Two ratios, and three components, may be depicted on a single facies map if a **lithofacies triangle** is utilized (Fig. 11.12d). Various areas on the triangle having certain compositional aspects in common are delineated by the two sets of ratios. Each area is indicated by a pattern or color, which is also used on the map. The various "pattern areas" on the map show where the unit is dominantly sandstone, shale, etc. They are bounded by lines representing the limiting ratio values. The standard facies triangle is divided into nine classes (Fig. 11.14). The one used in Figure 11.12d has been simplified to have only six classes.

Sample	A	B	C
sandstone (%)	9	22	81
shale (%)	7	56	12
limestone (%)	84	22	7
clastic ratio	0.2	3.5	13
sand:shale ratio	1.2	0.4	7
thickness (ft)	120	220	30

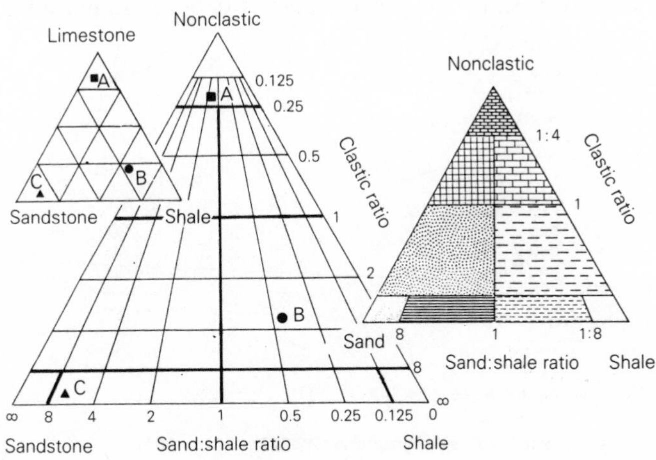

Figure 11.14 Lithofacies triangles showing ratio boundaries and nine major classes. A conventional 100% triangle is shown to the left. The three points plotted are also shown on the facies map in Figure 11.12. (Modified from Krumbein 1948.)

11.4.3 Vertical variability maps

Some facies maps are designed to show the vertical position of one or more lithologic components within a stratigraphic unit. To illustrate the problem refer to Figure 11.11. Observe that not only does the net sandstone thickness vary from section to section (Fig. 11.11a) but the distribution of sand beds within each section is variable (Fig. 11.11c). In section 1 they are rather uniformly distributed, but in section 2 they are concentrated in the upper half of the section and in section 3 in the lower half.

Such variability can be illustrated by utilizing the sandstone **center-of-gravity** map, which shows the relative, weighted mean position of the sandstone beds in terms of their distance from the top of the unit (Krumbein & Libby 1957). This value, expressed as a percentage of the total thickness of the unit (68% in Fig. 11.15), can be plotted on a map and the values contoured as on other facies maps. Other types of vertical variability maps include sandstone mean thickness maps, a number of sandstone maps, and interval–entropy maps.

11.4.4 Other special purpose maps

There are many other specially designed maps that one might use. They range from simple ones that show the regional extent of discrete sand layers in a stratigraphic unit (Bouma *et al* 1982: Fig. 19) to complex ones such as trend surface maps. As Pettijohn (1975: 523) notes, "the ingenious investigator can concoct a great many multicomponent parameters which show whatever aspect is deemed significant."

	Distance from top (d)	Thickness (t)	dh
bed 1	80	10	800
bed 2	110	30	3,300
bed 3	160	30	4,800
bed 4	200	30	6,000
		100 (A)	14,900 (B)

center of gravity = B/A = 149 ft

relative center of gravity = 149/220 × 100 = 68%

Figure 11.15 The calculation of the sandstone center of gravity. The center of gravity is 149 ft from the top of the section; the relative center of gravity is located at a point 68% below the top of the section. (Based on data derived from Section 3 in Figure 11.11.)

11.5 Facies models

Having described the rock, assigned the component beds to various facies, and established facies assemblages, we are now ready to interpret the depositional environment that best fits the sequence. This is one aspect of **facies modelling**. The model is based on the vertical sequence, generally depicted in a facies relationship diagram (Fig. 11.10) and its expression in a columnar section. Commonly the sequence is repeated in cycles. Although the temporal variations expressed by vertical transitions are important, spatial variations of the rock body represented by facies maps should not be overlooked. Interpretation of the environment is based on comparison with modern analogs and ancient examples. Even though environmental interpretation is important, it is not the only reason for facies modelling. Walker (1984: 6) suggests that facies models should also: (1) act as a norm, for purposes of comparison; (2) act as a framework and guide for future observations; (3) act as a predictor in new geologic situations, and (4) act as an integrated basis for interpretation of the environment or system that it represents.

We must keep in mind that the model proposed for a particular sedimentary sequence is not representative of all rock formed in the same general environment. The Battery Point Sandstone (Section 11.3.2), for example, is not a comprehensive model for all braided stream deposits. Its main value is that it can be compared with other sequences thought to have been deposited in the same general environment. The ways in which they are similar and the ways in which they are different may tell us a great deal about the processes in operation during deposition.

Facies analysis and modelling is a continuing process subject to constant modification as our knowledge and understanding grows. This point is beautifully expressed by Anderton (1985: 45), who writes:

> One can study a rock succession for years, without being able to interpret it satisfactorily, until work on a modern environment suddenly provides the key to a reasonable explanation. Years later an even better explanation may become possible as a result of continual progress in the subject. It does not mean that the original interpretation was wrong, just that it was the best that could be done at the time. One must have the courage and honesty to repeatedly change and update facies models as our understanding advances.

11.6 Exercise: facies relationship diagram

Analyze the section shown in Figure 11.6 using the methods described in Section 11.3.2. The tally matrix for this sequence is given in Table 11.2. Begin your facies relationship diagram with coal as the first (lowermost) facies. Analyze the transition "coal to shale" using the binomial probability method (see step h in Section 11.3.2).

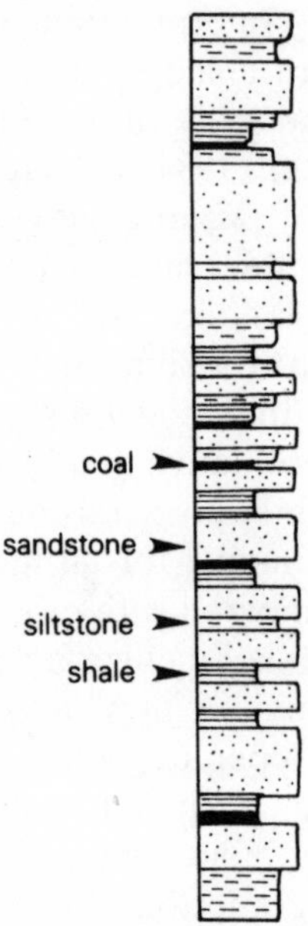

Figure 11.16 A stratigraphic section of a hypothetical coal measure (modified from Selley 1970).

Table 11.2 Tally matrix for hypothetical coal measure shown in Figure 11.16.

	Sandstone	Silt	Shale	Coal
sandstone		5	4	3
silt	8		1	1
shale	4	3		1
coal	1	1	3	

11.7 Exercise: isopach and facies maps

Table 11.3 contains data from 32 wells in the Williston Basin in the Great Plains of the United States and Canada. The total thickness of the

Table 11.3 Thickness of the Elk Point Group and its constituent lithologies. Calculate the clastic ratio (CR = sandstone + shale divided by carbonate + evaporite) and the evaporite ratio (ER = carbonate divided by evaporite) and add these values to this table.

Well number	Total thickness	Thickness (ft) Shale	Sandstone	Carbonate	Evaporite	Clastic ratio	Evaporite ratio
1	52	10	3	33	6		
2	133	25	10	82	16		
3	550	60	23	118	349		
4	420	42	21	89	268		
5	740	50	24	100	566		
6	160	20	4	116	20		
7	85	16	5	54	10		
8	490	41	18	73	358		
9	746	51	26	101	568		
10	240	35	10	70	125		
11	651	40	11	150	450		
12	157	10	3	124	20		
13	120	28	10	71	11		
14	310	30	12	179	89		
15	340	35	17	189	99		
16	140	10	4	113	13		
17	150	16	6	112	16		
18	360	42	19	75	224		
19	550	60	28	140	322		
20	450	38	7	134	271		
21	220	18	6	163	33		
22	140	11	4	100	25		
23	253	31	10	142	70		
24	345	29	6	176	134		
25	190	12	7	130	41		
26	110	21	7	62	20		
27	140	21	14	63	42		
28	400	30	10	151	209		
29	195	15	5	145	30		
30	197	16	4	133	44		
31	44	3	1	33	7		
32	41	4	1	32	4		

Devonian Elk Point Group is given, as well as the thicknesses of the following lithologies: shale, sandstone, carbonate, and evaporite.

Use tracing paper to make the maps indicated below. Put control points (well localities on Fig. 11.17) on the tracing paper in ink, but do all construction in pencil. When you are satisfied that all contour lines and isopachs are correctly located, ink them in and add appropriate title, north arrow, scale, and legend to each map.

1 Construct an **isopach map** (Section 11.4.1) using 100 ft isopachs. Follow the same procedure used in constructing topographic contour lines to interpolate between control points.
2 Construct a **lithofacies map** (Section 11.4.2). The first step is to determine the **clastic ratio** (CR = sandstone + shale divided by carbonate + evaporite) and the **evaporite ratio** (ER = carbonate divided by evaporite). Add these values to Table 11.3. Plot the data from each well on a full-scale facies triangle (Fig. 11.18). This facies

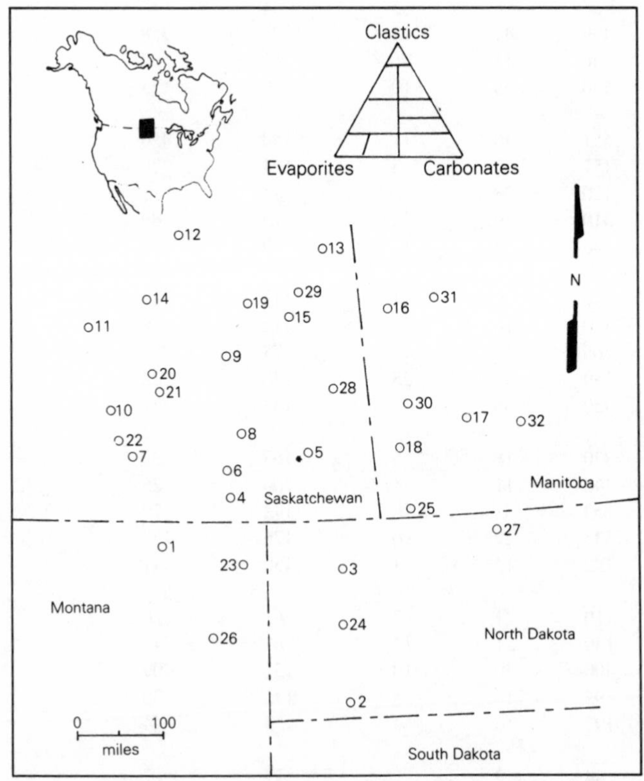

Figure 11.17 The location of wells with complete sections of the Elk Point Group.

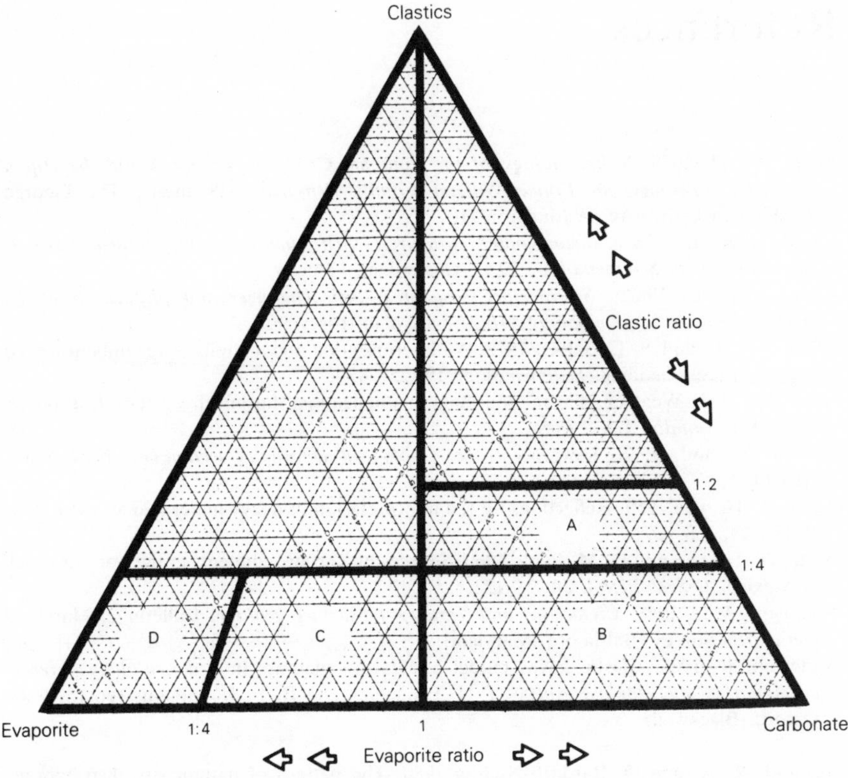

Figure 11.18 A facies triangle. Color the four labeled fields as follows: A, yellow; B, blue; C, purple; and D, red. Clastics include conglomerate, sandstone, and shale.

triangle is different from those shown in Figures 11.12 and 11.14 because of the dominance of nonclastic rock in the Elk Point Group. To simplify the final map only four fields (A–D) are used. They are delineated by the limiting ratio values ER 1, ER $\frac{1}{4}$, and CR $\frac{1}{4}$. Color each of the four fields as follows: A, yellow; B, blue; C, purple; D, red. Color each control point on the map the color of the field on the facies triangle in which the point occurs. This will aid you in determining the approximate location of the ratio contours (ER 1, ER $\frac{1}{4}$, and CR $\frac{1}{4}$). Use the ER and CR values in Table 11.3 to position the contours exactly. When the ratio contours are drawn, color the map following the scheme used on the facies triangle.

3 Construct an **interpretative map** showing the basinal axis (based on the area where the Elk Point Group is thickest) and the general source of terrigenous sediment. What lithology is dominant in the area of the basinal axis?

References

Adabi, M. H. 1978. *Sedimentology of the Potomac Group (Cretaceous) and the Aquia Formation (Tertiary) in Prince William County, Virginia*. MS thesis, The George Washington University, Washington DC.

Allen, J. R. L. 1982a. *Sedimentary structures: their character and physical basis I, Developments in Sedimentology 30A*. Amsterdam: Elsevier.

Allen, J. R. L. 1982b. *Sedimentary structures: their character and physical basis II, Developments in Sedimentology 30B*. Amsterdam: Elsevier.

Allen, J. R. L. and N. L. Banks. 1972. An interpretation and analysis of recumbent-folded deformed cross-bedding. *Sedimentology* **19**, 257–83.

Allen, P. 1972. Wealden detrital tourmaline: implications for north-western Europe. *J. Geol. Soc. London* **128**, 273–94.

Allman, M. and D. F. Lawrence 1972. *Geological laboratory techniques*. New York: ARCO.

Andel, T. H., van 1959. Reflections on the interpretation of heavy mineral analysis. *J. Sed. Petrol.* **29**, 153–63.

Andel, T. H., van and D. M. Poole 1960. Sources of Recent sediments in the northern Gulf of Mexico. *J. Sed. Petrol.* **30**, 91–122.

Anderson, J. L. 1948. *Cretaceous and Tertiary subsurface geology*. Bulletin 2, Maryland Geological Survey, Baltimore, Maryland.

Anderton, R. 1985. Clastic facies model and facies analysis. In *Sedimentology – recent developments and applied aspects*, P. J. Brenchley and B. P. J. Williams (eds), 31–48. Oxford: Blackwell.

Bagnold, R. A. and O. Bardorff-Nielsen 1980. The pattern of natural size distributions. *Sedimentology* **27**, 199–207.

Barnes, R. D. 1963. *Invertebrate zoology*. Philadelphia: Saunders.

Beal, M. and F. Shepard 1956. A use of roundness to determine depositional environments. *J. Sed. Petrol.* **26**, 9–60.

Billi, P. 1984. Quick field measurement of gravel particle size. *J. Sed. Petrol.* **54**, 658–60.

Blatt, H. and B. Sutherland 1969. Intrastratal solution and nonopaque heavy minerals in shale. *J. Sed. Petrol.* **39**, 591–600.

Blatt, H., G. Middleton and R. Murray 1980. *Origin of sedimentary rocks*. Englewood Cliffs, NJ: Prentice-Hall.

Boersma, J. R., E. A. Meene, van de and R. C. Tjalsma 1968. Intricated cross-stratification due to interaction of megaripple with its lee-side system of backflow ripple (upper pointbar deposits, lower Rhine). *Sedimentology* **11**, 147–62.

Bouma, A. H., H. L. Berryhill, H. J. Knebel and R. L. Brenner 1982. Continental shelf. In *Sandstone depositional environments*, P. A. Scholle and D. Spearing (eds), 281–328. Memoir 31, American Association of Petroleum Geologists, Tulsa, Oklahoma.

Boyde, D. W. 1975. *False or misleading traces*. In *The study of trace fossils*, R. W. Frey (ed.), 65–84. Berlin: Springer.

Briggs, D. 1977. *Sources and methods in geography – sediments*. London: Butterworth.

Byers, C. W. 1977. Biofacies patterns in euxinic basins: a general model. In *Deep-water carbonate sediments*, H. E. Cook and Paul Enos (eds), 5–17. Special Publication No. 25, Society of Economic Paleontologists and Mineralogists, Tulsa, Oklahoma.

REFERENCES

Cant, D. J. 1974. *Devonian braided stream deposits in the Battery Point Formation*. Msc thesis, McMaster University, Hamilton, Ontario.

Cant, D. J. and R. G. Walker 1976. Development of a braided-fluvial facies model for the Devonian Battery Point Sandstone, Quebec. *Can. J. Earth Sci.* **13**, 102–19.

Carr, T. R. 1982. Long-linear models, Markov chains and cyclic sedimentation. *J. Sed. Petrol.* **52**, 905–12.

Carroll, D. 1970. *Clay minerals: a guide to their X-ray identification*. Special Paper 126, Geological Society of America, Boulder, Colorado.

Chamberlain, C. K. 1975. Recent lebensspuren in nonmarine aquatic environments. In *The study of trace fossils*, R. W. Frey (ed.), 431–58. Berlin: Springer.

Chamberlain, C. K. 1978. Recognition of trade fossils in cores. In *Trace fossil concepts*, P. B. Basan (ed.), 125–74. Short Course No. 5, Society of Economic Paleontologists and Mineralogists, Tulsa, Oklahoma.

Chayes, F. 1949. Statistical analysis of two-dimensional fabric diagrams. In *Structural petrology of deformed rocks*, H. W. Fairbairn (ed.), 297–307. Reading, Mass.: Addison-Wesley.

Cheeney, R. F. 1983. *Statistical methods in geology – for field and lab decisions*. London: Allen & Unwin.

Collinson, J. D. and D. B. Thompson 1982. *Sedimentary structures*. London: Allen & Unwin.

Cook, H. E., M. E. Field and J. V. Gardner 1982. Characteristics of sediments on modern and ancient continental slopes. In *Sandstone depositional environments*, P. A. Scholle and D. Spearing (eds), 329–64. Memoir 31, American Association of Petroleum Geologists, Tulsa, Oklahoma.

Crimes, T. P. 1975. The stratigraphical significance of trace fossils. In *The study of trace fossils*. R. W. Frey (ed.), 109–30. Berlin: Springer.

Crimes, T. P. 1977. Trace fossils of an Eocene deep-sea fan, northern Spain. In *Trace fossils 2*, T. P. Crimes and J. C. Harper (eds), 71–90. *Geol. J.*, Special Issue No. 9. Liverpool: Steel House Press.

Curray, J. R. 1956a. The analysis of two-dimensional orientation data. *J. Geol.* **64**, 117–31.

Curray, J. R. 1956b. Dimensional grain orientation studies of Recent coastal sands. *Bull. Am. Assoc. Petrolm Geol.* **40**, 2440–56.

Dale, M. L. and C. K. Ballantyne 1980. Two statistics for the analysis of orientation data in geography. *Prof. Geogr.* **32**, 184–91.

Dalrymple, R. W., R. J. Knight and J. J. Lambiase 1978. Bedforms and their hydraulic stability relationships in a tidal environment, Bay of Fundy, Canada. *Nature* **275**, 100–4.

Davies, D. K. and W. R. Moore 1970. Dispersal of Mississippi sediment in the Gulf of Mexico. *J. Sed. Petrol.* **40**, 339–53.

Davies, I. C. and R. G. Walker 1974. Transport and deposition of resedimented conglomerates: the Cape Enrage Formation, Cambro-Ordovician, Gaspe, Quebec. *J. Sed. Petrol.* **44**, 1200–16.

Davis, R. A., Jr. 1983. *Depositional systems: a genetic approach to sedimentary geology*. Englewood Cliffs, NJ: Prentice-Hall.

Donovan, R. N. and R. Archer 1975. Some sedimentological consequences of the fall in the level of Haweswater, Cumbria. *Proc. Yorks Geol. Soc.* **40**, 547–62.

Dott, R. H., Jr. 1964. Wacke, graywacke and matrix – what approach to immature sandstone classification? *J. Sed. Petrol.* **34**, 625–32.

Dunham, R. J. 1962. Classification of carbonate rocks according to depositional texture. In *Classification of carbonate rocks – a symposium*, W. E. Ham (ed.), 108–21. Memoir 1, American Association of Petroleum Geologists, Tulsa, Oklahoma.

REFERENCES

Ehrlich, R. 1983. Editorial – size analysis wears no clothes, or have moments come and gone? *J. Sed. Petrol.* **53**, 1.

Ehrlich, R. and B. Weinberg 1970. An exact method for the characterization of grain shape. *J. Sed. Petrol.* **40**, 205–12.

Fagin, S. W. 1977. *The geology of the Culpeper Basin within Culpeper County, Virginia*. MS thesis, The George Washington University, Washington, DC.

Farrow, G. E. 1975. Techniques for the study of fossil and recent traces. In *The study of trace fossils*, R. W. Frey (ed.), 537–54. Berlin: Springer.

Folk, R. L. 1954. The distinction between grain size and mineral compositon in sedimentary rock nomenclature. *J. Geol.* **62**, 344–59.

Folk, R. L. 1955. Student operator error in determination of roundness, sphericity, and grain size. *J. Sed. Petrol.* **25**, 297–301.

Folk, R. L. 1959. Practical classification of limestones. *Bull. Am. Assoc. Petrolm Geol.* **43**, 1–38.

Folk, R. L. 1962. Spectral subdivision of limestone types. In *Classification of carbonate rocks – a symposium*, W. E. Ham (ed.), 62–84. Memoir 1, American Association of Petroleum Geologists, Tulsa, Oklahoma.

Folk, R. L. 1966. A review of grain-size parameters. *Sedimentology* **6**, 73–93.

Folk, R. L. 1969. Toward greater precision in rock-color terminology. *Bull. Geol. Soc. Am.* **80**, 725–28.

Folk, R. L. 1980. *Petrology of sedimentary rock*. Austin, Tex.: Hemphill.

Folk, R. L. and W. C. Ward 1957. Brazos River bar: a study in the significance of grain-size parameters. *J. Sed. Petrol.* **27**, 3–26.

Freeman, T. and Pierce, K. 1979. Field statistical assessment of cross-bed data. *J. Sed. Petrol.* **49**, 624–5.

Frey, R. W. 1971. Ichnology – the study of fossil and Recent lebensspuren. In *Trace fossils*, B. F. Perkins (ed.), 91–125. Miscellaneous Publication, 71–1, Louisiana State University, Baton Rouge.

Frey, R. W. 1978. Behavior and ecological implications of trace fossils. In *Trace fossil concepts*, P. B. Basin (ed.), 46–72. Short Course No. 5, Society of Economic Paleontologists and Mineralogists, Tulsa, Oklahoma.

Frey, R. W. and S. G. Pemberton 1984. Trace fossil facies models. In *Facies models*, 2nd edn, R. G. Walker (ed.), 189–207, Reprint Series 1, Geological Association of Canada, Geoscience Canada, Toronto, Canada.

Frey, R. W., S. G. Pemberton and J. A. Fagerstrom 1984. Morphological, ethological, and environmental significance of the ichnogenera *Scoyenia* and *Ancorichnus*. *J. Paleont.* **58**, 511–28.

Friedman, G. M. 1958. Determination of size distribution from thin-section data for sedimentary petrological studies. *J. Geol.* **66**, 394–416.

Friend, P. F., P. D. Alexander-Marrack, J. Nicholson and A. K. Yeates, 1976. Devonian sediments of east Greenland I. *Medd. om Gronland* **206** (1).

Füchtbauer, H. 1974. *Sediments and sedimentary rocks*. New York: Wiley.

Galloway, W. E., R. J. Finley and C. D. Henry 1979. *A South Texas uranium province–geologic perspective*. Guidebook 18, Texas Bureau of Economic Geology, Austin, Texas.

Gibbs, R. J. 1965. Error due to segregation in quantitative clay mineral X-ray diffraction mounting techniques. *Am. Mineral.* **50**, 741–51.

Gibbs, R. J. 1974. A settling tube system for sand-size analysis. *J. Sed. Petrol.* **44**, 583–8.

Goddard, E. N., P. D. Trask, R. K. Deford, O. N. Rove, J. T. Singlewald, Jr. and R. M. Overbeck 1948. *Rock color chart*. Boulder, Colo.: Geological Society of America.

Goldsmith, J. R. and D. L. Graf 1958. Relation between lattice constants and composition of Ca–Mg carbonates. *Am. Mineral.* **43**, 84–101.

Goldsmith, J. R. and O. Joensuu 1955. The occurrence of magnesia calcites in nature. *Geochim. Cosmochim. Acta* **7**, 212–30.

Griffin, G. M. and E. D. Goldberg 1963. Clay-mineral distributions in the Pacific Ocean. In *The sea – ideas and observations on progress in the study of seas*. 728–41. New York: Interscience.

Hallam, A. 1981. *Facies interpretation and the stratigraphic record*. New York: W.H. Freeman.

Hamblin, W. K. 1962. X-ray radiography in the study of structures in homogeneous sediments. *J. Sed. Petrol.* **32**, 201–10.

Hanley, S. 1981. *Nonparametric geostatistics*. New York: Wiley.

Hansen, E. 1971. *Strain facies*. Berlin: Springer.

Häntzschel, W. 1975. Trace fossils and problimatica. In *Treatise on invertebrate paleontology, pt. W, Miscellanea*, R. C. Moore (ed.). Lawrence, Kan.: Geological Society of America and University of Kansas Press.

Harms, J. C. and R. K. Fahenstock 1965. Stratification, bed forms, and flow phenomena (with examples from the Rio Grande). In *Primary sedimentary structures and their hydrodynamic interpretation*, G. V. Middleton (ed.), 84–114. Special Publication No. 12, Society of Economic Paleontologists and Mineralogists, Tulsa, Oklahoma.

Harms, J. C, J. C. Southard and R. G. Walker 1982. *Structures and sequences in clastic rocks lecture*. Short Course No. 9, Society of Economic Paleontologists and Mineralogists, Tulsa, Oklahoma.

Harper, C. W. 1984. Improved methods of facies sequence analysis. In *Facies models*, 2nd edn, R. G. Walker (ed.), 11–13. Reprint Series 1, Geological Association of Canada, Geoscience Canada, Toronto, Ontario.

Harrell, J. A. 1985. A visual comparator for degree of sorting in thin and plane sections. *J. Sed. Petrol.* **54**, 646–50.

Harrell, J. A. and K. A. Eriksson 1979. Empirical conversion equations for thin-section and sieve derived size distribution parameters. *J. Sed. Petrol.* **49**, 273–80.

Hauf, P. L. and J. Airey 1980. *The handling, hazards and maintenance of heavy liquids in the geological laboratory*. US Geological Survey Circular 827.

Hentz, T. F. 1981. *The sedimentology and structure of the Culpeper Group Lake Beds (Lower Jurassic) at Thoroughfare Gap, Virginia*. MS thesis, University of Kansas, Lawrence, Kansas.

Hester, N. C. 1974. Post-depositional subaerial weathering effects on the mineralogy of an Upper Cretaceous sand in southeastern United States. *J. Sed. Petrol.* **44**, 363–73.

Hill, G. W. 1981. Ichnocoenoses of a Paleocene submarine-canyon floor, Point Lobos, California. In *Upper Cretaceous and Paleocene turbidites, central California coast*, V. Frizzell (ed.), 93–117. Los Angeles, Calif.: Pacific Section, Society of Economic Paleontologists and Mineralogists.

Hiscott, R. M. 1981. Chi-square tests for Markov chain analysis. *Int. Assoc. Math. Geol.* **13**, 53–68.

Hobday, D. K., R. Tavener-Smith and D. Matthew 1975. Markov analysis and the recognition of paleoenvironments in the Ecca Group near Vryheid. *Trans Geol. Soc. S. Africa* **78**, 75–82.

Hopson, C. A. 1964. The crystalline rocks of Howard and Montgomery Counties. In *The geology of Howard and Montgomery Counties*. Maryland Geological Survey.

Howard, J. D. 1975. The sedimentological significance of trace fossils. In *The study of trace fossils*. R. W. Frey (ed.), 131–46. Berlin: Springer.

Howard, J. D. 1978. Sedimentology and trace fossils. In *Trace fossil concepts*, P. B. Basin (ed.), 13–45. Short Course No. 5, Society of Economic Paleontologists and Mineralogists, Tulsa, Oklahoma.

Hunter, R. E. 1977. Terminology of cross-stratified sedimentary layers and climbing-ripple structures. *J. Sed. Petrol.* **47**, 697–706.

Hunter, R. E. 1985. Subaqueous sand-flow cross-strata. *J. Sed. Petrol.* **55**, 886–94.

Imbrie, J. and E. G. Purdy 1963. Classification of modern Bahamian carbonate sediments. In *Classification of carbonate rocks*, W. E. Ham (ed.), 253–72. Memoir 1, American Association of Petroleum Geologists, Tulsa, Oklahoma.

Ingram, R. L. 1954. Terminology for the thickness of stratification units and parting units in sedimentary rocks. *Bull. Geol. Soc. Am.* **65**, 937–8.

Jenkyns, H. C. 1978. Pelagic sediments. In *Sedimentary environments and facies*, H. G. Reading (ed.), 314–71. Amsterdam: Elsevier.

Jopling, A. V. and R. G. Walker 1968. Morphology and origin of ripple-drift cross-lamination, with examples from the Pleistocene of Massachusetts. *J. Sed. Petrol.* **38**, 971–84.

Kennedy, W. J. 1975. Trace fossils in carbonate rocks. In *The study of trace fossils*, R. W. Frey (ed.), 377–98. Berlin: Springer.

Kidwell, S. M. 1982. Time scales of fossil accumulation patterns from Miocene benthic assemblages (abs). In *North American Paleontological Convention, Proceedings*, Vol. I, 295–300. Tulsa, Okla.: Society of Economic Paleontologists and Mineralogists.

Krinsley, D. H. and J. C. Doornkamp 1973. *Atlas of quartz sand surface textures*. Cambridge: Cambridge University Press.

Krumbein, W. C. 1934. Size frequency distribution of sediments. *J. Sed. Petrol.* **4**, 65–77.

Krumbein, W. C. 1939. Preferred orientation of pebbles in sedimentary deposits. *J. Geology* **47**, 673–706.

Krumbein, W. C. 1940. Flood gravels of San Gabriel Canyon, California. *Bull. Geol. Soc. Am.* **51**, 639–79.

Krumbein, W. C. 1941. Measurement and geological significance of shape and roundness of sedimentary particles. *J. Sed. Petrol.* **11**, 64–72.

Krumbein, W. C. 1948. Lithofacies maps and regional sedimentary–stratigraphic analysis. *Bull. Am. Assoc. Petrolm Geol.* **32**, 1909–23.

Krumbein, W. C. and W. G. Libby 1957. Applications of moments to vertical variability maps of stratigraphic units. *Bull. Am. Assoc. Petrolm Geol.* **41**, 197–211.

Krumbein, W. C. and F. J. Pettijohn 1938. *Manual of sedimentary petrography*. New York: Appleton-Century-Crofts.

Krumbein, W. C. and L. L. Sloss 1963. *Stratigraphy and sedimentation*. New York: W.H. Freeman.

Krynine, P. D. 1948. The megascopic study and field classification of sedimentary rocks. *J. Geol.* **56**, 230–165.

Lachenbruch, A. H. 1963. *Contraction theory of ice-wedge polygons: a qualitative discussion*. Publication No. 1287, 63–71, National Academy of Science, National Research Council, Washington, DC.

Leeder, M. R. 1982. *Sedimentology: process and product*. London: Allen & Unwin.

Lindholm, R. C. 1978. *Petrology of Potomac Group sand in Fairfax County, Virginia*. US Geological Survey Open File Report 78–512.

Lindholm, R. C. 1979a. Utilization of programmable calculators in sedimentology. *J. Sed. Petrol.* **49**, 615–20.

Lindholm, R. C. 1979b. Geological history and stratigraphy of the Triassic–Jurassic

Culpeper basin, Virginia. *Geol. Soc. Am. Bull.* Part II, **90**, 1702–36.

Lindholm, R. C. 1980. Intraclast orientation in Cambro-Ordovician limestones in Western Maryland. *J. Sed. Petrol.* **50**, 1205–12.

Lindholm, R. C. 1982. Flat stratification: two ancient examples. *J. Sed. Petrol.* **52**, 227–32.

Lindholm, R. C., J. M. Hazlett and S. W. Fagin 1979. Petrology of Triassic–Jurassic conglomerates in the Culpeper basin, Virginia. *J. Sed. Petrol.* **49**, 1245–62.

Lindsey, D. A. 1972. *Sedimentary petrology and paleocurrents of the Harbell Formation, Pinyon Conglomerate and associated coarse clastic deposits, northwestern Wyoming*. US Geological Survey Professional Paper 734B.

Lowe, D. R. and R. D. LoPiccolo 1974. The characteristics and origins of dish and pillar structures. *J. Sed. Petrol.* **74**, 484–501.

Margolis, S. V. and D. H. Krinsely 1974. Processes of formation and environmental occurrence of microfeatures on detrital quartz grains. *Am. J. Sci.* **274**, 449–64.

Martinsson, A. 1970. Toponomy of trace fossils. In *Trace fossils*, T. P. Crimes and J. C. Harper (eds), 323–30. *Geol. J.*, Special Issue No. 3, Liverpool: Steel House Press.

Mazzullo, J. M. and R. Ehrlich 1983. Grain-shape variation in the St. Peter Sandstone: a record of eolian and fluvial sedimentation of an Early Paleozoic cratonic sheet sand. *J. Sed. Petrol.* **53**, 105–20.

Mazzullo, J. M., R. Ehrlich and M. A. Hemming 1984. Provenance and aerial distribution of Late Pleistocene and Holocene quartz sand on the southern New England continental shelf. *J. Sed. Petrol.* **54**, 1335–48.

Mazzullo, J. M. and K. D. Withers 1984. Sources, distribution and mixing of Late Pleistocene and Holocene sand on the South Texas continental shelf. *J. Sed. Petrol.* **54**, 1319–34.

Mazzullo, J. M. and S. K. Kennedy 1985. Automated measurement of the nominal sectional diameters of individual sedimentary particles. *J. Sed. Petrol.* **55**, 593–4.

McBride, E. F. 1974. Significance of color in red, green, purple, olive, brown and gray beds of DiFunta Group, northeastern Mexico. *J. Sed. Petrol.* **44**, 760–73.

McCubbin, D. G. 1982. Barrier-island and strand-plain facies. In *Sandstone depositional environments*, P. A. Scholle and D. Spearing (eds), 247–80, Memoir 31, American Association of Petroleum Geologists, Tulsa, Oklahoma.

McKee, E. D. 1965. Experiments on ripple lamination. In *Primary sedimentary structures and their hydrodynamic interpretation*, G. V. Middleton (ed.), 66–83. Special Publication 12, Society of Economic Paleontologists and Mineralogists, Tulsa, Oklahoma.

Miall, D. A. 1973. Markov chain analysis applied to an ancient alluvial plain succession. *Sedimentology* **20**, 347–64.

Miall, D. A. 1984. *Principles of sedimentary basin analysis*. Berlin: Springer.

Miall, A. D. and M. R. Gibling 1978. The Siluro-Devonian clastic wedge of Somerset Island, Arctic Canada, and some paleogeographic implications. *Sed. Geol.* **21**, 85–127.

Middleton, G. V. 1973. Johannes Walther's law of correlation of facies. *Bull. Geol. Soc. Am.* **84**, 979–88.

Middleton, G. V. 1978. Facies. In *Encyclopedia of sedimentology*, R. W. Fairbridge and J. Bourgeois (eds), 323–5. Stroudsburg, Pa.: Hutchinson & Ross.

Miller, M. F. 1984. Distribution of biogenic structures in Paleozoic nonmarine and marine-margin sequences: an actualistic model. *J. Paleont.* **58**, 550–70.

Miller, M. F. and J. Rehmer 1982. Using biogenic structures to interpret sharp lithologic boundaries: an example from the lower Devonian of New York. *J. Sed. Petrol.* **52**, 887–96.

Miller, R. L. and J. S. Kahn 1962. *Statistical analysis in the geological sciences*. New York: Wiley.

Morris. R. C. 1971. Classification and interpretation of disturbed bedding types in Jackfork flysch rocks (Upper Mississippian), Ouachita Mountains, Arkansas. *J. Sed. Petrol.* **41**, 410–24.

Moussa, M. T. 1974. Rain-drop impressions. *J. Sed. Petrol.* **44**, 1118–21.

Müller, G. 1967. *Methods in sedimentary petrology*. New York: Hafner.

Nagle, J. S. 1967. Wave and current orientation of shells. *J. Sed. Petrol.* **37**, 1124–38.

Norcliff, G. B. 1977. *Inferential statistics for geographers*. New York: Wiley.

Pelletier, B. R. 1958. Pocono paleocurrents in Pennsylvania and Maryland. *Bull. Geol. Soc. Am.* **69**, 1033–64.

Pemberton, S. G. and R. W. Frey 1982. Trace fossil nomenclature and the *Planolites–Palaeophycus* dilemma. *J. Paleont.* **56**, 843–81.

Pettijohn, F. J. 1975. *Sedimentary rocks*, 3rd edn. New York: Harper & Row.

Pettijohn, F. J. and F. E. Potter 1964. *Atlas and glossary of primary sedimentary structures*. Berlin: Springer.

Phillips, W. J. and N. Phillips, 1980. *An introduction to mineralogy for geologists*. New York: Wiley.

Picard, M. D. and L. R. High, Jr. 1973. *Sedimentary structures of ephemeral streams*. Amsterdam: Elsevier.

Pierce, J. W. and R. R. Graus 1981. Use and misuses of the phi-scale: discussion. *J. Sed. Petrol.* **51**, 1348–50.

Pierce, J. W. and F. R. Siegel 1969. Quantification in clay mineral studies of sediments and sedimentary rocks. *J. Sed. Petrol.* **39**, 187–95.

Potter, P. E. 1978. Petrology and chemistry of modern big river sands. *J. Geol.* **86**, 423–49.

Potter, P. E and F. J. Pettijohn 1963. *Paleocurrents and basin analysis*, 1st edn. Berlin: Springer.

Potter, P. E., J. B. Maynard and W. A. Pryor 1980. *Sedimentology of shale*. Berlin: Springer.

Powers, D. W. and R. G. Easterling 1982. Improved methods for using embedded Markov chains to describe cyclic sediments. *J. Sed. Petrol.* **56**, 913–23.

Powers, M. C. 1953. A new roundness scale for sedimentary particles. *J. Sed. Petrol.* **23**, 117–19.

Pryor, W. A. 1973. Permeability–porosity patterns and variations in some Holocene sand bodies. *Bull. Am. Soc. Petrolm Geol.* **57**, 162–89.

Reading, H. G. 1978. Facies. In *Sedimentary environments and facies*, H. G. Reading (ed.), 4–14. Amsterdam: Elsevier.

Reineck, H. E. and I. B. Singh 1975. *Depositional sedimentary environments*. Berlin: Springer.

Reiche, P. 1938. An analysis of cross-lamination of the Coconino sandstone. *J. Geol.* **44**, 905–32.

Rhoads, D. C. 1975. The paleoecological and environmental significance of trace fossils. In *The study of trace fossils*, R. W. Frey (ed.), 147–60. Berlin: Springer.

Rittenhouse, G. 1943. A visual method of estimating two dimensional sphericity. *J. Sed. Petrol.* **13**, 79–81.

Ramsay, J. G. 1961. The effects of folding upon the orientation of sedimentary structures. *J. Geol.* **69**, 84–100.

Rupke, N. A. 1978. Deep clastic seas. In *Sedimentary environments and facies*, H. G. Reading (ed.). Amsterdam: Elsevier.

Salazar-Jimenez, A., R. W. Frey and J. D. Howard 1982. Concavity orientations of bivalve shells in estuarine and nearshore shelf sediments. *J. Sed. Petrol.* **52**, 565–86.

Schlee, J. 1957. Upland gravels in southern Maryland. *Bull. Geol. Soc. Am.* **68**, 1371–401.

Scholle, P. A and D. Spearing (eds) 1982. *Sandstone depositional environments*. Memoir 31, American Association of Petroleum Geologists, Tulsa, Oklahoma.

Seilacher, A. 1953. Studien zur Palichnologie über die methoden der Palichnologie. *Neues Jahrb. Geol. Paläont. Abh.* **98**, 87–124.

Seilacher, A. 1964. Biogenic sedimentary structures. In *Approaches to paleoecology*, J. Imbrie and N. D. Newell (eds), 296–316. New York: Wiley.

Seilacher, A. 1970. *Cruziana* stratigraphy of "non-fossiliferous" Paleozoic sandstones. In *Trace fossils*, T. P. Crimes and J. C. Harper (eds), 447–76. *Geol. J.*, Special Issue No. 3, Liverpool: Steel House Press.

Seilacher, A. 1978. Use of trace fossils for recognizing depositional environments. In *Trace fossil concepts*, P. B. Basin (ed.), 175–201. Short Course No. 5, Society of Economic Paleontologists and Mineralogists, Tulsa, Oklahoma.

Selley, R. C. 1970. Studies of sequences in sediments using a simplified mathematical device. *Geol. Soc. London Q. J.* **125**, 557–81.

Selley, R. C. 1976. *An introduction to sedimentology*. New York: Academic Press.

Shelton, J. W. and D. E. Mack 1970. Grain orientation in determination of paleocurrents and sandstone trends. *Bull. Am. Assoc. Petrolm Geol.* **54**, 1108–19.

Shepard, F. P. and R. Young 1961. Distinguishing between beach and dune sands. *J. Sed. Petrol.* **31**, 196–214.

Shrock, R. R. 1948. *Sequences in layered rocks*. New York: McGraw-Hill.

Simpson, G. G., A. Rowe and R. C. Lewontin 1960. *Quantitative zoology*. New York: Harcourt-Brace.

Simpson, S. 1975. Classification of trace fossils. In *The study of trace fossils*, R. W. Frey (ed.), 39–54. Berlin: Springer.

Sipple, R. F. 1971. Quartz grain orientation-I (the photometric method). *J. Sedimentol. Petrol.* **41**, 38–59.

Solohub, J. T. and J. E. Klovan 1970. Evaluation of grain-size parameters in lacustrine environments. *J. Sed. Petrol.* **40**, 81–101.

Sloss, L. L., E. C. Dapples and W. C. Krumbein 1960. *Lithofacies maps: an atlas of the United States and southern California*. New York: Wiley.

Smosa, R. and S. M. Warshauer 1979. A scheme for multivariate analysis in carbonate petrology with example from the Silurian Tonoloway Limestone. *J. Sed. Petrol.* **49**, 257–72.

Snedecor, G. W. and W. G. Cochran 1967. *Statistical methods*. Ames, Iowa: Iowa State University Press.

Sneed, E. D. and R. L. Folk 1958. Pebbles in the lower Colorado River, Texas – a study in particle morphogenesis. *J. Geol.* **66**, 114–50.

Stewart, J. H., F. G. Poole and R. F. Wilson 1972. US Geological Survey Professional Paper 690, Washington, DC.

Swan, D., J. J. Clayne and J. L. Luternauer 1978. Grain-size statistics I: Evaluation of Folk and Ward graphic measures. *J. Sed. Petrol.* **48**, 863–78.

Swan, D., J. J. Clayne and J. L. Luternauer 1979. Grain-size statistics II: Evaluation of grouped moment measures. *J. Sed. Petrol.* **49**, 487–500.

Taft, W. H. and J. W. Harbaugh 1964. *Modern carbonate sediments of southern Florida, Bahamas, and Espiritu Santo Island, Baja, California: a comparison of their mineralogy and chemistry*. Stanford University Publications, Geological Sciences 8, No. 2, Stanford, California.

Taira, A. and P. A. Scholle 1977. Design and calibration of a photo-extinction tube for grain size analysis. *J. Sed. Petrol.* **47**, 1347–60.

Tanner, W. F. 1967. Ripple mark indices and their uses. *Sedimentology* **9**, 89–104.

Tennant, C. B. and R. W. Berger 1957. X-ray determination of the dolomite–calcite ratio of a carbonate rock. *Am. Mineral.* **42**, 23.

Terry, R. C. and G. V. Chilingar 1955. Summary of "Concerning some additional aids in studying sedimentary rock formation" by M. S. Shvetsov. *J. Sed. Petrol.* **25**, 229–334.

Tickell, T. G. 1965. *The techniques of sedimentary mineralogy, developments in sedimentology, Vol. 4*. Amsterdam: Elsevier.

Tucker, A. D. 1981. *Sedimentary petrology: an introduction*. New York: Wiley.

Tucker, M. E. 1982. *The field description of sedimentary rocks*. Handbook Series, Geological Society, London. New York: Wiley.

Tucker, R. W. and H. L. Vacher 1980. Effectiveness of discriminating beach, dune and river sands by moments and cumulative weight percentages. *J. Sed. Petrol.* **50**, 165–72.

VanHouton, F. B. 1973. Origins of red beds: a review 1961–1972. *Ann. Rev. Earth Planet Sci.* **1**, 39–42.

Visher, G. S. 1969. Grain size distribution and depositional processes. *J. Sed. Petrol.* **39**, 1074–1106.

Waddell, H. 1935. Volume, shape and roundness of quartz particles. *J. Geol.* **43**, 250–80.

Walker, R. G. 1975. From sedimentary structures to facies models: examples from fluvial environments. In *Depositional environments as interpreted from primary sedimentary structures and stratification sequences*, 63–79. Society of Economic Paleontologists and Mineralogists, Tulsa, Oklahoma.

Walker, R. G. 1979. Facies and facies models, 1 General introduction. In *Facies Models*, R. G. Walker (ed.), 1–7. Reprint Series 1, Geological Association of Canada, Geoscience Canada, Toronto, Canada.

Walker, R. G. 1984. General introduction. In *Facies Models*, 2nd edn, R. G. Walker (ed.), 1–10. Reprint Series 1, Geological Association of Canada, Geoscience Canada, Toronto, Canada.

Walker, T. R. 1974. Formation of red beds in moist tropical climate: a hypothesis. *Bull. Geol. Soc. Am.* **85**, 633–8.

Warme, J. E. and E. J. McHuron 1978. Marine borers: trace fossils and their geological significance. In *Trace fossil concepts*, P. B. Basin (ed.), 73–124. Short Course No. 5, Society of Economic Paleontologists and Mineralogists, Tulsa, Oklahoma.

Weaver, C. E. 1958. Geological interpretation of argillaceous sediments. *Bull. Am. Assoc. Petrolm Geol.* **42**, 254–71.

Weimer, R. J., J. D. Howard and D. R. Lindsay 1982. Tidal flats. In *Sandstone depositional environments*, P. A. Scholle and D. Spearing (eds), 191–246. Memoir 31, American Association of Petroleum Geologists, Tulsa, Oklahoma.

Weir, G. M. 1976. *Cross-bedding of the Potomac Formation in Fairfax County, Virginia*. US Geological Survey Open File Report 76–193.

Wentworth, C. K. 1922. A scale of grade and class terms for clastic sediments. *J. Geol.* **30**, 377–92.

Whisonant, R. C., J. H. Giesen and L. A. Maloney 1985. *Use of paleocurrent data to recognize shallower versus deeper carbonate shelf environments in the Upper Cambrian of southwestern Virginia*. Geological Society of America Annual Meeting, Abstracts with Program.

Wilson, J. L. 1975. *Carbonate facies in geologic history*. Berlin: Springer.

Wyrwoll, K. H. and G. K. Smyth 1985. On using the log-hyperbolic distribution to describe the textural characteristics of eolian sediments. *J. Sed. Petrol.* **55**, 471–8.

Zeigler, J. M., G. G. Whitney and C. R. Hays 1960. Woods hole rapid sediment analyzer. *J. Sed. Petrol.* **30**, 490–5.

Zingg, T. 1935. Beitrage zur Schott eranalyse. *Mineral. Petrog. Mitt. Schweiz.* **15**, 39–140.
Zussman, J. 1967. *Physical methods in determinative mineralogy*. New York: Academic Press.

Index

acetylene tetrabromide 214
actinolite 219
aeolian
  dunes *1.1*, 10
  ripples 22
allochems *8.12*, 196
allocyclic mechanisms 28
amphibole 219
anatase 222
andalusite 222
angle of climb (cross-bedding) *1.18–19*, Table 1.4, 20, 21
Anjne's A (test statistic) 47
antidunes *1.27*, Table 1.1, 5, 6
  cross stratification **1.3.3e**, *1.27*
apatite 223
Arenicolites **4.4.1**, *4.17*, 99
arenite *8.6*, 189
arkose *8.6–8*, 195, 232
Asterosoma **4.4.2**, *4.18*, 71
asymmetrical ripples Table 1.1, 2–5, *1.6, 1.9*
  three-dimensional *1.2*
  two-dimensional *1.1*
augite 227
autocyclic mechanisms 28

backflow 2
  cross bedding *1.15, 1.22*, 22, 51
  ripples *1.15*, 22
ball-and-pillow structure *1.32c, 1.33*, 32
ballistic ripple Table 1.1
bar Tables 1.1, 1.2
Battery Point Formation *11.7–10*, 244, 255
bed 14
bedding
  convolute 34, 35, *1.34*
  flaser *1.20*, 21
  homogeneous **1.3.5**
  lenticular *1.20*, 21
  massive **1.3.5**
  terminology Table 1.3
  wavy *1.20*, 22
bedforms
  controlling factors **1.2.3**
  produced by wave action **1.2.4**
  produced by unidirectional water currents **1.2.1**, **1.2.2**
  superimposed 2
Bergiueria **4.4.3**, *4.19*
bidirectional aspect of cross-bedding 22

Bifungites **4.4.4**, *4.20*
bifurcation (ripple crestlines) *1.7*, 9
binomial probability 248
biotite 223
bioturbation *4.42*, 28, 62, 101, *3.4D*
borings 65, 70
bounce cast 1
Bragg equation 124
Brandywine Gravel *7.12b*
bromoform 214, 216
brookite 223
brush cast 1
Bull Run Formation *7.13*
burrows *4.3*, 13, 14, 35, 70, 72, *4.13*

calcarenite 196, **10.2.3**
calcilutite 196
calcirudite 196
calcite *6.6*, 130, 131
calclithite *8.8*, 191, 195
Cambrian carbonates 61
Carlisle Center Formation 102
center-of-gravity map (sandstone) 254
centripetal flow patter 53, *2.11a*
chevron cast 1
chi-square test 47, **5.5**
Chinle Formation *2.9*
chlorite *6.4*, Table 6.2, 128, 223, 232
chloritoid 224
Chondrites **4.4.5**, *4.21*, 98
classification
  conglomerate 8.3, *7.1*
  grain size **7.1**
  limestone **8.4.1**, **8.4.2**, *8.11, 8.13, 8.14*
  mudrock **8.2**, *7.2*
  sandstone **8.1**, *8.3, 8.6–8*
  trace fossils **4.2**
clastic ratio *11.12c*, 253
clay Table 7.1, *7.2*
  size analysis **7.2.2**, 174
  x-ray diffraction *6.4*, Table 6.2, **6.3**
climbing-ripple cross-lamination *1.18–19*, Table 1.4, 20
clinopyroxene 227
clinozoisite 224
coarse-tail grading *1.28b*, 26
coarsening upward sequences **1.3.4c**
coefficient of size-reduction *7.14*, 176
compound cross-bedding *1.24*, 24
color (rock) **10**

carbonate rock **10.2.3**
description **10.1**
mudrock **10.2.2**
sandstone **10.2.1**
variation with grain size *10.1*
cone-in-cone 100
conglomerate **8.3**, *7.1*, 110
grading 28
pebble orientation **3.3**
size analysis **7.3.3**
consistency ratio 47
contact matrix 245
content grading 26
convolute lamination (bedding) **1.5.3a**, 35, *1.34*
Copeza 4.6g
coset *1.17*, 15
Coulter Counter 160
counter-current ripples 22
cross bedding **1.3.3a** *1.15–17*
angle of climb *1.18–19*, Table 1.4, 20, 21
backflow *1.15, 1.22*, 22, 51
basis for classification 16
compound 24
deformed **1.5.3c**, *1.36*
dip azimuth variability **2.6**, *2.9–12*
epsilon *1.24*, 24
herringbone 22
large-scale 10, 18, 22
micro-scale 15
modifications in **1.3.3b**
overturned *1.36A*, 35
small-scale 18, 21, 22, 35
tabular *1.17B, 2.12*, 16, 54, *1.1*
trough *1.17B, 2.9, 2.12*, 16, 51, 54, *1.2*
set boundaries 15, 17
wave formed *1.21*, 21
cross-lamination 20
cross-stratification
antidune *1.27*, **1.3.3e**
hummocky **1.3.3d**, *1.26*
swash **1.3.3c**, *1.25*
Cruziana **4.4.6**, *4.22*, 98
association **4.7.1b**
Culpeper Basin *7.13, 8.9, 10.1*, 192
cumulative curve *7.9, 7.11*, **7.4.3**
current
crescents *1.30b*, 29, 43
ripples *see* asymmetrical ripples
rose *2.4, 3.3*, 46
Cylindrichnus **4.4.7**, *4.23*

Daedalus 4.3c
deformation (soft sediment) Table 1.5, **1.5.1**, 35
deformed cross-bedding *1.36*, **1.5.3c**
density inversion 31
depositional
environment (analysis of) **11**
-stoss climbing-ripple cross lamination 20, Table 1.4
desiccation cracks 11
difference matrix *11.9d*, 247
diffractograms (x-ray), 126
barite, *6.3*
calcite *6.6*
clay minerals *6.4*
dolomite *6.5–6*
practice exercises *6.7–10*
dikes
neptunian *1.38a*, 38
sandstone *1.38b–39*, 37
Diplichnites **4.4.8**, *4.6a*, *4.24*, 98
Diplocraterion **4.4.9**, *4.3a*, *4.25*, 98
Diplopodomorpha 4.6e
direction of movement 46, 59
data **2.4.1**
directional data (graphic presentation) **2.3**
dish and pillar structure **1.5.3b**, *1.35*, 12
dismicrite 197, *8.13*
dispersive stress 28
distribution grading *1.28a*, 26
dolomite *6.5–6*, 130, 131
dunes
aeolian Table 1.1, 10, 16, 18
subaqueous Tables 1.1, 1.2, 2, *1.5*

embedded Markov chain 247
enstatite 227
environmental analysis **11**
epidote 224
epireliefs (trace fossils) 66, *4.1*
epsilon cross-bedding *1.24*, 24
equivalent diameter 159
erosional-stoss climbing-ripple cross lamination 20, *1.18E*
Esopus Shale 102
exercises *see* practice exercises

facies
analysis of vertical sequences **11.3**
association 242
classification *11.5*, 240
definition **11.3.1**
description 241
Gressly's definition 240
maps **11.4**, *11.12*
models **11.5**
relationship diagram *11.10*, 245, 247
sequence *11.8*, 244
faults (gravity) 35
feldspar 186, 192
fining-upward sequences **1.3.4c**
fissil 157
flagstone 5
flame structures *1.31b*, 31

flaser bedding *1.20*, 22
flat
  bed 6
  stratification 15
flow
  régime 6, 15
  velocity *1.4–5*
flute cast *1.30a*, 29, 43, 46, 99
folds (slump) *1.37*, 35
foresets 15, 16, *1.16*
form sets (isolated ripple train) 21
fossils *8.12c*
  orientation fabrics **3.5**
Fourier analysis 110
frequency curve **7.4.2**, *7.8*
frosted grain surface 109
full reliefs (trace fossils) 66, *4.1*

garnet *9.5–6*, 213, 225
geometric mean 166
geopetal structure *8.16*
giant ripple Tables 1.1, 1.2
glauconite 190, 232
glaucophane 222
grade (size) 154
graded bedding **1.3.4**, *1.28*
  inverse **1.3.4b**, 16
  normal **1.3.4a**, *1.28*
  reverse **1.3.4b**, *1.28c*
grain
  fabric **3**
  flow 27
  morphology *see* particle morphology
grain size **7**
  classification **7.1**
  nomenclature **7.1.3**, *7.1–2*
  parameters **7.5**, *7.10*, Tables 7.3, 7.4
  variation with transport **7.6**, *7.12–14*
grain-size analysis
  conglomerate **7.3.3**
  gravel **7.2.3**
  pipette *7.4*, 159
  sand **7.2.1**, *7.3*
  sandstone **7.3.1**
  sediment **7.2**
  sedimentary rock **7.3**
  shale **7.3.2**
  silt and clay **7.2.2**, *7.4*
grainstone *8.15*, 198
graphic
  logs **11.2.3**, *11.3–4, 11.7*
  measures (grain-size) **7.5.3a**, *7.11*, Table 7.3
graphic presentation of data **7.4**
  cumulative curve **7.4.3**, *7.9*, *7.11*
  current rose *2.4*, *3.3*, 46
  facies maps **11.4**, *11.12*
  frequency curve **7.4.2**, *7.8*
  histogram **7.4.1**, *7.7*, 114
  moving average map **2.5**, *2.8*
graphical vector mean 47
gravel **7.2.3**, *7.1*, Table 7.1
gravity
  fault 35
  flow 28
  transport structures **1.5.4**
graywacke **8.1.4**, *8.6–7, 8.10*
greensand 190
Gressly (definition of facies) 240
groove cast 1, 30, 43, 50
growth position (bivalves) 62
Gulf of Mexico, (heavy mineral assemblages) *9.1*, 209

hand specimen study
  limestone **8.4.3**
  sandstone 186
heavy liquids 214
heavy minerals **9**
  assemblage **9.2**, **9.3**
  association 208
  descriptions **9.5**
  heavy liquid separation **9.4**, *9.7*
  identification keys *9.9–12*
  source-rock **9.3.1**, Table 9.1
  varietal studies 213
  zones *9.2–3*, 208, 210, 212
Helminthoida **4.4.10**, *4.26*, 99
hematite 218, 232
herring-bone cross-bedding 22
histogram **7.4.1**, 114, *7.7*
homogeneous bedding **1.3.5**
horizontal stratification 15, *1.3*
hornblende 222
hummocks 9
hummocky
  bedding surface *1.26*, 9
  cross-stratification **1.3.3d**, *1.26*
hydrometer 160
hypersthene 227
hyporeliefs (trace fossils) 66, *4.1*

ichnocoenose 100
ichnofossils *see* trace fossils
identification keys *see* keys
illite *6.4*, Table 6.2, 131, 232
ilmenite 218
imbrication (pebble) *3.2*, 60
inclined stratification **1.3.3**, 15
independent trials probability matrix *11.9c*, 245
interference ripple patterns *1.10*, 9, 99
intraclasts *8.12a*
  orientation **3.4**, *3.3*
intrastratal solution 212
isopach map *11.12a*, *11.13a*, 250

kaolinite *6.4*, Table 6.2, 128, 131
keys (identification)
  heavy minerals *9.9–12*
  sandstone textural maturity *8.4*
  trace fossils **4.3**
kinetic filtering 28
Kouphichnium 4.6f
Kurtosis 167, 168, *7.10*
kyanite 225

Lake Missoula 5
laminae Table 1.3, 14
  backwash 28
large
  ripples Table 1.2, 2
  -scale cross bedding 10, 18, 22
Lebensspuren 65
lee surface (side) *1.6*, 2
lenticular bedding *1.20*, 21
leucoxene 218
limestone **8.4**, *8.11, 8.13–15*
  hand specimen study **8.4.3**
  intraclast orientation **3.4**
Lincolnshire Limestone *3.3*
line of movement data **2.4.2**, 46, 59
liquefaction 31, 34, 35
litharenite *8.6–8*, 232
lithofacies triangle *11.12, 11.14*, 253
load
  casts *1.31a*, 31
  structures **1.5.2**
load-casted flutes 32
log
  -normal distribution **7.5.3f**
  hyperbolic distribution 174
logarithmic
  mean 166
  standard deviation 167
logs **11.2.3**, *11.2–3*
low angle inclined stratification 15
lower flow régime 6, 15

magnetite 218
Mann-Whitney U-test 8.5
maps
  facies **11.4**, *11.12*
  heavy mineral association *9.1*
  moving-average **2.5**, *2.8*
  multicomponent **11.4.2**
  single component **11.4.1**
  variation in grain size *7.13*
  variation in pebble size *7.12*
  vertical variability **11.4.3**
Markov chain 243
  embedded 247
marl *8.11*
Maryland
  coastal plain *9.2*
  piedmont 192
massive bedding **1.3.5**
matrix 184, 186, 195, 199, *8.1, 8.4, 8.6*
maturity
  mineralogic 186
  textural *8.4*, 186, 196
mean (grain size) 161, 166, *7.8, 7.10*, Table 7.2
measured sections **11.2.2**, *11.3, 11.7*
median (grain size) 166
megaripple *1.4*, Tables 1.1, 1.2, 2, 5, 6, 15, 16, 18, 22, 35, 54
meniscate structure *4.3*
method of moments **7.5.1**, Table 7.2, 172
micrite *8.13–14*, 196, 199, 200
micro-scale cross bedding 15
midpoint deviation 168
mineral identification
  hand specimen 186
  heavy minerals *9.9–12*
  x-ray diffraction **6**
mineralogic maturity 186
modal
  class 46, 114, 165
  size 26
mode 166, *7.8*
moment measures Table 7.2, 172
Monocraterion 4.4.11, *4.27*, 99
monozite 226
montmorillonite *6.4*, Table 6.2, 128, 131
morphology *see* particle morphology
moving-average maps **2.5**, *2.8*
mud curls *1.13a*, 12, 35
mud ripples 29
mudcracks **1.2.6**, *1.12–13*, 99
mudrock **8.2**, *7.2*
mullite 128
multicomponent (facies) maps **11.4.2**
muscovite 226

neptunian dike *1.38A*, 38
Nerites **4.4.12**, *4.28*, 99
  association **4.7.1c**
New England shelf 113
nominal section grain diameter 159
non-opaque heavy minerals 219, **9.5d**
nonorthogonal mudcracks *1.12*, 11
normal distribution **7.5.2f**, 165
  log- **7.5.2f**,
normative mineralogic composition **8.1.5b**, *8.10*
number frequency 173

Octopodichnus 4.6d
oolite *8.12b*
opaque grains (heavy minerals) **9.5a**
Ophiomorpha **4.4.13**, *4.29*, 71, 99
orientation (fabric) of fossils **3.5**

orthoconglomerate 195
orthogonal mudcracks *1.12*, 11
oscillatory planar lamination 15
overturned cross-bedding *1.36A*, 35

packstone *8.15*, 199
Palaeophycus **4.4.14**
paleocurrent analysis **2.1**, 60, 62
Paleodictyon **4.4.15**, *4.30*
paleoenvironmental interpretation **7.5.3g**, 43
paleoslope reconstruction 37
paraconglomerate 195
particle morphology **5**
  controlling factors **5.3**
  form **5.1.2**
  measurement **5.2**
  reasons for study **5.4**
  roundness **5.1.3**, *5.2–3, 5.5*, 110
  shape **5.1.2**, *5.1–2*, 110
  sphericity **5.1.1**
  surface textures **5.1.4**
  textural inversion *8.5*, 113
parting lineation *1.3*, 5, 43
pebble orientation **3.3**
pellets *8.12d*
penecontemporaneous deformation 31
percentile measures **7.5.2**, *7.11*
permeability 59
Permichnium 4.6b
phi notation **7.1.2**
photobatictic sensitivity 98
pillar structure 35
pipette analysis *7.4*, 159, 173
phyllarenite 191, *8.8*
Phycodes **4.4.16**, *4.31*, 98
planar
  lamination 15
  stratification **1.3.2**, 59
plane bed **1.2.2**, *1.3–4*, 5, 6, 15, 26
Planolites **4.4.17**, *4.32*
Pocono Formation *7.12a*
polymictic conglomerate 195
Potomac Group *2.8, 8.9*, 213
practice exercises
  binomial probability 256
  chi-square test **5.6**
  cumulative curve **7.7.5**
  cross bedding **2.7**
  current rose 55, 57, 63
  facies relationship diagram **11.6**
  forest dip azimuth measurement **2.7.3**
  fossil orientation **3.6**
  grain-size **7.7**
  histogram **5.6.1**, **7.7.3**
  isopach map **11.7.1**
  lithofacies map **11.7.2**
  Mann-Whitney U-test **8.6.5**
  mean roundness 121
  method of moments **7.7.6**
  millimeter-phi conversion 176
  paleocurrent direction 41, 64
  restoration of original bedding attitude **2.7.1**
  rock classification **8.6**
  sedimentary structures identification **1.6**
  stereonet 54
  two theta conversion
  trace fossil identification **4.8**
  vector mean and magnitude **2.7.2**
  x-ray diffraction **6.7**
primary
  sedimentary structure 1
  stratification 14
probability paper 168
prod cast 1, 30
protoquartzite *8.6e*
provenance 209
  heavy minerals Table 9.1
pseudonodules *1.32B*, 32
pumice 28
pyrite 218
pyroxene 226

quartz 186, 227
quartz arenite *8.6–7*, 232

radial line diagram 47
raindrop imprints **1.2.7**, *1.14*
Rayleigh test *2.7*, 47
reactivation surface *1.23*, 22
regressive ripples 22
reverse
  flow 2
  grading **1.3.4b**
Rhizocorallium **4.4.18**, *4.3, 4.33*, 98
Rhone delta 212
rib-and-furrow structure 17
ripple
  -drift Table 1.4
  index *1.11*, 2, 9, *1.6*, *1.8*
  symmetry index *1.9*, *1.11*, 9, *1.6*
ripple-drift cross-lamination Table 1.4
ripples
  aeolian 22
  asymmetrical *1.1–2, 1.6, 1.9*, 2–5
  backflow 22
  ballistic Table 1.1
  counter-current 22
  giant Tables 1.1, 1.2
  interference 9, 99, *1.10*
  large 2, Table 1.1
  mega- *1.4*, 2, 5, 6, 15, 18, 22, 35, 54, Tables 1.1, 1.2
  mud 29
  regressive 22

starved 21, 33
separated 21
symmetrical 9, *1.6–7, 1.9–10*, Table 1.1
unidirectional current **1.2.1**
wave **1.2.4**, 25, Table 1.1
wave-current 9, Table 1.1
wind-sand 9, Table 1.1
rock color *see* color
roll cast 1
rose diagram *2.4, 3.3*, 46
Rosselia **4.4.19**, *4.34*, 71
roundness (grain) **5.1.3**, *5.2–3, 5.5*, 110
Rusophycus 98
rutile 209, 227

saltation bombardment 22
sand Table 7.1, *7.1*
grain orientation **3.2**, *3.1*
-shale ratio *11.12b*, 251
-size analysis **7.2.1**
wave Tables 1.1, 1.2, 1.4, 1.5, 2, 5, 6, 15, 16, 18, 22, 24, 35
sandstone
aeolian 18
classification **8.1**, *8.3, 8.6–8*
dikes and sills *1.38B*, 38
Folk's five-fold name 191
grain-size analysis **7.3.1**
Scalarituba **4.4.20**, *4.35*
Scolicia **4.4.21**, *4.36*, 98
scour pits 2
Scoyenia **4.4.22**, *4.37*
sediment injection (structures) **1.5.5**
sedimentary structures **1**
analysis of **2**
primary 1
see various types by name
sedimentation tube 159
selective sorting **9.3.3**
semireliefs (trace fossils) 66, *4.1*
separated ripples 21
separation angle 37
set *1.17*, 15
boundaries 15, 17
settling
planar lamination 15
-tube 159
shaft (trace fossil) 70
shale **7.3.2**, *7.2, 7.6*
shape (grain) **5.1.2**, *5.1–2*, 110
sheet flood 29
shrinkage cracks 11
sieve
analysis *7.3*, 157
interval **7.5.2b**
sill (sandstone) *1.38D*, 37
sillimanite 228
silt **7.2.2**, Table 7.1, *7.2*
siltstone *7.2, 7.6*
single component (facies) map **11.4**
size grade **7.1.1**, Table 7.1
skewness 167, 168, Tables 7.2, 7.3, *7.10*
Skolithos **4.4.23**, *4.38*, 98, 99
association **4.7.1**
slipface 2
slump folds *1.37*, 35
small-scale cross bedding 18, 21, 22, 35
smectite 128
sodium polytungstate 215
soft-sediment deformation **1.5.1**, Table 1.5, 35
sole marks **1.4**, *1.29*
current crescents *1.30b*, 29
flute casts *1.30a*, 29, 43, 46, 99
groove casts 1, 30, 43, 50
load casts *1.31*, 31
mud ripples 29
prod casts 1, 30
tool casts 1, 30
South Texas continental shelf 113
sparite *8.13–14*, 197
sparry calcite (spar) 196, 200
sphene 228
sphericity (grain) **5.1.1**, 110
spinel 228
spoke diagram 47
spreite (in burrows) *4.3*, 72
St Peter Sandstone 113
standard deviation
arithmetic 167, *7.10A*
logarithmic 167
starved ripples 21, 33
statistics
Anjne's A test 47
binomial probability Table 11.1, 248
chi-square test **5.5**, 47
cumulative curve **7.4.3**, *7.9*, *7.11*
frequency curve **7.4.2**, *7.8*
grain-size parameters **7.5**, *7.10*, Tables 7.3, 7.4
graphic size parameters Table 7.3, **7.5.3a**, *7.11*
log-normal distribution **7.5.3f**
Mann-Whitney U-test **8.5**
Markov chain 243, 247
method of moments **7.5.1**, Table 7.2, 172
moving average map **2.5**, *2.8*
normal distribution **7.5.3f**, 165
percentile measures **7.5.2**, *7.11*, Table 7.3
Rayleigh test *2.7*, 47
staurolite 229
stereographic projection *2.1–3*, 43
Sternberg's Law *7.14*, 176
Stoke's Law 159
stoss surface *1.6*, 2
stratification Table 1.3

flat 15
horizontal 15, *1.3*
inclined **1.3.3**
planar **1.3.2**, 59
primary 14
also see bedding
surface
textures (grains) **5.1.4**
waves 2, 5
swash cross-stratification **1.3.3c**
Sykesville Formation *8.10*
symmetrical ripple 9, Table 1.1, 1.6, *1.7, 1.9–10*
synaeresis cracks 13
syndepositional basins *2.11a*, 53

tabular cross bedding *1.1, 1.17b, 2.12*, 16, 51, 54
tally matrix *11.9a*, 245
tectonic deformation Table 1.5
tectonic tilt – correction for **2.2**
linear structures *2.2*
planar structures *2.3*
Teichnichnus **4.4.24**, *4.3c, 4.39*
Tentaculites 63
ternary diagram (classification triangle) *8.3*, 156
test of significance 47
tetrabrom-ethane 214
Texas continental shelf 113
textural
inversions *8.5*, 113, 188
maturity 186, 196, *8.4*
Thalassinoides **4.4.25**, *4.40*
thigmotaxis 99
titanite 228
tool casts 1, 30
touch stimulus 99
tourmaline 208, 209, 229
trace fossils **4**
associations 100
behavioral classification **4.5**
biostratigraphy **4.7.4**
classification **4.2**
descriptions **4.4**
evolution **4.7.4**
identification keys **4.3**
ichnogeneric names 70
morphologic characteristics *4.2*
paleoenvironmental interpretation **4.7.1**
tracks *4.6*, 69
trackway 69
trails 69, *4.5*
transition probabilities matrix, *11.9b*, 245
tremolite 222
tribrom-methane 214
trough cross bedding *1.2, 1.17B, 2.9, 2.12*, 16, 51, 54
tunnels (trace fossils) 70
turbidites 27, 43, 61, 101
turbidity flows 20, 29
turbulent eddies 2
two-theta 125, *6.2*
values for selected minerals Tables 6.3–6

Udden-Wentworth grade scale Table 7.1, 154
unconformity 102
undulatory bedforms
unidirectional currents **1.2.1**
wave action **1.2.4**
wind action **1.2.5**
upper flow régime 6
upper traction planar lamination 15

variance Table 7.2, 168
varietal studies (heavy minerals) 213
vector magnitude and mean **2.4**
direction of movement data **2.4.1**
test of significance *2.7*
line of movement data **2.4.2**
vertical variability map **11.4.3**
volcanoclastic deposits 28

wacke *8.6*, 189
wackestone *8.15*, 199
Walther's law 242
water-surface wave 2, 5
wave
shell orientation *3.5c*, 63
cross bedding *1.21*, 22
-current ripples 9, Table 1.1
ripples 25, **1.2.4**, Table 1.1
wavy bedding *1.20*, 21
Wentworth grade scale *see* Udden-Wentworth
wind
sand ripple 9
ripple *1.1*, 9
Wissahickon Formation *8.10*, 194

X-ray diffraction **6**, *6.1*
Bragg equation 124
chemical composition **6.4**, *6.5*
clay mineral identification *6.4*, **6.3**, Table 6.2
diffractogram *6.3*, 126
mineral identification **6.2**
quantification **6.5**
relative intensity of reflections *6.3*, 126
sample preparation **6.6**

zircon *9.4–6*, 208, 209, 229
Zoisite 230
Zoophycos **4.4.26**, *4.41*, 99
association **4.7.1d**

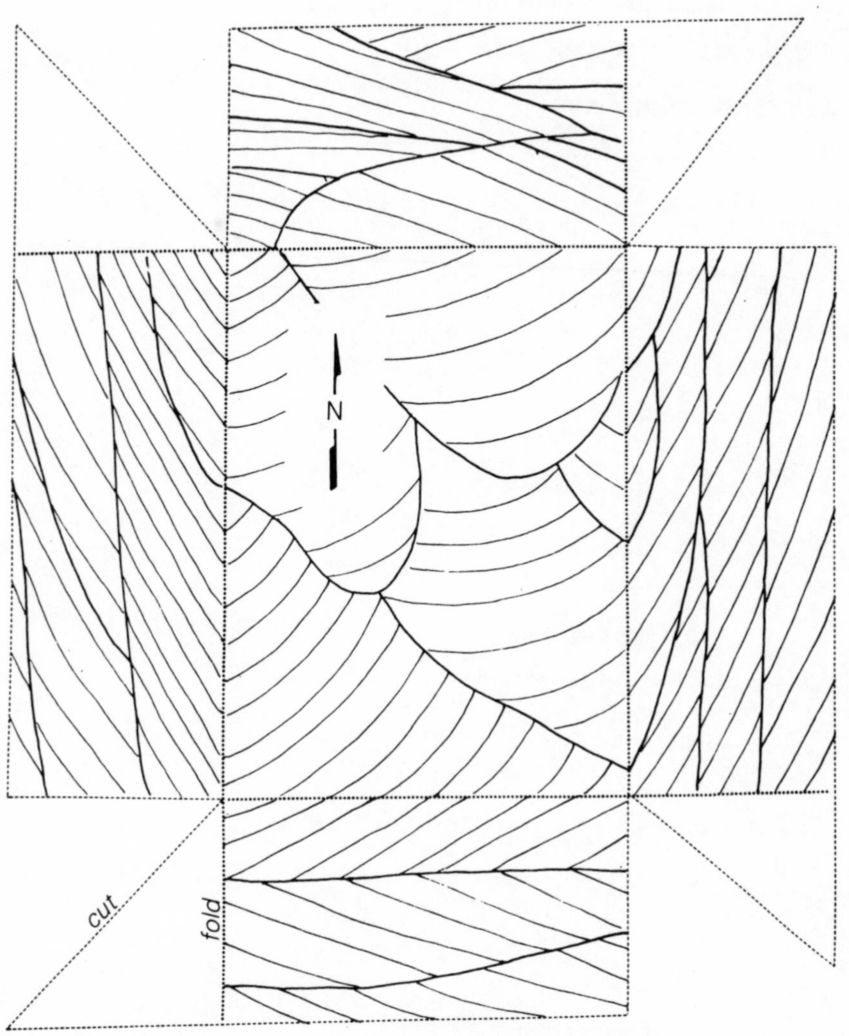
N
cut
fold

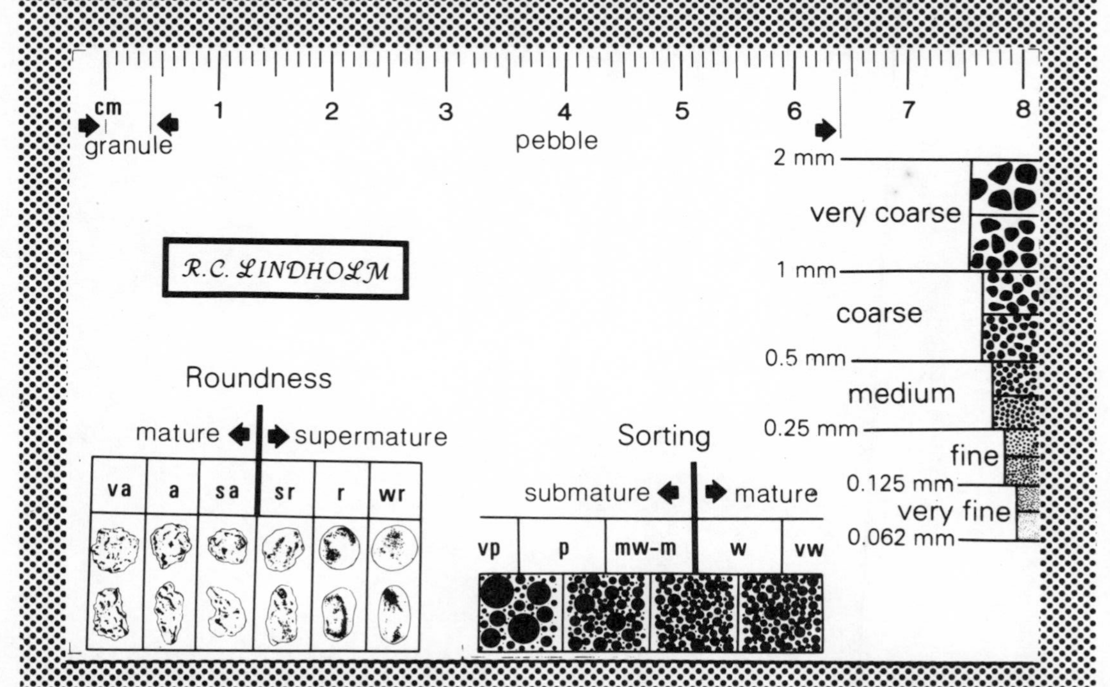
cm
1
2
3
4
5
6
7
8
granule
pebble
2 mm
very coarse
1 mm
coarse
0.5 mm
medium
0.25 mm
fine
0.125 mm
very fine
0.062 mm
R.C. LINDHOLM
Roundness
mature
supermature
va
a
sa
sr
r
wr
Sorting
submature
mature
vp
p
mw-m
w
vw